THE COMMONWEA

Joint Chairmen
Honorary Editorial Ad
Board   DEAN ATHELSTAN SPILHAUS
Minnesota

Publisher   ROBERT MAXWELL, M.C., M.P.

FUEL and OIL TECHNOLOGY DIVISION

General Editors   M. W. THRING, D. C. RHYS JONES
and T. F. GASKELL

FUELS AND FUEL TECHNOLOGY
VOLUME I

FUELS
AND FUEL TECHNOLOGY

A SUMMARIZED MANUAL
IN TWO VOLUMES

WILFRID FRANCIS
M.Sc. Tech., Ph.D., F.R.I.C., F.Inst. Fuel,
Consulting Chemist and Fuel Technologist

PERGAMON PRESS

Oxford · London · Edinburgh · New York · Paris · Frankfurt

PERGAMON PRESS LTD.	Headington Hill Hall, Oxford 4 & 5 Fitzroy Square, London W.1
PERGAMON PRESS (SCOTLAND) LTD.	2 & 3 Teviot Place, Edinburgh 1
PERGAMON PRESS INC.	122 East 55th Street, New York 22, N.Y.
GAUTHIER-VILLARS	55 Quai des Grands-Augustins, Paris 6
PERGAMON PRESS GmbH	Kaiserstrasse 75, Frankfurt-am-Main
FEDERAL PUBLICATIONS LTD.	Times House, River Valley Road, Singapore
SAMCAX BOOK SERVICES LTD.	Queensway, P.O. Box 2720, Nairobi, Kenya

Set in 10 on 12pt Times by   Printed in Great Britain by
Santype Ltd. of Salisbury   A. Wheaton & Co. Ltd. of Exeter

CONTENTS

VOLUME II

Preface
List of Illustrations

SECTION C: GASEOUS FUELS

SECTION D: FUEL TECHNOLOGY

PREFACE

THE subject of fuel technology is extremely complex and comprises portions of many sciences and technologies. The minimum requirements for a qualified practitioner of fuel technology are: (1) a basic knowledge of chemistry, physics and mathematics, at least to G.C.E. "Advanced Level" standard, or its equivalent; (2) a good working knowledge of the origin, constitution and properties of fuels; and (3) a knowledge of various engineering and technological subjects sufficient for subsidiary papers to a Degree or Diploma standard. The technological subjects required include oil technology, metallurgy and the properties of materials. The engineering subjects include chemical, combustion, electrical, gas, heating, and mechanical engineering.

In the leisured atmosphere of a University, which offers many, or all, of these subjects as full-time courses, it is comparatively easy for a student to obtain a Degree or Diploma in Fuel Technology, or in some other branch of applied science in which Fuel is a Principal Subject. Most part-time or evening students find the recognized syllabuses in Fuels and Fuel Technology (leading to a Professional Qualification) much too extensive and difficult, unless they are already qualified in one branch of the subject, or are employed in a research or technological undertaking relating to fuels.

Unfortunately, in many districts in Great Britain, including the Greater London area, full, part-time or evening courses in Fuel Technology, leading to a recognized "Professional Qualification", are not available. Moreover, the various aspects of the subject are not covered adequately, or at all, in any one text book. A student requires access to many different text books, and must possess the knack of rapid and selective reading if he is to acquire a working knowledge of all aspects of the subject in a reasonable time. For these reasons, and others, the intake of students at technical colleges offering part-time or evening courses in Fuel Technology is small and, of those entering, few survive to the end.

I have found, during a number of years of part-time and evening lecturing, that the only way to keep students of fuel, and to enable them to pass qualifying examinations, is to undertake personally this abstracting and selecting of the literature and to present the abstracts in a simple and concise form as separate lectures covering all important aspects of the syllabuses. In other words, to prepare a number of "Data Sheets" for the students, each being suitable for from one to three lectures. These are issued to the students before lectures, which obviates the necessity for time-consuming note-taking and assists concentration on the substance of each lecture.

The notes and abstracts that I have prepared for this purpose over the years are collected here as a manual, in two volumes (Volume I: Solid Fuels, Liquid Fuels; Volume II: Gaseous Fuels). The complete manual should be helpful to three types of student:

1. The executive or operative wishing to obtain a working knowledge of the subject without having to read through, and abstract a mass of literature.
2. The part-time day or evening student wishing to obtain a qualification in the subject of fuels, or fuel technology, and without the time, or the background, to study by existing facilities.
3. The full-time student, as an "Aide memoire" and to short-circuit the laborious task of note making.

In effect, the manual is a kind of "Fuel Technology without Tears" or "Fuels made Easy". The two volumes are complementary, and numerous cross-references obviate the necessity for repetition of subject matter.

The complete set of Data Sheets represents a cross section of the subjects of fuels and fuel technology and includes all items that are of primary importance and are usually selected for examination questions. They are couched in the simplest possible terms, with the maximum economy of words. There has been no attempt made to write an essay or treatise on any phase of the subject; brevity and conciseness being considered to be of more importance than good English or well rounded phrases.

The manual summarizes the best known text books relating to the various items covered. Those consulted are listed as unnumbered references at the end of each Data Sheet. Where it has been necessary to refer to original papers in the technological literature, these are listed as numbered references.

The student is recommended to follow his study of each Data Sheet, and any related lectures in courses which he attends, by further reading of the appropriate references. This is particularly important in advanced work, after the student had obtained minimum basic qualifications in Fuel Technology. The total literature consulted during the preparation of this manual, of approximately 800 small pages, extends to well over 10,000 large pages. This ensures a very considerable saving in the effort required from the student. As far as possible, the treatment of each Data Sheet has been made to conform to that in the references quoted, so that the student should have no difficulty in following the fuller subject treatment in the latter. To assist those with an engineering background, particular pains have been taken to explain chemical terms and notations in a simple manner. Similarly, to assist the student with a background of "Pure" science, the subject of heat engines and certain engineering items have been developed from first principles.

Because the English-speaking practitioner of Fuel Technology will normally work in English units, these are mainly used in the manual. In some cases, particularly in high temperature measurement, it is more usual to use Continental units and so these are used, with the English units placed in brackets. In Data Sheets where units are defined, both English and Continental units may be used, and references to text books giving more complete conversions are included.

In this manual, which is merely a concise and reasonably accurate summary of the existing knowledge and literature relating to fuel technology, no claim is made to originality of subject matter. Indeed I wish to acknowledge my debt to the authors of the excellent text books and original papers mentioned in the references and hope that they will be widely read by students who are introduced to the subject by this manual and who wish to proceed further in the matter. I also wish to thank the following firms and organizations who have supplied illustrations or information on various phases of the subject: Babcock & Wilcox Ltd., British Petroleum Co. Ltd., Davy–Ashmore Ltd., The Morgan Crucible Co. Ltd., Lurgi Ges. für Wärmetechnik m.b.H., South Eastern Gas Board, Shell Mex and B.P. Ltd.

My special thanks are due to Mr. M. C. Peters, who has read through the manuscript and provided many useful suggestions and additions; and to my Secretary, Mrs. Sheila Price, for her laborious and painstaking effort in converting a mass of scrappy notes into something approaching an ordered manual.

Kingston-on-Thames   WILFRID FRANCIS
April 1963

ILLUSTRATIONS

VOLUME I

Section A

Section B

Volume II

Section C

Section D

SECTION A
SOLID FUELS

DEFINITIONS AND UNITS

Fuels are organic combustible substances used solely or mainly for the production of useful heat. They may be divided into the three natural classes, solid, liquid and gaseous fuels.

Solid Fuels. The most important of these are:

Natural	*Artificial*
Wood	Wood charcoal
Peat	Peat charcoal
Lignites	⎰ Lignite briquettes
	⎱ Lignite coke
	⎧ Coal briquettes—uncarbonized
Hard coals—ranging from	⎪ Coal briquettes—carbonized
bituminous coals to anthra-	⎨ Low temperature coke
cites	⎪ Medium temperature coke
	⎩ High temperature coke

Liquid and Gaseous fuels—see Data Sheets Nos. 51 and 101

Calorific value—the heat evolved by the combustion of unit quantity of the fuel. (Weight for solid fuels; weight or volume for liquid fuels; volume for gaseous fuels.)

Gross calorific value—the heat evolved when all the products of combustion are cooled to atmospheric temperature, as in a bomb calorimeter. This includes the sensible and latent heat of evaporation of the water in the products of combustion.

Net calorific value—is the gross calorific value, less the sensible and latent heats of the water in the products of combustion when cooled to 60°F (15·5°C). The value of this deduction is 1055 B.t.u./lb (586 cal/g) of water condensed.

UNITS OF HEAT

British thermal unit (B.t.u.)—the amount of heat required to raise the temperature of 1 lb of water by 1°F from 60°F to 61°F.

Gram calorie or calorie (g cal or cal)—the amount of heat required to raise the temperature of 1 g water by 1°C from 15°C to 16°C.

1 B.t.u. = 252 g cal.

These units are inconveniently small for industrial purposes. Larger units of heat are:

Therm = 100,000 B.t.u. (gas industry)

Kg cal = 1000 g cal

Tonne. cal = 1000 kg cal

UNITS OF CALORIFIC VALUE

(a) *Solid Fuels*

English units—B.t.u./lb—the number of B.t.u. evolved by the combustion of 1 lb of fuel.

C.G.S. units—cal/g—the number of calories evolved by the combustion of 1 g of fuel.

Kcal/kg—the number of kilogram calories evolved by the combustion of 1 kg of fuel.

$$1 \text{ cal/g} = 1 \text{kg cal/kg} = 1.8 \text{ B.t.u./lb}$$
$$\text{cf. } 1°C = 1.8°F.$$

Sometimes, also, the unit kcal/g is used = 1000 cal/g.

(b) *Liquid Fuels*—as for solid fuels, by weight, or as B.t.u./gal.

(c) *Gaseous Fuels*

English units—B.t.u./ft^3

C.G.S. units—kg cal/m^3

Note that the temperature, pressure and humidity of a gas should be specified to prevent ambiguity, e.g.

1 B.t.u./ft^3 at 30 in., 60°F, wet

= 8.9 kg cal/m^3 at 760 mm, 15°C, wet.

Thermal Capacity or Specific Heat—The quantity of heat required to produce unit change of temperature in unit mass of a substance.

Units: B.t.u./lb/°F and cal/g/°C.

(Units are equal in both systems.)

Alternatively, Specific heat is the ratio of the thermal capacity of a substance to that of water at 60°F (15·5°C), since the thermal capacity of water at 15·5°C = 1·000.

In the case of gases, it is necessary to distinguish between the specific heat at constant volume, C_v, and the specific heat at constant pressure, C_p. These may be expressed on a weight or volume basis.

OTHER UNITS AND CONVERSION FACTORS

Temperature $1°C = 1·8°F$

$$°C \text{ to } °F: °C \times \tfrac{9}{5} + 32 = °F$$
$$°F \text{ to } °C: (°F - 32)\tfrac{5}{9} = °C$$

$°K$, or $\begin{matrix} °Abs \\ °R \end{matrix} \begin{cases} °C + 273 \\ °F + 460 \end{cases}$

Length

    1 inch = 2·54 cm = 0·0254 metres

    1 foot = 30·48 cm = 0·3048 metres

Area

    1 sq. inch = 6·45 cm^2 = 0·000645 m^2

    1 sq. ft = 929 cm^2 = 0·0929 m^2

    1 sq. yd = 8361 cm^2 = 0·8361 m^2

Volume

    1 cubic inch = 16·39 cm^3 = 0·01639 litres

    1 Imperial gallon = 4546 cm^3 = 4·546 litres = 1·201 U.S. gallons

    1 U.S. gallon = 3785 cm^3 = 3·785 litres

    1 cubic foot = 28·32 litres = 0·02832 m^3

    1 cubic metre = 35·315 ft^3

Mass

    1 gram = 15·432 grains = 0·0022 lb

    1 pound = 453·6 g = 7000 grains

    1 ton = 1016 kg = 1·016 tonnes = 1·12 U.S. tons

    1 U.S. ton = 907 kg = 0·907 tonnes = 0·893 tons

    1 tonne = 1000 kg = 2204·6 lb

Pressure

 1 atmosphere = 760 mm Hg at 0°C = 29·92 in. Hg
         = 33·9 ft H_2O = 1·033 kg/cm^2 = 14·695 lb/in^2
         = 2116 lb/ft^2

 1 in. w.g. = 0·036 lb/in^2 = 5·2 lb/ft^2

Heat and Work

 1 kg cal = 3·968 B.t.u. = 3087 ft lb = 4186 Joules

 1 Watt = 3·413 B.t.u./hr

 1 kilowatt hour = 3413 B.t.u./hr

 1 h.p. = 550 ft lb/sec = 33,000 ft lb/min

 1 therm = 100,000 B.t.u. = 25,200 kg cal

 1 B.t.u. = 0·252 kg cal = 778·3 ft lb^2 = 1055 Joules

 The quantity 778·3 ft lb is known as Joules' equivalent.

Thermal Conductivity

 1 B.t.u./ft^2/hr/°F/in. thickness = 0·124 kg cal/m^2/hr/°C/m

 1 B.t.u./ft^2/hr/°F/ft thickness = 1·488 kg cal/m^2/hr/°C/m

Sulphur in Flue Gases or Air

 1 grain sulphur per cubic ft = 2·3 mg sulphur per litre
            = 1·61 volumes SO_2 per million vols.

EXOTHERMIC AND ENDOTHERMIC REACTIONS

In fuel technology, an exothermic reaction or process is one in which heat is evolved, for example in combustion processes. An endothermic reaction or process is one in which heat is absorbed, for example in the production of water gas by the reaction of steam upon red-hot coke. cf. Data Sheet No. 107.

TERMS USED IN THE ANALYSIS OF SOLID FUELS

(coal specifically)
(for details see Data Sheet No. 28)

Proximate Analysis—the analysis in terms of percentages of moisture, volatile matter, ash, fixed carbon and sulphur; plus the calorific value (B.t.u./lb or cal/g).

Ultimate Analysis (elementary composition)—the analysis in terms of the percentages by weight of the elements present, viz.—carbon, hydrogen, oxygen, nitrogen and sulphur. Carbon and hydrogen are determined by combustion in oxygen, weighing the water and carbon dioxide produced. Sulphur and nitrogen are determined by the methods described in Data Sheet No. 28. Oxygen is calculated by taking the sum of the percentages of C, H, N and S from 100.

Moisture Content: Free—the percentage lost when moist, ground, coal is allowed to reach equilibrium with the atmosphere at 60°F (15·5°C).

Moisture Content: Fixed—the percentage of moisture present in the air-dried coal. Sometimes called "Interent" or "Equilibrium' moisture.

Ash Content—the percentage of residue obtained when coal is burned in air at 800°C in a muffle furnace under standard conditions.

Volatile Matter Content—the percentage of products evolved when coal is heated in a covered crucible to a temperature of 925°C under standard conditions.

Fixed Carbon—One hundred minus the sum of the percentages of ash, volatile matter and moisture.

Calorific Value—the gross calorific value of the coal as determined in a bomb calorimeter.

BASES OF REPORTING

The following bases are generally used for reporting analyses:
(a) As-received
(b) Dry
(c) Moisture and ash-free
(d) Mineral matter free.
For details see Data Sheet No. 28.

CAKING INDICES

(a) *Crucible swelling number*—Heat 1 g at 825°C for $2\frac{1}{2}$ min in a standard closed crucible. Compare the profile of the coke button with those outlined in a series of standards of increasing swelling indices from 1 to 9 by $\frac{1}{2}$ units.

(b) *Carbonization assay—Gray–King method*—Heat 20 g of coal in a standard cylindrical horizontal glass retort at 600°C for $1\frac{1}{4}$ hr and compare the profile of the carbonized residue (low temperature char or coke) with those formed from a series of standard coals producing coke types A to G_3 and G_4 to G_{10}.

Coking Coal—a coal that can be used for the production of commercial varieties of coke by carbonization.

REFERENCES

FRANCIS, W. *Boiler House and Power Station Chemistry*. London, 1962.
SPIERS, H. M. *Technical Data on Fuel*. London, 1952.

WOOD

WOOD may be burned directly as a fuel, or it may first be converted into charcoal or producer gas. It is used extensively in semi-tropical or tropical countries where forests are abundant and coal is not available cheaply.

COMPOSITION

The principal chemical components of wood are cellulose and ligno-cellulose. Other important inflammable components are resins and waxes. The major non-inflammable component of wood is water. Freshly cut trees contain between 25 and 50% of water. Air-dried wood contains between 10 and 15%. Ash is very small, usually less than 0·6%. Volatile products at 900°C = 60 to 75%. Variations in the proportions of organic components determine the observed variations in the calorific values of wood. The calorific value of pure cellulose is 4150 cal/g (7480 B.t.u./lb). Wood resin and wood wax approximate to 9450 cal/g (17,000 B.t.u./lb). The proportions of resins and waxes in most woods are small, as shown in the table below:

COMPOSITION OF SOME COMMON TREES (AIR-DRIED ASH FREE)

	Beech	Chestnut	Pine
Moisture %	12·6	12·0	12·9
Cellulose %	45·5	52·6	53·3
Resin + wax %	0·4	1·1	1·6
Water soluble %	2·4	5·4	4·0
Lignin %	39·1	28·9	28·2

The formation of wood in nature is an endothermic process, absorbing approximately 555 cal/g (1000 B.t.u./lb). This is liberated at about 270°C (518°F) during carbonization or combustion.

The calorific values of the dried woods from the above trees vary from about 4450 cal/g (8000 B.t.u./lb) to about 5000 cal/g (9000 B.t.u./lb). Ultimate analyses on the dry–ash free basis are: Carbon 49 to 51%, hydrogen 5·9 to 6·2%, oxygen 45 to 43%. Density $\ngtr$ 1.0. cf. coals 1·4–1·5.

COMBUSTION CHARACTERISTICS OF WOOD

1. Easily ignited.
2. Does not burn readily in large pieces because of layers of semi-fused ash forming on the surface.
3. Produces a long, non-smoky, flame when burned in excess air.
4. Sawdust burns readily—can be made into binderless briquettes at pressures of 2 to 5 ton/in^2.

CARBONIZATION OF WOOD — WOOD CHARCOAL

1. Ancient "charcoal-burning" process—wood burned in large heaps with restricted air. Yield of charcoal less than 20%. Gas and by-products lost.
2. At low temperatures in metal retorts. Maximum temperature 350°C (662°F). Yields as in table page 15:
   Wood charcoal has the following characteristics:
   Low ash < 2·5%
   Volatile matter 12–17%
   Easily ignited and burns at low rates
     (C.A.B. value 0·007. Cf. Data Sheet No. 25.)
   High absorptive capacity for vapours
   Calorific value 13,700–14,000 B.t.u./lb (7600–7800 cal/g)
   Uses: Reducing agent for Swedish iron ores
           Fuel for producer gas vehicles
           Fuel for heating food in mobile canteens, etc.

LOW TEMPERATURE CARBONIZATION OF WOODS

	Pine	Beech
Charcoal %	37·8	35·0
Gases % CO_2	10·1	10·9
C_2H_4	0·2	0·2
CO	3·7	4·2
CH_4	0·6	0·5
Methyl alcohol %	0·9	2·1
Acetone %	0·2	0·2
Methyl acetate %	0·01	0·03
Acetic acid %	3·5	6·0
Sodium acetate soluble material %	8·0	5·9
Stockholm tar %	11·8	8·1
Water %	22·3	26·6

3. At high temperatures (1000°C to 1200°C). For town gas. Yields on dry fir: Charcoal 20%, gas 30,000 ft^3/ton, gross C.V. of gas 360 B.t.u./ft^3.

PRODUCER GAS FROM WOOD

Wood has recently been used successfully for the production of producer gas in India. The gas may be used as fuel, or for the synthesis of ammonia.

Yield of gas per 1000 lb dry wood (used with natural water content)	260,000 ft^3
$CO + H_2$ in gas	42%
C. V. of gas	150 B.t.u./ft^3

REFERENCES

BRAME, J. S. S. and KING, J. G. *Fuel—Solid, Liquid and Gaseous*. London, 1956.
BUNBURY, H. M. *The Destructive Distillation of Wood*. London, 1923.

PEAT

PEAT is a brown fibrous mass of partially decayed plant material that has accumulated *in situ* under waterlogged conditions. The agencies causing decay are mainly aerobic bacteria, near the surface (oxidizing conditions) and increasingly anaerobic (reducing) with increasing depth. Peat bogs occur in many locations at the present time. World resources of peat are estimated at 1200×10^8 tons, of which some 700×10^8 tons exist in the U.S.S.R. The present annual consumption of peat is about 0.2×10^8 tons (air-dried basis).

TYPES AND COMPOSITION

Composition depends upon type, depth in the deposit, and age. Bog peat consists mainly of mosses. Forest peat consists of the decayed products of massive trees. It is analogous to the deposits of plant debris forming coal (cf. Data Sheet No. 4). The basic change in chemical composition is the formation of humic acids (cf. the "humus" of soils) from the celluloses and proteins of the parent woody tissues.

Moisture Wet Peat $> 95\% H_2O$
            Cut peat $80-90\% H_2O$
            Air-dried peat $25\% H_2O$

Ash—usually about 3.0%, $> 10\%$ in areas subject to flooding.

Calorific Value
  Average values, dry basis   7000 to 9000 B.t.u./lb
                              4000 to 5000 cal/g

Resins and Waxes
Montan wax—varies from 3 to 12%
Resin content of wax—varies from 10 to 45%

ULTIMATE ANALYSIS (ash-free–dry basis)

	Moss Peat; recent	*Forest; recent*	*Peat; old*
Carbon %	51·1	55·5	59·5
Hydrogen %	6·1	5·8	5·8
Nitrogen %	1·8	1·5	2·3
Sulphur %	0·6	0·8	1·0
Oxygen %	40·4	36·4	31·4

COMMERCIAL PRODUCTION OF PEAT

Hand winning—bog drained—peat sods cut by hand in spring— air dried in stacks for 2–3 months.
Mechanical
    (a) use of bucket dredgers on endless chain
    (b) maceration, mixing, and extruding
    (c) air drying of extruded blocks
Milled Peat—half-inch surface layers are milled from the surface and air dried to 45% moisture. Product used directly in boilers or briquetted.
Hydro Peat—high pressure water jets wash peat into shallow layers of about 8 in. Drained mass cut into sods for air drying.

COMBUSTION CHARACTERISTICS OF PEAT

1. Low C.V. and high proportion of moisture reduces furnace temperature and efficiency.
2. Low bulk density—20 lb per ft^3—reduces capacity of furnace and increases storage and transport capacity.
3. Friable nature causes appreciable losses on handling.

Powdered Peat—now used extensively for power stations in Sweden, Russia and Eire.

Briquetting—self-binding briquettes made readily from air-dried peat in extrusion type (or ring-roll) machines.

Peat charcoal—made by carbonizing peat, or peat briquettes, at low temperatures in steel retorts, as in the carbonization of wood (cf. Data Sheet No. 2) or by carbonizing peat briquettes by the Lurgi Spülgas process (cf. Data Sheet No. 4).

LOW TEMPERATURE CARBONIZATION OF PEAT

Products obtained from air-dried peat carbonized in a Lottman oven are shown below:

LOW TEMPERATURE CARBONIZATION OF PEATS

	Light Fibrous Peat	Compact Fibrous Peat	Woody Peat
Charcoal %	30·00	33·43	30·34
Tar %	6·00	4·68	6·96
Water %	33·00	42·50	37·50
Gases %	31·00	19·29	25·20
% ash in peat	1·34	1·35	1·87
% ash in charcoal	3·33	2·99	4·93
Density of peat	0·26	0·52	0·48
Density of charcoal	0·230	0·208	0·355

The gas is used for heating the ovens. The products obtained from 100 lb of tar are:

> 10 lb paraffin wax
> 58 lb illuminating oil
> 12 lb creosote oil (similar to wood creosote)

From 200 gal of water are obtained:

> 10 lb ammonium sulphate
> 15 lb calcium acetate
> 15 lb methyl alcohol

TYPICAL ANALYSES OF PEAT AND
WOOD CHARCOALS

	Peat	Wood
Carbon %	84·2	85·2
Hydrogen %	1·9	2·9
Oxygen + nitrogen %	7·8	3·5
Ash %	3·1	2·5
Moisture	3·0	5·9
Calorific Value B.t.u./lb.	12,600	13,500

PRODUCER GAS FROM PEAT

Producer gas can be made from air-dried peat in conventional gas plants (cf. Data Sheet No. 106) at efficiencies of 80–85%. The natural water content of the peat obviates the necessity for the addition of water to the blast, which is the normal practice with coal. In Germany pressure and suction type producers have operated satisfactorily, with high yields of gas and good recovery of ammonia. In the Körting type of producer two fire zones are used; the gases from the upper part of the producer, containing tarry matter, are fed to the lower fire zone, which decomposes the tar. The clean gas, which is very suitable for gas engines has the composition:

CO_2	13·3%
CO	17·6%
H_2	10·9%
CH_4	2·5%
N_2	55·7%
Gas yield:	90,000 ft³/ton
C.V.	110 B.t.u./ft³
Ammonium sulphate	120 lb/ton

REFERENCES

BRAME, J. S. S. and KING, J. G. *Fuel—Solid, Liquid and Gaseous*. London, 1956.
MARTIN G. and FRANCIS W. *Industrial and Manufacturing Chemistry*, Part II, Vol. I. London, 1954.

B

LIGNITES AND SUB-BITUMINOUS COALS

LIGNITES are immature coals that are intermediate in composition between peat and bituminous coals. They are of tertiary or late mesozoic age (cretaceous), that is between 10 and 100×10^6 years old. They often occur in thick seams, varying from a few feet in Pakistan and Borneo to over 1000 ft thick in Victoria, Australia. In Germany and Victoria they are of industrial importance as fuels, including the manufacture of synthesis gas and towns gas. Sub-bituminous coals, which are included in this general class of coals and are harder and more mature than lignites and brown coals, occur in the U.S. in Montana, Wyoming, Colorado and Utah. The most immature coals, soft brown coals, cannot be distinguished chemically from mature peats. Some mature lignites, e.g. in Pakistan, Borneo and Utah possess coking properties.

TYPICAL ULTIMATE ANALYSES (ash-free–dry basis)

Origin	Description	C%	H%	O + N + S%
Nigeria	Earthy brown lignite	64·5	6·5	29·0
Victoria	Brown lignite	67·4	4·7	27·9
Nigeria	,, ,,	70·8	6·4	22·8
Wyoming, U.S.A.	,, ,,	71·9	5·4	22·7
N. Dakota, U.S.A.	,, ,,	72·9	4·9	22·2
Borneo	Black lignite	72·1	4·9	23·0
Pakistan	,, ,,	74·0	6·7	28·3
Colorado, U.S.A.	Sub-bituminous	78·4	5·1	16·5

Proximate Analyses
H$_2$O—as mined, varies from 20% to 75%
—air dried, varies from 12% to 20%

Ash (dry basis) varies from ca. 3% to $>30\%$
Volatile Matter
  (ash-free dry basis)varies from ca. 40% to $>50\%$
Sulphur   varies from $<1\%$ to $>12\%$ (Pakistan)
Calorific Value
  (ash-free–dry basis) varies from ca. 9000 B.t.u./lb to 12,600
                                    B.t.u./lb
                                ca. 5000 cal/g to 7000 cal/g

UTILIZATION

1. *Raw Lignite*

(a) Small scale–air dried-in furnaces fitted with a "fore set" hearth.
(b) Pulverized fuel—as mined lignite is ground in mills. through which passes preheated air at 800°F (425°C)—hot mixture passes directly into furnace.

2. *Briquettes*

(a) Binderless briquettes—air dried lignite at equilibrium moisture content ($12\frac{1}{2}$ to 15%) briquetted without binder by extrusion press (2 to 5 tons/in^2 pressure) or by ring-roll press (>10 ton/in^2 pressure).
(b) Carbonized binderless briquettes—Lurgi Spülgas process. The lignite briquettes (if a strong coke is required) or the raw lignite (if small, weak, coke is required) are dried at 200–250°C and carbonized at 650–800°C by direct contact with hot gases from the combustion of Lurgi gas in a carbonizing retort of capacity 350–450 tons per day (see FIG. 1). The fuel passes down the plant in three zones: (1) drying, (2) carbonizing, (3) cooling. Circulating gas in zones (1) and (3) dries the lignite and cools the coke. Gas from the process burns in an external chamber and passes through zone (2). The gases from zone (2) then pass through coolers and by-product plant for the recovery of motor spirit, oil, paraffin

wax, and tar. Pure phenols may be recovered from the oil during the refining process and the tar may be processed by several alternative refining processes.

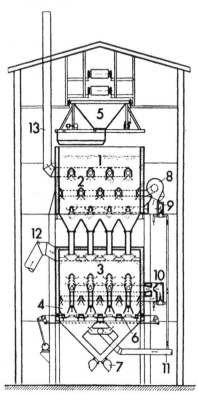

FIG. 4.1. Elevation of a Lurgi Direct Heating Carbonization Plant.

1. Coal hopper
2. Drying zone
3. Carbonizing zone
4. Coke cooling zone
5. Coal charging car
6. Coke discharging mechanism
7. Coke discharging pockets
8. Circulating fan for drying zone
9. Combustion chamber for drying zone
10. Combustion chamber for carbonizing zone
11. Admission of purified circulating gas
12. Offtake for mixture of circulating gas and carbonization gas
13. Offtake for waste gas from drying zone

MATERIAL AND HEAT BALANCES FOR A LURGI DIRECT HEATING
PLANT, PER LB OF FUEL

Brown coal briquettes containing 16% of water and 14·6%
tar (Fischer Assay)

	lb	B.t.u./lb	Percentage of Heat
Input:			
Brown coal briquettes	1·000	9876·6	99·92
Air for combustion	0·425	8·1	0·08
Total	1·425	9884·7	100·00
Output:			
Semi-coke	0·445	5627·5	56·96
Surplus gas*	0·253	676·7	6·84
Refined tar	0·116	2086·9	21·10
Light spirit			
(boiling below 200°C)	0·023	434·0	4·39
Liquor	0·081	2·9	0·03
Residue	0·009	122·2	1·23
Gas loss	0·001	12·4	0·13
Heat in cooling water	—	225·9	2·28
Waste gases	0·487	185·3	1·88
Loss	0·010	510·9	5·16
Totals	1·425	9884·7	100·00

* 7400 ft³/ton (at 30 in. and 60°F)

NATURE OF COKE

The coke from the ring-roll briquettes, obtained as slightly
shrunken replicas of the uncarbonized briquettes, is hard and of high
calorific value (ca. 12,000 B.t.u./lb). That from unbriquetted lignite
is small and weak. It is suitable for domestic purposes and for the
manufacture of sintered briquettes for metallurgical processes.

REFERENCE

MARTIN, G. and FRANCIS, W. *Industrial and Manufacturing Chemistry*, Part II,
Vol. I. London, 1954.

THE ORIGIN OF COAL

DEFINITION

Coal is a compact, stratified mass of mummified plant debris, interspersed with smaller amounts of inorganic matter and covered by sedimentary rocks. The chemical properties of any coal depend upon the proportions of the different chemical components present in the parent plant debris; the nature and extent of the changes which these components have undergone since their deposition; and the nature and quantity of the inorganic matter present.

Peat may be considered to be an immature coal and closely resembles, in composition and properties, the most immature of true coals, viz. young brown coals.

Agencies causing the change from plant tissues to coal are:

1. Bacteria—as during the formation of peat (cf. Data Sheet No. 3) —mainly before the deposit is covered by an impervious sedimentary layer.
2. Temperature and time—operating mainly after bacterial action has ceased.
3. Pressure—increasing with increasing depth of burial and accentuated by severe earth movements, e.g. during the folding or buckling of strata.

RANK

The degree of change of chemical composition of a coal, within the series of fossil fuels from peat to anthracite, is known as the rank of that coal. The rank of a coal may be measured by several parameters, the most important of which are ultimate and proximate analyses (see Data Sheets Nos. 1 and 28).

MODE OF FORMATION OF COAL FORMING DEPOSITS

1. *Drift origin*—the deposition from water of masses of plant debris in shallow basins, lakes, deltas and estuaries. If the water is fresh or brackish and the deposits are shallow, attack by aerobic bacteria is mainly oxidizing in character and the resultant coal contains a lower hydrogen/carbon ratio than the mean. If sea water is the carrying agent, or if the deposit is covered by marine inorganic sediments, reducing conditions occur. The resulting coals are relatively rich in hydrogen and possess coking properties (within certain limits of rank).

2. In situ *origin*—plants grew and died in the same place, under conditions generally similar to those existing in the formation of modern forest-type peat bogs. The growth of the resulting peat bog was arrested by covering with sedimentary inorganic deposits. Conditions of decay during the peat stage were oxidizing or reducing according to the depth in the peat deposit. Flooding by sea water, or cover by marine deposits, favoured reducing conditions. Shallow deposits, or fresh water deposits, favoured oxidizing conditions.

CYCLIC FORMATION OF DEPOSITS

The cycles of accumulation of plant debris (by either process) and cover by sedimentary deposits were repeated several (or many) times in one area, causing several seams of coal to be formed, each separated by many feet of sedimentary rocks. Such a formation of stratified coal seams and sedimentary rocks is known as a Coal Measure.

AGE OF COAL MEASURES

Geological System		Approximate Mean Age, in years	Rank of Coals Formed
Era	Period		
Upper Paleozoic	Carboniferous Permian	250×10^6 210×10^6	Bituminous coals, carbonaceous coals and anthracites
Mesozoic	Triassic Jurassic Cretaceous	180×10^6 150×10^6 100×10^6	Bituminous Bituminous Sub-bituminous and bituminous
Tertiary	Eocene Oligocene Miocene	60×10^6 40×10^6 20×10^6	Lignites and sub-bituminous Lignites Lignites
Quaternary	Pleistocene	1×10^6	Peat only

APPROXIMATE PERCENTAGES OF CARBON AND HYDROGEN IN THE ABOVE RANKS OF COAL (pure coal basis)

	Carbon %	Hydrogen %
Anthracites	93–95	3·8–2·8
Carbonaceous	91–93	4·25–3·8
Bituminous	80–91	5·6–4·25
Sub-bituminous	75–80	5·6–5·1
Lignites	60–75	5·7–5·0

THE CHANGE FROM FOREST DEBRIS TO PEAT

The principal chemical components of trees, such as were the parents of forest peats and coals, with their average ultimate analyses and probable empirical formulae are shown in the table on page 23.

Plant Tissue	Compounds Present	Percentage of Tissue	Average Ultimate Analysis %					Typical Empirical Formula
			C	H	O	N	S	
Wood, Xylem or Cortex	Cellulose	45–65	44·4	6·2	49·4			$(C_6H_{10}O_5)n$
	Lignin	20–40	63·2	6·1	30·7			$C_{30}H_{33}O_{11}$
	Water and proteins in solution	12–16	53·5	7·0	22·0	15·5	2·0	$C_{72}H_{112}N_{18}O_{22}S$: (Protein only)
	Resins	0·5–15·0	80·0	10·0	10·0			$C_{20}H_{30}O_2$
	Waxes	0·2–4·0	82·0	14·2	3·8			$C_{29}H_{60}O$

In a peat bog the bacterial processes are only partially completed, because some of the products which accumulate in the deposit are aseptic and prevent the complete breakdown of the plant tissues. Resins and waxy plant skins resist bacterial decay more strongly than wood, so these compounds tend to accumulate in the deposit. The celluloses, lignin and protein are partially decomposed and their residuals combine to form products of varying composition that resemble humus (known by gardeners to be an essential feature of

MODE OF DECAY OF PLANT DEBRIS IN PEAT BOG

Condition	pH	Mode of Decay	Nature and Composition of Main Product
In shallow water	4·5–6·0	In top layers of peat bog, with medium aeration. Partial loss of cellulose and hemi-cellulose. Hydrolysis and partial oxidation of lignin, tannin and proteins. Formation of gels of sub-hydrous humic acids, plus attritus (resins, cuticles, etc.)	Sub-hydrous humus $C = 50\%$ $H = 4·5\%$ $O = 44·7\%$ $N = 0·5\%$ $S = 0·3\%$
In stagnant shallow water	3·0–4·5	Moderately deep in peat-bog. Little aeration, less destruction of cellulose. Start of mild reducing conditions. Formation of normal humus from less oxidized cellulose, lignin, tannin and protein. Structured or unstructured gels of humic acids, slimes and attritus.	Normal humus $C = 55\%$ $H = 5·5\%$ $O = 37·5\%$ $N = 1·5\%$ $S = 0·5\%$
Lowest layers of peat deposit	3·0	Maximum depth of peat bog. No aeration—reducing conditions. Maximum preservation of plant tissues. Formation of per-hydrous humus, with or without attritus.	Per-hydrous humus $C = 60\%$ $H = 6·0\%$ $O = 29·0\%$ $N = 2·5\%$ $S = 2·0\%$

fertile soil). More precisely, the products are known as humic acids, since they are soluble in dilute alkaline solutions. This property is suppressed during the later conversion to mature coals. In the latter, the derivatives of humus (humic acids) are known as ulmins.

The variations in chemical composition of the humus with the different conditions of bacterial decay in a wet deposit of peat-forming plants are shown in the table on page 24.

The type chemical compounds of peats can be separated by solvent extraction or sometimes, by physical means. The humus or humic acid occasionally occurs as a thick jelly, called Dopplerite (after its discoverer Doppler). Typical analyses of Dopplerite, resins, and waxes (Montan wax) found in peat are shown below.

Material	Compounds Present	Percentage on Peat	Average Ultimate Analysis % C H O	Empirical Formula
Peat	(Dopplerite) Humic acid	70–90	56·5 5·5 38·0	$(C_{30}H_{35}O_{15})n$ or $(C_6H_7O_3)n$
	Resins	5–30	80·0 11·0 9·0	
	Waxes		80·5 13·0 6·5	

THE CHANGE FROM PEAT TO MATURE COAL

Soon after burial under an impervious cover, all bacterial action ceases and subsequent chemical changes taking place in the deposit are caused by:

(a) Temperature—in normal coals not exceeding 300°C (572°F)
—increasing with increasing depth.

(b) Pressure—from a few pounds to many hundred pounds per sq. in.
—important mainly in its effect on temperature.
—particularly dynamic pressure due to resistance to earth movements.

(c) Time—extending from ca. 10×10^6 years for young brown coals to ca. 300×10^6 years, in the case of the most mature coals.

HILT'S LAW

The rate of a chemical change doubles for a rise of 5°C to 10°C; so that coals in the lower seams of coal measures are generally more mature (i.e. of higher rank) than those of higher seams because of the temperature gradient of the earth's crust (e.g. increasing by 1°C per 100 ft depth in India). This variation of rank with depth is known as Hilt's Law.

NATURE OF CHEMICAL CHANGES ASSOCIATED WITH INCREASE IN RANK

1. Progressive decrease in equilibrium moisture content (inherent water, characteristic of the colloidal structure of coal).
2. Progressive loss of hydrogen, oxygen, nitrogen and sulphur, with a corresponding increase in carbon.
3. Progressive loss of volatile matter.
4. Progressive increase in calorific value, up to the rank of carbonaceous coals (smokeless steam coals).
5. Development, over a certain range of rank, of coking properties.
These changes will be discussed further in relation to the classification of coals in Data Sheet No. 6.

OVERALL CHANGE IN COMPOSITION OF WOOD DURING THE FORMATION OF COAL

1. Cellulose to bituminous coal according to Renault (1900)
$$(C_6H_{10}O_5)_4 = C_9H_6O + 7CH_4 + 8CO_2 + 3H_2O$$
cellulose → bituminous coal + methane + carbon dioxide + water
2. Cellulose to lignite and bituminous coal — Parr (1910)
$$(C_6H_{10}O_5)_5 = C_{20}H_{22}O_4 + 3CH_4 + 8H_2O + 6CO_2 + CO$$
cellulose → lignite
$$(C_6H_{10}O_5)_6 = C_{22}H_{20}O_3 + 5CH_4 + 10H_2O + 8CO_2 + CO$$
cellulose → bituminous coal

3. According to Mott[1] the following changes occur in the series wood to anthracite:

Stage	Products Evolved	Yield % (Wood = 100)	Gases ft^3/ton CH₄	CO₂
Wood to low rank lignite	$64H_2O + 8CH_4 + CO_2$	73·5	1350	150
Low rank lignite to low rank bituminous coal	CO_2	53·4	nil	5180
Low rank bituminous coal to semi-anthracite	*1st stage* $1·42\ H_2O + 0·43CH_4 + CO_2$	47·4	475	1220
	2nd stage $5H_2O + 3CH_4 + CO_2$	45·1	510	105
	3rd stage $1·45\ H_2O + 5·8\ CH_4 + CO_2$	41·3	2600	430
Semi-anthracite to anthracite	$36CH_4 + H_2O$	37·2	5140	nil

The changes suggested by Mott account for the following phenomena:

1. The increasing rate of fall of the hydrogen content of bituminous coals in the final stage of change from bituminous coals to semi-anthracites (carbonaceous coals) between carbon percent 88 to 92·3, corresponding to an increase in methane evolved.
2. The more pronounced fall in hydrogen observed during the transition from semi-anthracite (carbonaceous or smokeless steam coal) to anthracite, carbon percent 92·3 to 95, because of the considerable increase in methane evolved.
3. The large quantities of methane (fire-damp) associated with coal measures containing carbonaceous coals and anthracites.
4. The small reduction in calorific value of coal during the transition from smokeless steam coal to anthracite (methane has a calorific

value of ca. 1000 B.t.u./ft^3, equivalent to 22,400 B.t.u./lb, which is far greater than the maximum value of any pure coal, viz. 15,800 B.t.u./lb).

USE OF "PURE-COAL" BASIS IN COAL TERMINOLOGY

Because of the varying proportions of water and inorganic matter in commercial varieties of coal, it is usual, when dealing with fundamental issues, to refer all data and observations to the "pure-coal" substance (sometimes called the "organic" portion of coal, or the "dry-mineral matter-free" portion).

When dealing with practical, or commercial issues, data or discussions, reference is to the "as-received" basis, or to some other suitable basis after the coals have been prepared for commercial utilization. In this data sheet, the discussion has been centred round the pure coal substance. In subsequent sheets the data usually relate to coals containing both moisture and mineral matter.

REFERENCES

1. Mott, R. A. *Fuel*, **21**, 129 (1942): **22**, 20 (1943).
Francis, W. *Coal—its formation and composition*. London, 1961.

THE CLASSIFICATION OF COALS

GENERAL

1. Most systems are based upon some characteristic property of the coal series that changes uniformly and progressively with increase in "maturity" or "rank" as the series is ascended.

2. The properties generally used for this purpose are either "Ultimate analysis" (often called the "Elementary composition") or "Proximate analysis" (cf. Data Sheet No. 1).

3. The items of proximate analysis used include water (free and inherent), volatile matter and calorific value. Recent classifications developed primarily for commercial purposes, such as the N.C.B. and E.C.E., also include the coking properties of coals.

4. Since coals contain varying amounts of inorganic matter (not related to rank) most scientific systems of classification are based on the "mineral matter free" or "ash-free-dry" basis of analysis.

5. The simplest method for determining the amount of mineral matter present in a coal is to determine the ash and sulphur contents and to make corrections for the changes taking place in these during combustion. The Parr formula for doing this is:

Total Inorganic Matter = Moisture + 1·08 Ash + 0·55 Sulphur

where moisture, ash and sulphur represent the percentages

29

of these substances found by analysis of the coal. A recent, more detailed, method is used in para II b. of this Data Sheet.

I. METHODS BASED UPON ULTIMATE ANALYSIS

1. *Regnault, 1837.* The first satisfactory classification in terms of ultimate analysis.
2. *Grüner, 1874.* A development of the Regnault classification in which numerical limits were given for carbon, hydrogen and volatile matter to the higher rank coals defined by Regnault.
3. *Grüner–Bousquet, 1911.* Grüner's son, with Bousquet, modified the earlier classifications and divided coals above the rank of lignite into six classes based upon their carbon content and drew up a table in which the principal features of the six classes were defined in terms of hydrogen, fixed carbon, volatile matter, calorific value, the nature of the residue obtained on carbonization and the behaviour of the coals during combustion. Names were given to the six classes of coals based upon the latter characteristic, e.g. "Dry, long flame", "Fat, short flame" etc. Later, Brame, and then Bone, modified this classification to make it more applicable to coals found in Great Britain. See table on page 31.
4. *Grout and Ralston (U.S.A.).* Grout, in 1907, plotted the ultimate analyses of a large number of coals, calculated to the ash-free–dry basis, on a tri-axial diagram and found that humic coals lie on a narrow band, with cannel coals, which are rich in hydrogen, well above the band.

   Ralston, in 1915, plotted all analyses then published by the U.S. Government on a tri-axial diagram in which $C + H + O = 100\%$ and confirmed the observations made by Grout. He found that coals of equal volatile matter and equal calorific value fall on approximately straight lines inclined at an angle to the C, H and O axes.
5. *Seyler, 1900–1957.* In 1900 Seyler proposed a system of classification for high rank coals in which they were divided into a series of species, according to carbon content, and genera,

No. of Class	Character of Coal	C %	H %	F.C. %	V.M. %	C.V. cal/g	Nature of Coke
I	Dry, long flame, non-caking	75–80	4·5–5·5	60–55	40–45	8000–8500	Powdery or slightly coherent
II	Fat, long flame	80–85	5·0–5·8	68–60	32–40	8500–8800	Caked, but friable
III	Fat, "properly named"	84–89	5·0–5·5	74–68	26–32	8800–9300	Caked, moderately compact
IV	Fat, short flame	88–91	4·5–5·5	82–74	18–26	9300–9600	Caked, very compact, lustrous
V	Lean coals—semi-anthracites	90–93	4·0–5·5	90–82	10–18	9200–9600	Powdery or slightly coherent
VI	Anthracites	93–95	4·0–2·0	92–90	8–10	9110–9200	Non-coherent—powdery

N.B. (1) Data are on the ash-free-dry basis.
(2) Calorific values are too high, by modern standards, by ca. 600 cal/g.

C

according to hydrogen content. He gave limits to the C and H percentages in the various classes and, later, plotted all available analyses for high rank coals on rectangular co-ordinates, representing % carbon and % hydrogen on the "pure coal basis" (C + H + O = 100). He found that all normal

SEYLER'S CLASSIFICATION — SIMPLIFIED

Coal Rank	Carbon Range %	Hydrogen %	V.M. %	C.V. B.t.u./lb	B.S. Swelling Index
Anthracite	>93·3	3·0–3·8	5–10	15,400	1
Carbonaceous					
Semi-anthracite	93·3–91·2	3.8–4.4	10–14	17,500	1
Semi-bituminous		4·4–5·0	14–20	15,800	3½
Bituminous					
Meta-	91·2–89·0	4·4–5·4	20–28	15,700	9
Ortho-	89·0–87·0	4·7–5·6	28–31	15.500	9
Para-	87·0–84·0	4·9–5·7	31–36	15,000	6
Lignitous					
Meta-	84·0–80·0	5·0–5·7	36–42	14,300	2
Ortho-	80·0–75·0	5·0–5·7	42–49	13,300	1
Lignite	<75·0	5·0–5·7	49–59	11,700	1

high rank coals are placed within a narrow band between C = 75% and 95·0% and hydrogen from 3·0% to 5·7%, with a maximum width equivalent to 0·7% hydrogen. Any coals falling above this band he considered to be abnormally rich in hydrogen and so may be called "per-hydrous" and any coals falling below this band may be called "sub-hydrous". He also found that lines of equal volatile matter (called "iso-vols") and of equal calorific value (called "iso-cals") are approximately at right angles to each other and are equally spaced, except for anthracites. He therefore added subsidiary axes to his chart for volatile matter and C.V. and devised mathematical equations to express the relationship between C:H:V.M: and

C.V. (Cf. Data Sheet No. 8). He later added lines of equal caking characteristics to his chart (as determined by the B.S. Swelling Index). The table on page 32 gives the essential features of Seyler's classification.

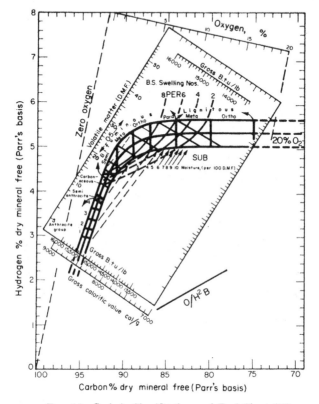

FIG. 6.1   Seyler's Classification and Fuel Chart 47B.

Seyler's classification, chart and relationships, together provide the most accurate and useful data obtainable from any classification based primarily upon ultimate analysis.

Seyler's Classification Chart is reproduced as Fig. 6.1.

II. METHODS BASED UPON PROXIMATE ANALYSIS

Three major classifications have been developed in recent years based upon the proximate analyses of coals. These are the A.S.T.M. Classification, developed in the U.S.A.: the Fuel Research Board/ N.C.B. classification, developed in England; and the International Classification of Hard Coals by Type, by the Economic Commission for Europe (E.C.E.)

1. *A.S.T.M. Classification.* Coals containing less than 31 % V.M. on the mineral matter free basis (Parr Formula) are classified only on the basis of "Fixed Carbon", i.e. $100 - \%$V.M. They are divided into five groups: $>98\%$ F.C.; $98-92\%$ F.C.; $92-86\%$ F.C.; $86-78\%$ F.C. and $78-69\%$ F.C.

The first three of these groups are called Anthracites and the last two are called Bituminous coals. The remaining bituminous coals, the sub-bituminous coals and lignites are then classified into groups as determined by the calorific value of the coals containing their "Natural bed moisture", that is the coals as mined but free from any moisture on the surface of the lumps. The classification includes three groups of bituminous coals with moist C.V. from $>14,000$ to $>13,000$ B.t.u./lb; three groups of sub-bituminous coals with moist C.V. $<13,000$ to $<8,300$ B.t.u./lb and two groups of lignitic coals with moist C.V. <8300 B.t.u./lb. The classification also differentiates between consolidated and unconsolidated lignites and between the weathering characteristics of sub-bituminous and lignitic coals.

2. *F.R.B./N.C.B.—Coal Rank Code Numbers.* The system was devised during the 1939–1945 war with a numerical background in order to facilitate the mechanical card indexing of data; but it has come into general use because of its simplicity and convenience. The revised 1956 code is summarized below, and is based upon the volatile matter, expressed upon the dry, mineral matter free basis and the coking power of clean material (containing not $>10.0\%$ ash) as determined in the Gray-King Assay. (Cf. Data Sheet No. 28.)

Group	Class	Sub-class	Volatile Matter % (d.m.m.f. basis)	Gray-King Coke Type	General Description
100			< 9·1	A	
	101		< 6·1	A	*Anthracites*
	102		6·1–9·0		
200			9·1–19·5	A to G.8	*Low Volatile steam coals*
	201		9·1–13·5	A to C	
		201a	9·1–11·5	A to B	Dry steam coals
		201b	11·6–13·5	B to C	
	202		13·6–15·0	B to G	
	203		15·1–17·0	E to G.4	Coking steam coals
	204		17·1–19·5	G.1 to G.8	
	206		9·1–19·5	A to B for V.M. 9·1–15·0 A to D for V.M. 15·1–19·5	Heat altered low volatile steam coals
300			19·6–32·0	A to > G.9.	*Medium Volatile coals*
	301		19·6–32·0		
		301a	19·6–27·5	> G.4	Prime Coking Coals
		301b	27·6–32·0		
	305		19·6–32·0	G to G.3	Mainly heat
	306		19·6–32·0	A to F	altered coals
400–900			> 32·0	A to > G.9	*High Volatile Coals*
400			> 32·0		Very strongly
	401		32·1–36·0	G.9 or >	caking coals
	402		> 36·0		
500			> 32·0		Strongly caking
	501		32·1–36·0	G.5 to G.8	coals
	502		> 36·0		
600			> 32·0		Medium caking
	601		32·1–36·0	G.1 to G.4	coals
	602		> 36·0		
700			> 32·0		Weakly caking
	701		32·1–36·0	E to G	coals
	702		> 36·0		
800			> 32·0		Very weakly caking
	801		32·1–36·0	C to D	coals
	802		> 36·0		
900			> 32·0		Non-caking coals
	901		32·1–36·0	A to B	
	902		> 36·0		

The volatile matter is calculated to the dry mineral matter free basis after correcting the ash to "mineral matter" by one of the usual formulae, such as

Mineral Matter $= 1 \cdot 13$ ash $+ 0 \cdot 5 \ S_{pyr} + 0 \cdot 8 \ CO_2 - 1 \cdot 1 \ SO_{3ash}$
$+ 0 \cdot 5 \ Cl$.

Where S_{pyr} $= \%$ pyritic sulphur in the coal
   CO_2 $= \%$ carbon dioxide, as carbonate, in the coal
   SO_{3coal} $= \%$ sulphate in the coal.
   Cl $= \%$ Chlorine in the coal
   SO_{3ash} $= \%$ sulphate in the ash from the coal

The various groups of coals by the N.C.B. classification may be plotted on Seyler's later charts and by these means fairly complete data can be obtained on the combustion and caking characteristics of all the coals found in Great Britain. For coals of lower rank than the bituminous groups, i.e. for sub-bituminous coals and lignites, the A.S.T.M. classification should be used, though Seyler's coal band can be extrapolated to include lignites, with a fair degree of accuracy.

3. *E.C.E. Classification.* This system was devised by the Coal Committee of the Economic Committee for Europe to prevent confusion and inconvenience in the post-war handling of coals. It is based partly on the N.C.B. Code system and partly upon the A.S.T.M. classification.

The parameters used are caking and coking properties for coals containing less than 33% of volatile matter, and calorific value on the moist, ash-free basis ($30°C$, 96% humidity) for coals containing more than 33% of volatile matter.

Alternative indices of caking properties are the crucible swelling number (B.S. 1016) or the Roga Index (measure of agglutinating power).

Alternative indices of coking properties are the Gray–King coke type (as in the N.C.B. method) or the Audibert–Arnu dilatometer number.

A system of three digit code numbers for groups and classes

is used, in which the first digit is the group number, the second the caking index, and the third the coking index.

Thus a coal containing 10 to 14% of volatile matter, with a crucible swelling index of 1 to 2 and a Gray-King coke type E–G, would be given a code number 212. In general, the code numbers resemble those used in the N.C.B. code, ranging from 100 for anthracites to 900 for high volatile, non-caking coals (of low calorific value), but the parameters used for sub-groups and class types are more appropriate; therefore the system of classification is more scientific.

The Roga and the Audibert–Arnu indices are not used in Great Britain for routine purposes.

The distinction between "caking" and "coking" properties is in the rate of heating; a high rate of heating being considered to be applicable to the determination of "caking" and a slow rate being more nearly related to industrial coking practice. Further details will be found in the official E.C.E. Publication (Geneva) or in the references below.

REFERENCES

FRANCIS, W. *Coal—its Formation and Composition.* London. (1961).
FRANCIS, W. *Boiler House and Power Station Chemistry.* London (1962).

PETROLOGY
AND CHEMICAL COMPOSITION

COAL is a non-homogeneous sedimentary rock, containing many types of organic and inorganic compounds that are mainly distributed in layers or bands parallel to the bedding plane of the seam. The kinds of coal present in a seam depend upon the variations in composition of the masses of plant debris and mineral matter deposited originally, and upon the changes in them that have taken place subsequently. The latter determine the rank of the coals: the former determine their type.

The non-homogeneity of coal seams is recognizable, macroscopically (to the unaided eye) as bands or striations parallel to the bedding plane; microscopically, as differences in reflectivity or transparency of polished or thin sections and, chemically, by the separate examination of layers or small samples of different appearance.

Petrology. Petrology is the study of the individual mineral components of a mass of rock or coal by visual means.

Rational analysis. Rational analysis is the resolution into chemical types of a mass of rock or coal.

BANDED COMPONENTS OF COAL

Stopes and Wheeler[1] published the first comprehensive account of the relationship between the appearance and properties of the banded components of bituminous coals. Four banded components were recognized, viz:

    1. *Vitrain*—Narrow bands of brilliant, or vitreous, uniform appearance.

2. *Clarain*—Bands of varying thickness, with a pronounced gloss or shine and with a subdued striated texture.

   (Vitrain and clarain together comprise the portions of coal seams sold as "Brights")

3. *Durain*—Dull, hard bands of varying thickness, with a matt or granular texture.

   (Durain forms the bulk of the "Hards" of commerce, also the type known as "Splint coal" in some localities).

4. *Fusain*—Bands, patches or wedges of soft, fibrous material resembling charcoal (previously called "mineral charcoal" in some localities). The component of coal that dirties the hands!

The chemical properties of these banded components of bituminous coals were studied initially by R.V. Wheeler and associates. Typical variations in analyses and properties for a medium volatile bituminous coal are shown below:

CHEMICAL EXAMINATION OF COMPONENTS OF MID-RANK BITUMINOUS COAL

Analysis	*Vitrain*	*Clarain*	*Durain*	*Fusain*
Proximate				
Moisture, air-dried, %	1·7	1·4	1·2	0·9
Volatile matter	34·6	37·6	32·2	19·1
Ash	0·6	3·5	4·6	9·6
Ultimate				
Carbon, ash-free–dry %	84·4	82·2	85·8	88·7
Hydrogen ,,	5·4	5·7	5·3	4·0
Sulphur ,,	1·0	2·3	0·9	1·0
Nitrogen ,,	1·5	1·9	1·4	0·7
Oxygen ,,	7·7	7·9	6·6	5·6
Calorific Value B.t.u./lb A.F.D.	14,790	14,790	15,100	14,840
Caking power (crucible)	Swollen coke	Swollen coke	Non-swollen coke	No coke formed

In any seam the caking power of the vitrain and the clarain is always greater than that of the durain. Fusain is invariably non-caking.

RATIONAL ANALYSIS

The correlation between petrological type and chemical composition for the individual entities present in coals was established mainly by R. Thiessen in the U.S.A. and by W. Francis in Great Britain.

Thiessen correlated the brightest portions of coals (Anthraxylon) with the woody tissues of the original plants, and the dull portions of coal with miscellaneous tissues, spore exines, pollen grains, plant and amorphous material (attritus). Later he divided attritus into two types, *opaque attritus* and *translucent attritus*.

Francis, by rational analysis, identified the bulk of the coal substance of anthraxylon with coal ulmins, equivalent to the humus of peat and the amorphous matter of translucent attritus with resin, wax, or hydrocarbon. Recent experience shows that attritus can best be divided into three groups of material:

1. Opaque matter — finely divided, fragmentary woody cells with dark amorphous material (micrinite)

USUAL RANGE OF CHEMICAL COMPOUNDS IN BANDED COAL
(Rock types)

The terms in brackets refer to the micro-components now called *macerals* (q.v.)

| Chemical Component (Maceral) | Rock Type | | | |
	Vitrain %	Clarain %	Durain %	Fusain %
Ulmins (vitrinite)	90–97	70–95	20–80	33–66
Opaque matter (micrinite)	nil	0–5	5–50	nil
Spore exines and cuticles (exinite)	nil	2–25	5–35	nil
Waxes, resins, hydrocarbons (resinite)	3–9	3–10	3–15	0·2
Carbonized fibres (fusinite)	nil	0–2	0–10	66–33

2. Translucent attritus — spore exines, pollen grains, cuticles (exinite), resins, waxes, hydrocarbons (resinite)
3. Carbonized fibres — small fragments of woody cells converted into fusain (fusinite).

ESTIMATED ANALYSES OF TYPICAL CHEMICAL INGREDIENTS (MACERALS) OF A COAL OF AVERAGE COMPOSITION C = 80·7%   H = 5·4%

Ingredient	Ultimate Analysis	
	Carbon %	Hydrogen %
Ulmin (vitrinite)	80·5	5·2
Opaque matter (micrinite)	83·3	3·7
Carbonized fibres (fusinite)	94·0	2·3
Plant skins (exinite)	77·0	7·1
Resins (resinite)	80·5	7·5
Hydrocarbons	88·5	11·5

ESTIMATED LIMITING ANALYSES AND PROPORTIONS OF MACERALS IN THE ABOVE BITUMINOUS COAL

	Vitrains per cent		Clarains per cent				Durains per cent			
Rational analysis										
Ulmin	91	97	91	87	85	81	72	67	52	47
Resins	6	2								
Hydro-carbons	3	1	(3)	(3)	(9)	(9)	(3)	(8)	(3)	(8)
Plant Skins	—	—	1	10	1	10	15	15	5	5
Opaque matter	—	—	5	—	5	—	10	10	40	40
Ultimate analysis										
Carbon	80·75	80·6	80·7	80·2	80·85	80·4	80·3	80·4	81·5	81·65
Hydrogen	5·55	5·3	5·25	5·5	5·45	5·7	5·45	5·65	4·8	5·0

GREY AND BLACK DURAINS

Wandless and Macrae[2] showed that two types of durain exist, viz:

1. Black durain—rich in spore exines, with little fusinite—resembles cannel coal (q.v.) in spore content and oil yield.
2. Grey durain—relatively deficient in spores, but contains high proportions of fusinite and material intermediate in composition between fusain and vitrain (micrinite)—low oil yield.

The results of the Gray–King assays on samples of grey and black durain from the same seam are shown below:

GRAY–KING ASSAY ON BLACK AND GREY DURAINS
(Wandless and Macrae)

Yields per 100 g (dry coal)	Black durain	Grey durain
Coke (g)	61·35	75·72
Tar (g)	25·00	10·88
Liquor (g)	3·89	5·93
Gas (g)	7·76	7·17
Gas volume (ml)	9470	8810

CANNEL COALS

Dull, hard portions of seams containing more hydrogen than the associated coal—high yield of oil and gas of good illuminating value is obtained by carbonization—Gray–King assay results are generally similar to those obtained with black durains (above). Petrology is similar to black durains but Boghead cannel, or Torbanite, also contains remains of algae.

RECENT PETROLOGICAL TERMINOLOGY

1. **Lithotype or rock type**—a macroscopic component of coal, equivalent to the banded component, vitrain, clarain, durain or fusain, of Stopes.
2. **Maceral**—an individual chemical entity, identified by microscopic (or chemical means) as a component of a lithotype. Name termination "-inite", e.g. vitrinite, resinite, fusinite, etc.
3. **Micro-lithotype**—an association of macerals present in a coal band of maximum width 50 microns. Name termination "-ite" e.g. vitrite, clarite, durite, fusite.

REFERENCES

1. STOPES, M. C. and WHEELER, R. V. *Monograph on the Constitution of Coal*, H.M.S.O., London, 1918.
2. WANDLESS, A. M. and MACRAE, J. C., *Fuel* **14**, 1935.
FRANCIS, W. *Coal—its formation and composition*. London, 1961.
BRAME, J. S. S. and KING, J. G. *Fuel—solid, liquid and gaseous*. London, 1956.

COAL—RELATIONSHIP BETWEEN CARBON, HYDROGEN, VOLATILE MATTER AND CALORIFIC VALUE

DULONG FORMULA

The earliest reasonably accurate formula for calculating the calorific value of coal from the proportions of carbon and hydrogen found by ultimate analysis was the Dulong formula, viz:

$$Q = 80.8 \ C + \left(H - \frac{O}{8}\right)344 \text{ cal/g.}$$

where Q is the gross C.V. of the fuel.

C, H, O, are the percentages of carbon, hydrogen and oxygen, respectively, in the cool.

ASSUMPTIONS IN DULONG'S FORMULA

1. That the gross C.V. of carbon and hydrogen in coal are 8080 and 34,400 cal/g respectively.
2. That oxygen is combined with hydrogen as in water, so that surplus hydrogen available for combustion $= H - \dfrac{O}{8}$.

3. That the heat of formation of coal is zero.

The last assumption is not correct, since the heat of formation of wood is about 1000 B.t.u./lb and this amount of heat is liberated during the combustion of wood. Coals derived from wood retain this characteristic to an extent depending upon the degree of chemical charge that has taken place during the transition from wood. For example, low rank bituminous coals decompose with an exothermic reaction equivalent to the release of about 100 B.t.u./lb. With anthracites heat is neither absorbed nor evolved during decomposition.

Dulong's formula may be expressed as English units, to include sulphur as

$$Q = 146\,C + 620\left(H - \frac{O}{8}\right) + 40S \text{ B.t.u./lb}$$

where S = percentage of sulphur in the coal.

These formulae suffice for practical purposes, but Seyler's formulae (q.v.) should be used when greater accuracy is required.

SEYLER'S FORMULAE

Seyler modified the Dulong formula to allow for the increasing exothermic character of coals with decreasing rank and also established relationships between the percentages of carbon, hydrogen, volatile matter and the calorific value of coals, which take into consideration petrological characteristics; as follows:

1. Modification of Dulong formula to eliminate the factor $\left(H - \dfrac{O}{8}\right)$:

$$Q_D = 388\,H + 124C - 4270 \text{ cal/g} \tag{1}$$

2. Correction for exothermic decomposition of low rank coals:

$$Q_g = Q_D + \tfrac{1}{4}O^2 \tag{2}$$

In these equations Q_D = gross calorific value calculated from equation (1) and Q_g = gross calorific value corrected for exothermic reaction.

3. Relationship between volatile matter (V.M.) and ultimate analysis:

(a) V.M. = $10\cdot61H - 1\cdot24C + 84\cdot15$ for coals below the rank of anthracite $\hspace{2cm}$ (3)

(b) Log   V.M. $= 0.23364H - 0.02706C + 2.579$,   for   anthracites.   (4)

4. Calculation of C and H from determination of C.V. and V.M.:

$$H = 0.069\left(\frac{Q}{100} + \text{V.M.}\right) - 2.86 \qquad (5)$$

$$C = 0.59\left(\frac{Q}{100} - \frac{1.1.\text{V.M.}}{3}\right) + 43.4 \qquad (6)$$

ACCURACY OF SEYLER'S RELATIONSHIPS

When calculating $H.C$ V.M. and C.V. from equations (1) to (6)

1. *For bright coals* Hydrogen, accuracy $\pm 0.05\%$
   - Carbon,   ,, $\pm 0.25\%$
   - V.M.   ,, $\pm 0.75\%$
   - C.V.,   ,, ± 25 cal/g

2. *For dull coals*   Hydrogen: calculated value is too high by 0.14% to 0.57%
   Carbon: calculated value too low by 0.53% to 1.88%
   V.M.: calculated value too low by 2.13% to 8.38%

For dull coals, the smaller differences between calculated and determined values relate to the petrological types known as grey durains: the larger differences relate to the types known as black durains.

CORRECTION OF FORMULAE FOR DIFFERENCES IN PETROLOGICAL TYPE

The greatest errors relate to equation (3) and in this equation Seyler introduced a term called "Volatile Displacement", thus:

$$\text{V.M.} = 10.61H - 1.24C + 84.15 + \Delta V \qquad (7)$$

The volatile displacement (ΔV) may be determined experimentally for any coal if the ultimate analysis and volatile matter are known, when:

$$\Delta V = \text{V.M.} - V_u \tag{8}$$

where V.M. = laboratory determination of volatile matter
and V_u = V.M. calculated from equation (3), assuming that the coal is a bright coal. (Vitrain)

USE OF SEYLER'S CHART
(cf. Data Sheet No. 6, Fig. 6.1.)

If one pair of variables, carbon and hydrogen, or volatile matter and calorific value, are plotted on Seyler's chart, the other pair may be read off from the appropriate axes.

REFERENCE

FRANCIS, W. *Coal—its Formation and Composition*. London, 1961.

COALFIELDS OF GREAT BRITAIN AND WORLD RESOURCES

GREAT BRITAIN

The known coalfields of Great Britain are shown in the attached map Fig. 9.1. as shaded areas, with N.C.B. code numbers (cf. Data Sheet No. 6) giving the types of coal found therein and arrows indicating the general direction of increase in rank. Details of the coals in the more important areas, with typical analyses and commercial uses are summarized below.

ANALYSIS (PURE COAL BASIS) AND COMMERCIAL USES OF COALS IN THE COALFIELDS OF GREAT BRITAIN

Fife and Lothians

Analysis: $C = 82 \cdot 5 \%$, $H = 5 \cdot 4 \%$, V.M. $= 35 \cdot 5 \%$
N.C.B. 700–900.
Local occurrences of low volatile coal. N.C.B. class 201.
Uses: House and steam.

Central Scotland

Analysis: $C = 80–84 \%$, $H = 5 \cdot 2–5 \cdot 4$, V.M. $= 40–44 \%$
Types. N.C.B. 500–900. Uses: House, steam, gas.
Some small deposits of pseudo-anthracite (produced by igneous intrusions).
N.C.B. 100. $C = 92 \cdot 5 \%$, $H = 3 \cdot 2 \%$, V.M. $= 5 \cdot 3 \%$

FIG. 9.1   The Coalfields of Great Britain.

Ayr

N.C.B. 800–900 Non-coking.
Uses: House, steam, producers.

Cumberland

Analysis: C = 84·5%, H = 5·7%, V.M. = 33%
N.C.B. 500. Uses: Coking and gas

Northumberland

Analysis: C = 80·8%, H = 5·5%, V.M. = 40·5%
N.C.B. 600–900 Non-coking. Uses: steam, producer, house.

Durham

Analysis: C = 85·9%, H = 5·3%, V.M. = 30%
N.C.B. 300–500. Excellent coking coals—high swelling.
Uses: Coking, gas, house.

Yorkshire

Analysis: C = 84·5%, H = 5·2%, V.M. = 34%
N.C.B. 400–800. Uses: Coking, gas, steam, house.

Notts and Derby

Analysis: C = 82·0%, H = 5·4%, V.M. = 40%
N.C.B. 700–800 Uses: House and steam.

South Derby and Leicester

Analysis: C = 79·0%, H = 5·6%, V.M. = 44%
N.C.B. 800–900 Non-coking. Uses: House, steam, producer.

Lancashire

Analysis: C = 81·8%, H = 5·0%, V.M. = 35%
N.C.B. 500–800. Uses: Gas, house, steam. Some coking.

North Wales

Analysis: C = 83·0%, H = 5·5%, V.M. = 38%
N.C.B. 600–700. Uses: House, steam. Some gas.

North Staffs.

Analysis: C = 83·5%, H = 5·4%, V.M. 37%
N.C.B. 400–900. Uses: House, steam. Some coking.

South Wales

Analysis: Anthracite   C = 94·0%, H = 3·4%, V.M. = 5·0%
           Carbonaceous   C = 92·0%, H = 4·4%, V.M. = 14·0%
           Coking   C = 88·0%, H = 5·1%, V.M. = 21·0%
           Gas   C = 84·0%, H = 5·2%, V.M. = 36·0%
N.C.B. 100–500. Uses: Steam, producer, coking, gas, central heating.

Forest of Dean and Somerset

Analysis: C = 84·5%, H = 5·4%, V.M. = 37%
N.C.B. 500–700. Uses: House and gas.
Note: These coals sometimes contain high proportions of sulphur, e.g. 4·5%. cf. average value 1·25%

Kent

Analysis: C = 89·5%, H = 4·4%, V.M. = 14%
N.C.B. 100–301. Uses: Steam (low volatile coals) Coking (high volatile coals)

REGIONAL VARIATION IN PROPERTIES
(Regional metamorphism)

All coalfields show variations in rank and type, with depth in the coal measures (Hilt's Law), and laterally. The lateral variation is called regional metamorphism. The causes are either:
1. Local variations in temperature, due to earth movements subsequent to deposition, or
2. Depth in original basin of coal-forming material.

Examples in Great Britain

1. Coalfields of Lancashire, Yorkshire, Nottingham, Derbyshire, Leicester and Staffordshire once formed a large continuous basin. The centre portion is now incomplete, but there is a marked tendency for increase in rank of the coals towards the centre of the original basin (cf. Fig. 9.1, arrows showing direction of increase in rank on map). Alternatively, the elevation of the Pennine chain could have caused a rise in temperature and consequent increase in rank at the centre.
2. S. Wales, Forest of Dean and Somerset coalfields once formed a large basin with the centre to the north-west of the present limits of the coalfield. The highest rank coals (anthracite) are found in the north-west portion of the coalfield. Elevation of the Welsh mountains could also have caused a rise in temperature of strata with corresponding increase in rank.

CONTACT WITH IGNEOUS INTRUSIONS
(molten rocks)

Molten rocks sometimes intrude upon coal measures, causing local changes in composition, similar to those taking place during the manufacture of coke. Characteristics of these changes, which should not be confused with regional metamorphism, are:

1. Formation of coke, or coke plus ash, in regions nearest to the hot rock.
2. Increase in rank and ash content, inversely proportional to the distance from the area of contact.
3. Effect is only observed over a comparatively small distance (say within 1 mile) from the igneous rock.

Examples: Pseudo-anthracite formation in central coalfields of Scotland. Cinder coals in Busty Seam, Northumberland. Generally, coals of classes 305 and 306 of the N.C.B. Classification.

OUTPUT OF COAL CLASSES IN GREAT BRITAIN

200×10^3 tons of coal are produced annually in Great Britain. The following is an analysis of the breakdown into the major coal classes, based on N.C.B. publications:

Coal Class	Annual Output tons 10^6	Type
100 ...	3·8	Anthracites
201 and 202	6·6	Smokeless steam
203 and 204	6·4	Low vol. steam-caking
206	0·4	Low vol. non-caking
300, 301 and 401	15·8	Very strongly caking
400	13·2	Very strongly caking
500	35·2	Strongly caking
600	27·6	Medium caking
700	33·6	Weakly caking
800 and 900	57·4	Non-caking
Total	200·0	

WORLD RESERVES OF COAL

The known approximate amounts of hard coals and lignites in the world in seams of greater thickness than 1 ft and at depths less than 400ft are given in the table on page 54.

WORLD RESOURCES OF HARD COAL AND LIGNITE
tons x 10^8

Country	Hard coal (bituminous and anthracite)	Lignite and Sub-bituminous
U.S.S.R.	9800	2000
Germany	2750	560
U.K.	1700	nil
Poland	800	nil
France	60	4
Canada	560	320
U.S.A. (including Alaska)	20,240	900
S. Africa	2000	2
China	10,000	5
India and Pakistan	600	3
Japan	160	5
Australia	140	400
New Zealand	1	1
Others	350	164
Total	49,161	4364

WORLD AVAILABILITY OF COKING COALS

As shown earlier, the output of good quality coking coals in Great Britain is only about 30% of the total output. The world's reserves contain a similar, or smaller, proportion of good quality coking coals. The main areas in which good quality coking coals exist are: Great Britain, U.S.A., Germany, U.S.S.R., India (Jahria, Girindih, Raniganj and Bokhara), Australia (New South Wales and Queensland), South Africa and Rhodesia, Canada (Nova Scotia).

REFERENCES

The Efficient Use of Fuel, H.M.S.O. London, 1958.
BRAME, J. S. S. and KING, J. G. *Fuel, Solid, Liquid and Gaseous*. London, 1955.
FRANCIS, W. *Coal—its Formation and Composition*. London, 1961.

COAL PREPARATION—GRADING AND CRUSHING

OBJECT

Coal as mined, called "Run of mine" coal, varies in size from fine dust to large lumps and contains much impurity in the form of inorganic material present in the coal seam or introduced from floor or roof during mining operations. Every combustion appliance burning coal requires a quality and size grading within well defined limits. The object of coal preparation is to provide each user with fuel of optimum specification for the appliance used.

PROCEDURE

Coal preparation includes some or all of the following processes:
1. Separation of coal types at the coal face, e.g. into "Hards" and "Brights".
2. Screening or grading into fractions of different size.
3. Hand-picking of large sizes to remove separate lumps of impurity.
4. Crushing of larger sizes to provide the smaller sizes mostly required by industry.
5. Cleaning to remove inorganic impurities when low-ash coal is required.
6. Drying, when small sizes coal particles are washed to remove impurities.
7. Blending, to modify the properties of a coal.

Items 1 to 4 will be discussed here, leaving 5 to 7 for later data sheets.

1. SEPARATION OF COAL TYPES AT THE FACE

Thick seams containing well defined bands of bright or dull coal, or zones or parts of seams containing much ash or high sulphur, may be cut and removed separately at the coal face.

2. SCREENING

The coal is passed over bars, perforated plates, or wire mesh screens, so that sizes smaller than the openings fall through.

Types of Screens

(a) Cylindrical screens (on rollers) or Trommels (with centre shaft mounted nearly horizontally and fitted with round or square holes) revolve slowly at 3–4 r.p.m. Coal passes through the inside: smalls pass through the holes. There is excessive breakage with fragile coals—output is low and costs high.

STANDARDIZATION OF SIZES (B.C.U.R. 1946)

Name	Size	Use
Large cobbles	6 in. × 3 in.	House
Cobbles	4 in. × 2 in.	House
Trebles	3 in. × 2 in.	Vertical gas retorts
Doubles	2 in. × 1 in.	Vertical gas retorts
Singles	1 in. × $\frac{1}{2}$ in.	Mechanical stokers
Peas	$\frac{1}{2}$ in. × $\frac{1}{4}$ in.	Mechanical stokers
Smalls	1 in. to 0 in. or $\frac{1}{2}$ in. to 0 in.	Mechanical or hand fired industrial furnaces

(b) Shaking screens, or "Jiggers"—Horizontal rectangular trays with reciprocating motion in lengthwise direction caused by eccentric crank. Driving crank speed is 80 to 120 r.p.m. Capacity of 10 ft. × 20 ft. jigger ca. 500 tons/hr.

(c) High speed vibrating screens—used particularly for screening out smaller sizes, e.g. $\frac{1}{2}$ in to 0 from washed coal before sending to market. Best results with dry coal. Small units, 24 in. to 60 in. wide and 4 ft to 8 ft. long.

Electrically vibrated—up to 3000 vibrations per min.; amplitude small, e.g. $\frac{1}{8}$ in.

3. HAND PICKING

Large screened coal > 4 in. is placed on a slowly moving "picking belt" of about 100 ft length and a team of about six workers pick out obvious pieces of shale or dirt. Output per manshift is 10 to 12 tons, with high efficiency of separation; with smaller sizes efficiency and output fall rapidly.

4. CRUSHING OR BREAKING

Process is designed to reduce the size of large pieces with minimum production of dust. Two main types of breakers are used in Great Britain, viz.: (a) Pick Breaker, and (b) Bradford Breaker. Other crushers commonly used are jaw crushers, roll crushers, disc crushers, cone crushers and hammer crushers.

(a) *Pick Breaker*—designed to imitate the action of miners' picks. Strong pick blades are mounted rigidly on a solid steel frame moving slowly up and down. Coal passes under the picks on a slowly moving horizontal plate conveyor belt. The amount of breakage is roughly controlled by the height to which picks are raised—upper limit 20 in. Typical performances; 450 ton/hr with a 72 in. wide machine. Size reduction from 20 in. to 12 in. Several machines may be placed in series with screens in between to remove fines. Main advantage—minimum production of fines can be achieved. Fines production is controlled by the diameter and spacing of picks. Reduction in diameter and increase in spacing decrease proportion of fines.

(b) *Bradford Breaker*—Screens, breaks, and removes large pieces of accidental material, e.g. pit props, chains or tramp iron, in one operation. Consists essentially of a massive cylindrical screen or Trommel, with fins fitted longitudinally inside the screen. These raise the lumps of coal as the cylinder rotates, until they fall, break, and are screened. Unbroken material passes out of the end of the cylinder. Production of fines is also small. Capacity of machine; up to 600 ton/hr.

TYPICAL PERFORMANCE — SCREEN ANALYSIS OF PRODUCT.

	Soft Coal	Hard Coal
> 4 in. %	0·2	0·7
4 — 3 in. %	5	13
3–2½ %	14	20
2½–1¾ %	28	28
1¾–1 %	24	17
1–3/16 in. %	22	15
< 3/16 in. %	6·8	6·3
Total	100	100

(c) *Blake Jaw Crusher*—consists of a heavy corrugated crushing plate, mounted vertically in a hollow rectangular frame. A similar moving plate (moving jaw) is attached at a suitable angle to a swinging lever, arranged so that the reciprocating movement opens and closes the gap between the plates, the greater movement being at the top. The machine is available with top opening up to 66 in. × 86 in. Usual capacity up to 300 ton/hr. Horsepower required: up to 150.

(d) *Corrugated and Toothed Roll Crushers*—two heavily toothed, or corrugated, cylindrical rollers (Fig. 10.1) are mounted horizontally and revolve in opposite directions. (Towards each other at the top side or nip, one being spring loaded.) Alternatively, a single roll may revolve against a breaker plate. Capacity of a 5 ft long machine with a 6 in. opening and roll speed 40 r.p.m. is about 350 ton/hr, with a power consumption of about 200 h.p. Best results are obtained by the use of several rolls in series, with screens between.

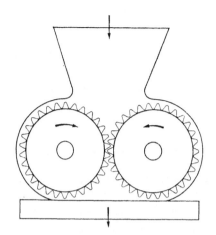

FIG. 10.1   Diagram of Double Roll Crusher.

REFERENCE

PERRY, J. H. *Chemical Engineers Handbook*. New York, 1953.

COAL PREPARATION — MECHANICAL CLEANING — THEORY

OBJECTIVE

To reduce the amount of ash formed from the coal in a combustion appliance to an acceptable degree in an economical manner.

Most large furnaces can burn effectively coals producing between 15 and 20% of ash, but the upper desirable ash limit for smaller furnaces is 10% and for carbonization 5%. Cleaning processes should not increase the cost of coal by more than about five shillings per ton.

METHODS

Successful coal cleaning requires the application of some physical property that can be used to separate clean coal from associated impurity within the size range required for commercial purposes.

Physical properties that are used for this purpose include size, shape, density, friction, resilience, electrical conductivity and wetability. Density, for a given size or size distribution, is the most important property used in commercial coal cleaning processes. Those now in use may be classified thus:

A. *Dry Processes*

1. Pneumatic tables   } Differences in density and dry
2. Spiral separators   }   friction
3. Berrisford   Differences in resiliency

B. *Wet Processes*

1. Dense medium ⎫
2. Jigs ⎪ Differences in density, size
3. Upward current ⎬ and shape
4. Troughs ⎭
5. Tables — Density and wet friction
6. Froth flotation — Wetability and density

THEORY OF SEPARATION BY DENSITY
(specific gravity)

The specific gravity of coal varies between the limits 1·2 and 1·7, depending upon the rank and moisture of the coal and the nature and amount of the associated mineral matter. This varies as follows:

Shale, clay and sandstone	2·0 to 2·6
Pyrites	4·0 to 4·9
Calcite	2·7
Gypsum	2·3
Coaly-shale	1·4 to 2·0

The possibility of cleaning a coal by a gravity separation process can be determined by carrying out a float and sink test, in which a prepared sample is suspended in a series of liquids of increasing density from 1·3 to 1·6 by increments of 0·1. The percentage, and the ash content, of the floats are determined at each stage. The results are recorded graphically as "washability curves" following calculations of yields and ash contents, as set out in Table 11A.

TABLE 11A

WASHABILITY DATA FOR COAL OF ASH CONTENT 19·0%(A) FOR FRACTION < ⅛ in. > 1/32 in.

Sp. Gr. of Liquid	Fractional Floats		Ash in Fraction as % Total	Ash, Cumulative Wt. %	Cumulative Floats		Fractional Sinks	Cumulative Sinks	
	% wt	% ash			% wt	% ash	% ash	% wt	% ash
1·3	60·0	2·3	1·38	1·38	60·0	2·3	17·62	40·0	44·0
1·4	13·2	10·0	1·32	2·70	73·2	3·7	16·30	26·8	60·7
1·5	8·0	26·0	1·68	4·32	81·2	5·3	14·68	18·8	79·0
1·6	3·0	36·8	1·10	5·42	84·2	6·8	14·58	15·8	84·0
1·7	7·0	82·0	5·58	11·00	91·2	12·0	8·0	8·8	91·5
1·8	4·8	87·5	4·20	15·20	96·0	15·8	3·8	4·0	95·0
Key: Code letter	F	FA	$TA = \dfrac{F \times FA}{100}$	CA	CF	CFA	FSA	CS	CSA
Method	Direct weighing	Direct determination		Cumulation of TA	Cumulation of F	$\dfrac{CA}{CF} \times 100$	A−CA	100−CF	$\dfrac{FSA}{CS} \times 100$
Example			$\dfrac{60 \times 2·3}{100}$ $= 1·38$	$1·38 + 1·32$ $= 2·70$	$60 + 13·2$ $= 73·2$	$\dfrac{2·7}{73·2} \times 100$ $= 3·7$	$19 - 2·7$ $= 16·3$	$100 - 73·2$ $= 26·8$	$\dfrac{16·3}{26·8} \times 100$ $= 60·7$
Use	For increment curve				For clean coal curve			For dirt curve	

The washability curves are shown in Fig. 11.1.

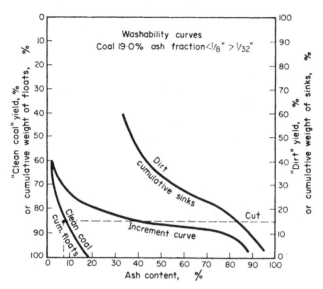

FIG. 11.1   Washability Curves.

INFORMATION OBTAINED FROM TABLE AND CURVES:

1. If a "cut" is made at specific gravity 1·6:

Yield of "clean" coal   = 84·2%   } From clean coal curve
Ash in "clean" coal   = 6·8%   }
Ash in dirt   = 84·0%—from dirt curve
Ash content of dirtiest
particle included in
clean coal   = 36·8%—from increment curve.

2. If clean coal is required to contain 5·3% ash the cut should be made at 1·5 specific gravity, and the yield of clean coal would be 81·2%.

3. The clean coal curve represents the maximum possible cleaning efficiency by gravity or jig separtion for this size grading of coal.

4. The limitation in practice is the variation in ash content of different sized fractions of coal. In any sized fraction of coal, only dirt that appears as separate particles or lumps, substantially free from coal, can be separated by the aid of gravity.

5. The increment curve (instantaneous ash curve) shows the rate of change of ash content for different yields. If a coal gives a curve that is L-shaped (that is the ash content increases rapidly for a small increase in yield in the middle portion of the curve) the coal is easy to clean. If the curve is more nearly straight, the coal is hard to clean and a high proportion of "middlings" is obtained (coal of medium to high ash content).

6. A middlings curve (specific gravity distribution curve) is sometimes drawn by plotting the difference in yields at two chosen densities against the mean of these densities. This gives the weight of coal falling within, say, ± 0.1 of a given density. If this weight is less than 10%, the coal is easy to clean.

THEORY OF CLEANING BY JIGGING OR WASHING

The terminal velocity of a solid particle settling in a fluid is determined by the opposing forces of gravity and frictional resistance.

Two formulae are used to determine the terminal velocity, due to Stokes and Newton.

Stokes' formula

$$vt = \frac{2}{g} \frac{D-d}{\eta} r^2 g$$

where vt = terminal velocity
D = sp. gr. of particle
d = ,, ,, of fluid
r = radius of particle
g = acceleration due to gravity
η = viscosity of fluid

Newton's formula

$$vt = \sqrt{\frac{8}{3Q} \cdot \frac{D-d}{\eta} rg}$$

Q is an experimental coefficient of resistance of the fluid.

These formulae apply only to a limited range of conditions and can be used only as an approximate indication of the behaviour of a particle in washing practice. In practice, also, particles do not fall freely but are interfered with by other particles and by the apparatus. Two cases can be considered, viz. free settling and hindered settling.

Free Settling

Consider two spheres of sp.gr. D_1 and D_2 and radii r_1 and r_2, falling separately in the same fluid at the same terminal velocity. From the Stokes formula

$$\frac{r_1}{r_2} = \left(\frac{D_2 - d}{D_1 - d}\right)^{1/2}$$

From the Newton formula

$$\frac{r_1}{r_2} = \frac{D_2 - d}{D_1 - d}$$

Generally

$$\frac{r_1}{r_2} = \left(\frac{D_2 - d}{D_1 - d}\right)^m$$

where m varies from $\frac{1}{2}$ to 1.

$$\text{When } r_1 = r_2 \quad R = \left(\frac{D_2 - d}{D_1 - d}\right)^m$$

R is called the free settling ratio and determines the rate of settlement of the two spheres.

Hindered Settling

Under free settling conditions, large light particles fall at the same rate as small heavy particles. With hindered settling, that is in a restricted area, dense particles fall at a greater rate than light particles of the same settling rate under free settling conditions. The density of a suspension of solid particles in a fluid is the mean density of the suspension. This affects the settling rate as compared with free settling as follows:

Consider a small number of equal-sized particles of shale, sp.gr. 2·0 and coal, sp.gr. 1·4, in water, sp.gr. 1·0. Taking $m = 1$, then

$$R_{free} = \frac{2 \cdot 0 - 1 \cdot 0}{1 \cdot 4 - 1 \cdot 0} = 2 \cdot 5$$

This means that the shale particles sink 2·5 times as quickly as the coal particles of equal size.

Now consider a suspension of equal volumes of coal and shale particles in water, together occupying 40% of the volume of the suspension. The equivalent density of the suspension is calculated from the mass proportion of water, coal and shale in the suspension, thus:

$$
\begin{aligned}
\text{Mass proportion of water} \quad &= 1 \cdot 0 \times 0 \cdot 6 = 0 \cdot 6 \\
\text{,, \qquad ,, \qquad ,, coal} \quad &= 1 \cdot 4 \times 0 \cdot 2 = 0 \cdot 28 \\
\text{,, \qquad ,, \qquad ,, shale} \quad &= 2 \cdot 0 \times 0 \cdot 2 = 0 \cdot 40 \\
\text{Total mass per unit volume (sp.gr.)} \quad &= 1 \cdot 28
\end{aligned}
$$

Then $R_{hindered} = \dfrac{2 \cdot 0 - 1 \cdot 28}{1 \cdot 4 - 1 \cdot 28} = 6 \cdot 0$

Hence the separation of shale from coal will take place more than twice as quickly as under free settling conditions. Suspensions of heavy particles in water, equivalent to fluids of known specific gravity, are used in modern dense medium washing processes (q.v.) (cf. Data Sheet No. 12).

Effect of Particle Size

Under any given conditions the ratio of particle sizes for equal settlement rate can be found. Outside this ratio, small, dense particles may settle more slowly than large, light, particles. Hence:

1. Washers operating on the principle of differential settlement must be fed with a limited size range of particles for efficient operation.
2. A greater size range can be accommodated under conditions of hindered settling than with free settling.

Effect of Motion of Fluid

More complete gravity separation may be effected when the fluid is in motion than when it is static. If the fluid flows upwards, the rate of fall of the particles will be diminished, or the light particles may be caused to float if the upward velocity of the fluid is greater than the rate of settlement of these in the still fluid. If the fluid moves horizontally, the lighter particles are carried greater distances than the heavier particles. These principles are applied to the design of upward current and trough washers, q.v. (cf. Data Sheet No. 12).

REFERENCES

PERRY, J. H. *Chemical Engineers Handbook*. New York, 1953.

COAL PREPARATION — Mechanical Cleaning
— Types of Plant

A. DRY CLEANING PROCESSES

Advantages: these processes eliminate the cost of drying wet coal and the difficulty of disposal of slurries of water and fine coal or dust.

Disadvantages: (1) close screening is necessary to obtain good separation; (2) with increased mechanization in the mines, combined with the use of water to suppress dust during cutting, only a small proportion of coal in Britain comes from the pits dry.

Types of Plant

1. *Pneumatic Tables* (Birtley and Sutton–Steele)

Air tables and wet concentrator tables are of similar design except that in the former air is used as the separating fluid and in the latter water is used. The table is fitted with wooden ripple bars, from $1\frac{1}{2}$ in. to $2\frac{1}{2}$ in. high, in a longitudinal direction, and is tilted cornerwise. The coal is fed in a thin stream from the upper corner and travels down and across the table. The table is given an oscillating or vibrating motion and air passes up, through the ripples, continuously or with a pulsating motion. The combined effect of the vibration, the air flow and the downward and forward movement, causes a separation of the dirt from the shale. The latter falls through the ripples and the coal passes over the lower corner of the table.

The capacity of the table varies with the sizing of the coal, e.g. 55 tons/hr for 4 in. to 2 in. coal; 30 tons/hr for 1 in. to $\frac{1}{2}$ in. and 20 tons/hr for $\frac{1}{4}$ in. to $\frac{1}{8}$ in.

With closely graded coal fractions, efficiency of cleaning is high, e.g. Durham gas coal containing $8\cdot5\%$ ash in fraction $> \frac{1}{8}$ in.

Products: 92% clean coal containing 3·7% ash.
7·2% dirt containing 66·4% ash.

2. *Spiral Separators*

These were formerly much used for the cleaning of anthracite. The separator consists of a tall, vertical spiral with a pitch between 28 in. and 38 in. (see Fig. 12.1). The dirty coal slides down the spiral

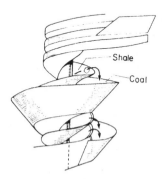

FIG. 12.1   Spiral Separator.

and the clean coal, which has a lower coefficient of friction than the dirt, slides to the outside. It is collected separately from the dirt, which follows the inside of the spiral.

Limitations:
1. Coal sizes < ⅜in. cannot be cleaned efficiently.
2. Close grading is required for fractions > ⅜in.
3. Rust or moist patches on spiral cause uneven operation.

3. *Berrisford Process*

The Berrisford process depends upon the difference in resiliency between coal and dirt particles.

Method: Dirty coal is fed in a jigging motion on to an inclined plane containing a gap of suitable width. Coal particles bound higher than dirt particles, which slide down the plane and fall through the gap. The result obtained depends upon the grading of the coal, the height of fall on to the plane, the angle of the plane, and the position and width of the gap.

B. WET CLEANING PROCESSES

1. *Dense Medium*

Dense medium is usually a suspension of closely graded mineral particles in water, for example sand, sp.gr. 2·6 (Chance process), barytes, sp.gr. 4·2 containing 2% by volume of clay (Barvoys process) and magnetite, sp.gr. 5·2 (Tromp).

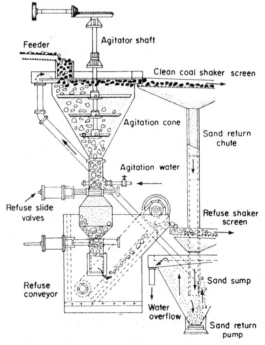

FIG. 12.2   Chance Gravity Washer.

In the Chance process (Fig. 12.2) coal is floated in a cone in a 40 % suspension of sand (grain size 0·2 to 0·5 mm) and water, equivalent to a solution of density 1·64 (cf. Data Sheet No. 11). The mixed sand, clean coal and water, flow from the top of the cone on to a shaker screen, which removes water and sand. These are returned to the process.

With magnetite, a gradation in specific gravity occurs due to settlement of the heavy mineral, varying from 1·53 at the top to 1·83 at the base. Coal middlings remain suspended within the bath and are removed by a gentle horizontal cross flow of the medium on to an elevator. Heavy shale or pyrites settle to the base of the cone. Thus a three-product separation is possible.

All dense medium washers can treat material with a wide range of particle size, the lower limit being usually the size of the mineral particles in the dense medium. A usual range of size is <6 in. > 1 in. the material passing through a 1 in. screen being washed separately in a jig washer (q.v.).

2. *The Baum Jig Washer* (Fig. 12.3)

This is one of the oldest and most commonly used types of washer. Though capable of treating unsized feeds up to a maximum of 4 in., Baum washers are now often used to wash only the small coal, say < 1 in. size, removed during a preliminary screening operation. In a jigging operation, a bed of coal, resting on a perforated plate, is subjected to the action of periodic upward and downward currents of water. In the Baum jig this motion is obtained by alternately admitting and releasing compressed air over the surface of water in compartments adjoining the jigging chamber. Pulsation rate is 30 to 60 cycles per min. The dirty coal flows on to the jig at one end of the chamber and the clean coal out at the far end over a weir. The dirt passes through the holes in the jig and falls to the bottom of the washer. It is removed by elevator.

Separation of middlings is not efficient with this type of washer. It is therefore used for coals showing good washability characteristics (cf. Data Sheet No. 11).

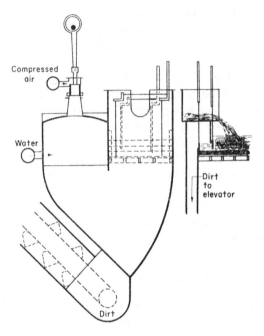

Fɪɢ. 12.3   Baum Jig Washer.

3. *Upward Current Washers*

The Robinson washer (Fig. 12.4) is typical of these washers. Closely graded dirty coal is added at the top centre of the cone and water enters through the base. A horizontal revolving frame gives the water a rotary and a vertical movement. Clean coal is carried over the top edge of the cone. Dirt settles to the base and is removed by elevator. The dirt settling in the water has some of the properties of a dense medium and the coal size range treated can therefore be greater than would be the case under free settling conditions (cf. Data Sheet No. 11).

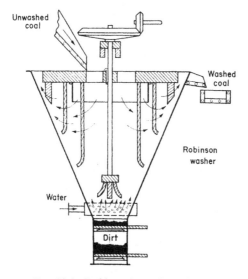

FIG. 12.4   Robinson's Coal Washer.

4. *Trough Washers*

The Rheolaveur trough washer (Fig. 12.5) consists of large inclined troughs into which screened fractions of coal and water enter
at the top. Each trough contains a series of orifices through which
the heavy particles of shale or dirt fall against an upward current of
water. The material passing through each orifice may be rewashed
in another trough, before being discarded, the whole plant being
operated on a battery or cascade principle. In a plant treating
material < 5 in. there may be three sets of troughs, each dealing
with separate sized fractions, e.g. 5 in. to $\frac{1}{2}$ in, $\frac{1}{2}$ in. to 2 mm, and
< 2 mm. Each set contains 2 or 3 troughs. Middlings may be
separated efficiently by recirculation at various stages.

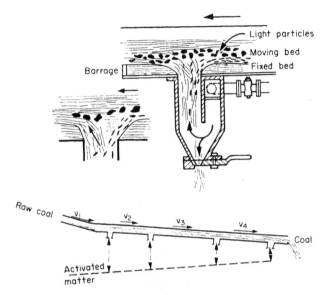

FIG. 12.5　Rheolaveur Trough Washer.

5. *Concentrator Tables*

These are similar to the dry tables described earlier, but the fluid used is water. Wet tables are more efficient in dealing with unsized feeds than dry tables.

6. *Froth Flotation*

None of the above processes is suitable for cleaning fine coal dusts, for example screenings < 0.5 mm. Separation of clean coal from shale in such fractions can be achieved by froth flotation, using the principle of differential wetability.

Coal particles are wetted by bubbles of froth, made by agitating air and water in the presence of certain oils and frothing agents. If fine coal is added to such a system the bubbles adhere to the coal particles, which float. The shale and dirt particles are not wetted, and sink. "Collecting" oils used include light spindle oil and creosote oil. Frothing agents (frothers) are usually cresol, pine oil or heavy alcohols. The amount of oil used is 1 to 3 lb per ton of coal. In practice the approximate ratio of water to fine coal is 10 : 1 by weight. The clean fine coal forms a scum at the top of the frothing chamber or cell. It is removed by an arrangement of paddles and subjected to vacuum filtration. The filter cake contains from 25% to 30% of water and ca. 5% of ash. It is mixed with washed smalls for sale. Power consumption is about 3 h.p. per ton of coal. Cost of washing is ca. 2 to 3 times conventional washing cost. Tailings (fine slurry of shale) are thickened and pumped to waste dump.

Elmore Vacuum Process—operates under vacuum, without mechanical agitation. Froth is formed by introducing "Conditioned" pulp to frothing chamber under vacuum. Dissolved gases in water form the air bubbles. The main advantages claimed are:

(a) Low power

(b) Collapse of froth–coal concentrate on leaving vacuum chamber—improves handling and dewatering.

7. Auxiliary Processes

(a) *Flocculation*

Recovery of water from coal cleaning products which contain fine coal dust, and from "tailings". *Principle:* Rate of settling of fine particles in water is increased by the addition of colloids, such as glue, starch, alginates, pectates and/or alum. These neutralize the electrical charge on the fine particles of mineral, causing flocculation into large aggregates, which settle correspondingly rapidly. The flocculated slurry is fed into a thickener (large circular cone) where the solids settle at the base of the cone and are pumped into vacuum filters. The clean water flows over the rim of the cone for re-use, or for disposal as effluent. Cyclones are sometimes used to supplement. the action of thickeners. Amount of flocculating agent used = 5 to 10 lb/ton dry solids. Use of "wetting agent" e.g. sulphonated castor oil, improves results. Electrolytes flocculate coal particles up to 0·07 mm diameter and organic colloids flocculate those up to 0·3 mm diameter.

(b) *De-watering*

Washed coals are de-watered by passing over shaker screens fitted with wire sieve bottoms—effective with coal $> \frac{1}{2}$ in. size. Small sizes are de-watered by draining in bunkers, or by the use of centrifuges. Vacuum filters of the drum or disc type are used for fine clean coal. Pressure filters are used for thickened shale suspensions (tailings).

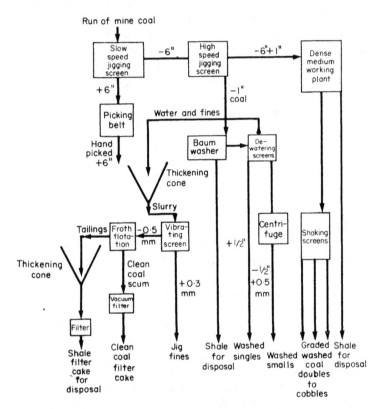

Fig. 12.6   Flow Sheet—Coal Preparation Plant.

(c) *Blending*

To produce grades suitable for a specific purpose, e.g. gas-making, low temperature or metallurgical coke, blends of highly swelling with low swelling coals, or blends containing fractions rich in fusain.

8. *Comprehensive Flowsheet*

A typical flowsheet for handling the preparation of run of mine coal from a colliery is shown in Fig. 12.6 (p. 76).

COAL CLEANING — Representation of Washer Performance

WASHABILITY curves based on float and sink tests (cf. Data Sheet No. 11) enable an assessment to be made of the possibility of cleaning a coal fraction by density separation. Related methods are used to assess the performance of commercial washing plants. These methods fall into two categories:

1. Block diagrams representing performance.
2. Graphical methods for comparing performance data.

1. BLOCK DIAGRAMS

A. *Block Distribution Diagrams*

These are made up to represent the yields obtained at different density levels for a number of screened sizes of coal. The width of each panel shows the relative proportion of each size fraction floating in a series of liquids of increasing density.

B. *Mirror Diagrams*

Block diagrams are prepared for the same coal, before and after washing. The diagram for the washed coal is drawn above that for the unwashed coal and is inverted. If separation is ideal, one diagram is the mirror image of the other. Any difference is a measure of the inability of the washing plant to make clean cuts on the coal tested.

C. *Hancock Efficiency Chart* (Fig. 13.1)

Shaded areas are marked on a square. These show the weights of the fractions of refuse obtained at each interval of specific gravity, expressed as a percentage of the raw coal. The total shaded area represents the total amount of refuse. The area of the square represents the weight of raw coal.

The block distribution diagrams give a simple overall picture of the

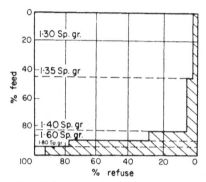

FIG. 13.1　Hancock Efficiency Chart.

nature of the separation effected. The mirror diagrams give a comprehensive visual indication of the differences between ideal and practical washing processes. For most purposes the simpler Hancock chart is sufficient. For more detailed information than can be obtained by these diagrams, graphical methods, with derived formulae, are required.

2. GRAPHICAL METHODS

An ideal washing process is one in which all coal of lower specific gravity than a predetermined value, which may be called the specific gravity of separation, appears in the clean coal fraction and all material of higher specific gravity is rejected as dirt. No commercial washing process approaches closely the ideal because of the differing effects of the factors of particle shape and size on the results. This imperfection of performance may be represented and evaluated by plotting the proportion of material included in the wrong product, for any specific gravity, against the difference between that specific gravity and the specific gravity of separation for the coal.

These values, from float and sink test data or from washing practice, may be plotted conveniently in the form shown in Fig. 13.2

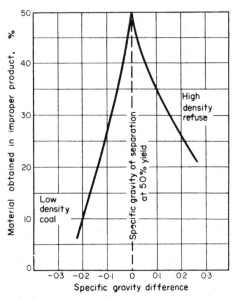

FIG. 13.2 Typical Separation effected in Practice (Yancey[1] *et al.*).

(Yancey, Geer and Shinkowskey[1]). Coal of low density, and refuse of high density, are obtained as washed coal and refuse, respectively. As the specific gravity of separation is approached, the proportion of material obtained in the improper product increases rapidly. Tromp (q.v.) observed that the shape of the curve resembles a Gaussion error distribution curve, and he developed methods for assessing washing performance based on the construction of "Error curves" ("Partition" or "Distribution factor" curves). These curves represent practical results and float and sink data. They demonstrate the difference between practical and theoretical results. The results may also be represented by three significant coefficients (q.v.).

A. *Tromp Error Curves* (Horsley and Whelan[2])

Data Required:

1. Percentage by weight of clean coal produced for each interval of specific gravity (density).
2. Percentage by weight of sinks discarded for each interval of specific gravity (density).
3. Yields of clean coal and dirt obtained.

Method:

Plot specific gravity, as abscissa, against percentage sinks per specific gravity interval, as ordinate (Fig. 13.3). Characteristics of curve:

1. The value of the ordinate corresponding to any point on the abscissa gives the probability that a particle will be found in the sinks. 100 minus the value of the ordinate gives the probability that the same particle will be found in the floats.

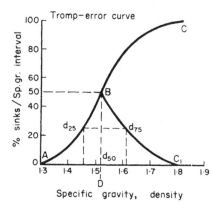

Fig. 13.3   Tromp Error Curve.

2. The value of the density corresponding to ordinate 50% is called the partition density (*D* in Fig. 13.3). It is the density of a particle which has an equal chance of appearing as clean coal or dirt.

3. Since the partition density is obtained from the curve, it need not coincide with any density used in practice, or with the "Specific gravity of separation" mentioned above.

4. If the upper half of the curve is inverted (B C in Fig. 13.1) the area under the curve, $ABCDA$, measures the variation of the curve from the ideal. The smaller the area, ("Tromps area" or "Error area") the more closely does the washing process conform to the ideal. The performance of two washers can be compared by determining the areas obtained with each when washing the same coal. With perfect separation the area would be zero, the curve running at zero ordinate to the point D, then rising vertically to the value 100. *The error area* is the first Coefficient deduced from the curve.

5. *Probable error* (Second Coefficient)
   If d_{50} = the partition density (D) and d_{25} and d_{75} are densities corresponding to ordinates 25% and 75% respectively,

   Then probable error $E = \frac{1}{2}(d_{75} - d_{25})$.

   If the curve is symmetrical about the vertical through D,

   then $E = d_{75} - d_{50} = d_{50} - d_{25}$

   This coefficient is a better indication of the efficiency of a washer near the partition density than is the error area. However E determines the width of the area, so is also a measure of the separation errors.

6. *Imperfection* (Third Coefficient)

$$\text{Imperfection } (I) = \frac{\text{Probable error}}{\text{Partition density} - 1} = \frac{E}{d_{50} - 1}$$

Imperfection varies little with partition density and is the coefficient to be preferred in expressing the performance of a washer.

7. It is found that the error curve is a function of particle size, larger particles giving closer separation. Hence coals of the same size grading should be used when comparing the performance of different washers.

B. *The Mayer Curve* (Dell[3])

In this simple curve, cumulative ash content of the floats, expressed as a percentage by weight of the coal feed, is plotted against cumulative percentage yield of floats over a range of specific gravity intervals, (1·3 to 1·8 by +0·1) as shown in Fig. 13.4. This gives

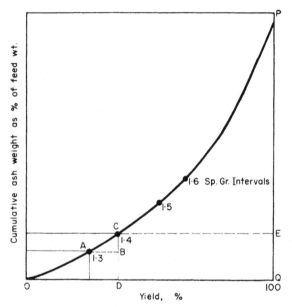

FIG. 13.4   The Mayer Curve — Dell [3].

directly, for any point and for any specific gravity, the percentage of ash in the floats. In Fig. 13.4 *AB* represents the % wt. of floats for sp.gr. interval 1·3 to 1·4. *BC* represents the weight of ash in this fraction. *OD* represents the combined % wt. of fractions *OA* and *AC*, i.e. % <1·4 sp.gr. *CD* = the weight of ash in fractions *OA* and *AC*. *QP* represents the weight of ash in the whole sample.

∴ *PE* = *QP* − *CD* = wt. of ash in fraction >1·4 sp.gr.

Ratio *CD/OD* gives % ash in 1·4 float fraction

and *PE/CE* gives % ash in 1·4 sink fraction.

C. *Mayer Middlings Curve* (Horsley and Whelan, *loc. cit.*)

This is a more detailed treatment of (B) relating to a three product separation (including a "Middlings" product) and a two product separation (without middlings).

Method

Plot cumulative yield of floats, as abscissa, against ash points (left hand ordinate). Ash points represent the cumulative products of the percentage yields of floats and the ash contents of the floats. The right hand ordinate shows the ash points divided by 100, i.e. the percentage of ash.

Typical Data

Sp. Gr. Interval (A)	Ash Points $\Sigma d = \Sigma(B \times C)$	Yield %(B)	Ash %(C)
< 1·3	105·6	24	4·4
1·3–1·35	333·6	32·1	7·1
1·35–1·4	420·4	10·1	8·6
1·4–1·45	491·8	7·1	10·2
1·45–1·50	534·3	3·4	12·5
1·5–1·55	555·8	1·5	16·3
1·55–1·6	576·7	1·0	18·0
1·6–1·7	598·5	1·1	19·8
1·7–1·8	620·1	1·0	21·6
> 1·8	1889·1	18·8	67·5

These data are plotted in Fig. 13.5.

In this figure:

O = no separation

Q = complete recovery

OR = Total yield of floats (100 units)

OS = Total ash points for coal (S units) (1889)

RQ = Total ash in coal (18·89%)

1. *Two Product Separation*

Take separation at any gravity (sp. gr. curve gives yields of floats) and let P on middlings curve represent this point.

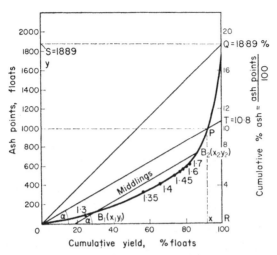

FIG. 13.5   Mayer Middlings Curve (Horsley and Whelan).

$$\therefore \text{ Cum. ash of floats } = \frac{\text{ash points of floats}}{\text{cumulative float yield}} = \frac{980}{90\cdot5} = 10\cdot8$$

$$= \frac{\text{ordinate of } P}{\text{abscissa of } P} = \frac{980}{90\cdot5} = 10\cdot8\,\%$$

$$\therefore \text{ Cum. ash of sinks } = \frac{S - \text{ordinate of } P}{OR - \text{abscissa of } P} = \frac{909}{9\cdot5} = 95\cdot5\,\%$$

2. *Three Product Separation*

Middlings are limited by points B_1 and B_2 on curve. Let the co-ordinates of these points be: x_1 and x_2 (yields)

$$y_1 \text{ and } y_2 \text{ (ash points)}$$

$\therefore$ yield of middlings $= (x_2 - x_1)$ and

$$\text{cumulative ash} = \frac{(y_2 - y_1)}{x_2 - x_1}$$

$$\frac{(y_2 - y_1)}{x_2 - x_1} = \tan \alpha$$

where B_1B_2 makes $\angle \alpha$ with OR

α is also $\angle$ between OR and line through O, parallel with B_1B_1, meeting RQ in T

$\therefore$ Tan $\alpha = RT/OR$ (ash points) $= RT/100$ ash points

But RT, read from right hand scale $= RT/100$ ash points

$\therefore$ Tan $\alpha = RT = 10\cdot 8\%$ ash.

Middlings Curve has the Following Properties:

1. Cumulative ash is measured by the gradient, i.e. Tan α, of the line drawn parallel to the line joining two points corresponding to the middlings product, and passing through O (RT on right hand scale).

2. All lines parallel to this line represent products with the same ash content, i.e. a series of middlings with the same ash contents but different yields.

3. The parallel line which is tangential to the curve meets it at a point representing 2 product separation in which the dirtiest particle in the floats, and the cleanest particle in the sinks, have ash contents of $10\cdot 8\%$.

4. The tangent to the curve at O gives the lowest ash content of the product.

5. The tangent to the curve at Q gives the highest ash content of the product.

6. Every straight line through O cutting the curve at a point P gives the ash content of the floats where it cuts RQ.

7. The line OQ gives the ash content of the raw coal.

D. *Calculation of Washer Efficiency*

Three formulae have been used generally:

1. *Fraser and Yancey:*

$$\text{Efficiency} = \frac{\text{yield of washed coal}}{\text{yield of floats of same ash content}} \times 100$$

2. *Drakeley:*

$$\text{Efficiency} = \frac{100 - \% \text{ floats in refuse } \times \% \text{ refuse}}{\% \text{ floats in feed}}$$

3. *Modified Drakeley:*

$$\text{Efficiency} = \frac{\% \text{ recovery} \times \% \text{ sinks in washed coal}}{\% \text{ sinks in feed}}$$

REFERENCES

1. YANCY, H. F., GEER, M. R. and SHINKOWSKEY, R. E. U.S. Bur. Mines. Rept. Investigations, 3372, 1938.
2. HORSLEY, R. M. and WHELAN P. F. *Can. Min. Met. Bulletin*, Feb. 1955.
3. DELL, C. C. *Colliery Engineering*, Oct. 1956.

THE STORAGE OF COAL — OXIDATION AND SPONTANEOUS COMBUSTION

COALS deteriorate during storage by low temperature oxidation, accentuated by weathering and handling. If the rate of oxidation is high, and storage conditions are bad, spontaneous combustion may result.

A. FACTORS AFFECTING DETERIORATION BY OXIDATION

1. Rate of oxidation varies inversely with rank, i.e. oxidation of high volatile coals (low rank) is rapid and oxidation of low volatile coals (high rank) is slow.
2. Rate of oxidation increases with increase in surface area, i.e. with decrease in lump or particle size.
3. Oxidation generates heat, which causes rise in temperature of the coal mass unless heat is removed, as generated, by ventilation or other means.

4. If the temperature rise due to oxidation does not exceed a critical value (varying from about 50°C for lignites to about 80°C for bituminous coals) spontaneous combustion does not result, but the physical and chemical properties of the coal change in proportion to the degree of oxidation. The main effects observed are:
   (a) Decrease in calorific value
   (b) Decrease in carbon and hydrogen
   (c) Increase in oxygen
   (d) Reduction of caking power
   (e) Reduction in size grading
5. If the temperature rise exceeds the critical value, spontaneous combustion results and the coal is destroyed by fire.

B. QUANTITATIVE ASSESSMENT OF THESE FACTORS

1. No exact quantitative relationship between rank of coal and rate of oxidation has yet been formulated because of the difficulties of measurement and interpretation of data. For the bituminous range of coals, under standardized conditions of alkaline permanganate oxidation, the following relationship has been found by the author[1] between oxidizability (as "k" = the velocity constant of the reaction) and percentage carbon (by ultimate analysis).

Oxidizability ($k \times 10^3$)	Carbon %
80	80
33	82
18	84
13	86
7	88

This relationship may be extrapolated to lower rank coals to give an approximate measure of their oxidizabilities.

2. There is also no exact proportionality between surface area and rate of oxidation, but the following results were obtained by the Fuel Research Board for the loss of calorific value of sized fractions of Forest of Dean coal on storage:

Size of coal (in.)	Loss of calorific value %	
	1 year	2 years
2–3	0·11	0·24
0·5–0·125	0·5	1·0
0·0125–0·0084	1·0	2·1
0·0025–0	1·8	3·0

3. By heating carefully sized fractions of coal to varying temperatures in air or oxygen, a temperature is found at which spontaneous combustion ensues. The following results, due to Burian, illustrate this point:

Temp. from which coal ignites in 60 min. °C	Liability to spontaneous combustion
100–109	Very liable
130–138	Medium liability
above 150	Not liable

In practice, coals placed in storage piles commence to oxidize and heat up immediately. Freshly mined coals also contain methane (0·02 ft³/lb for bituminous coals) which is evolved gradually, creating an additional fire hazard in an enclosed place. The heat liberated is about 360 B.t.u./ft³ of oxygen reacting and the rate of oxidation doubles, approximately, for a rise in temperature of 10°C.

If the rate of removal of heat, by ventilation or other means, is greater than the heat liberated by low temperature oxidation, the temperature cannot rise. If the rate of removal of heat is less than the heat developed, then the temperature will rise at an accelerating rate till spontaneous combustion occurs. Such heating may be detected by the formation of carbon dioxide, carbon monoxide and water, which becomes appreciable at temperatures in excess of about 120°C.

4. The most important effect of deterioration in storage, in the absence of spontaneous combustion, is the loss of caking power. With fine washed smalls of low caking power (N.C.B. classes 500 to 600) storage over the week-end may prevent the coals from forming a satisfactory metallurgical coke. Finely divided strongly caking coals lose their property of forming good cokes

when stored in the laboratory in the presence of air for several months. These changes cannot be detected by the methods of proximate or ultimate analysis.

Longer storage affects coking properties, analyses, gas and tar yields. For example, small Durham gas coal stored for 12 months and 24 months showed the following variations in carbonization products (Stanier):

Therms/ton, dry, ash-free coal	Original	12 months storage	24 months storage
Gas	84	81½	79
Tar	22	19½	17½
Coke breeze % increase	—	—	5
Swelling Index of coal	8	4	0

Reduction in Size Grading

Over a period of 12 months there is usually a decrease of 10% in the proportion of the larger sizes of coal stored. The friability of coals in storage decreases more rapidly than the size grading. Often more than twice as quickly.

C. PRACTICAL CONDITIONS OF STORAGE

From these considerations, and from practical experience in the bulk handling and storage of coal, the following points emerge:

1. Oxidation and Temperature Control

Oxidation is accelerated by temperature rise, by access to diffused air, by the presence of small particles, by the presence of porous or friable particles (fusain, vitrain) and by storage in large heaps with small surface/volume ratios. Oxidation is retarded by cooling, including cooling by adequate ventilation or by storage under water, by reducing access to air, for example by storage in compressed piles or by storage under water; by reducing the size of storage piles so that losses of heat by convection and conduction are high; by the storage of only large sizes of coal, for example by screening out fractions below 1/16 in.

2. *Size and Nature of Storage Piles*

These should be determined by the rank and type of coal. The lower the rank of the coal, the more shallow and the smaller the pile, and the smaller the proportion of fines $<\frac{1}{8}$ in. that may be accommodated without risk. Hards (consisting mainly of durain), cannels, dry steam coals and anthracites may be stored with less risk than bright bituminous coals, sub-bituminous coals and lignites. Maximum safe size of individual storage piles for bituminous coals is 200 ton and maximum depth 8 ft. Maximum safe size for lignites is 50 ton and depth 3 ft.

3. *Ventilation and Temperature Control*

The ventilation and temperature control during storage is ensured by the use of shallow piles, fitted with gas vents and temperature recorders. Contact with hot pipes or hot surfaces must be avoided.

4. *Age of Coals and Spontaneous Combustion*

Spontaneous combustion usually occurs within 4 to 5 weeks of mining but may occur up to about 4 months. Coals already stored longer than six months that have had access to air are not usually liable to spontaneous combustion.

5. *Summary*

Factor	Conditions favourable to safe storage	Conditions not favourable to safe storage
Size grading	Exclusion of fine coal $< \frac{1}{8}$ in. Washed coals free from fines.	Run of mine, or mixed coals containing natural fines; dirty coals containing finely divided pyrites.
Size of pile	Less than 200 ton for bituminous and higher ranks. Less than 50 ton for lignite	More than 200 ton bituminous coal. More than 50 ton lignite.
Height of pile	Less than 8 ft for bituminous coals. Less than 3 ft for lignite	> 8 ft, bituminous > 3 ft, lignite
Period of storage after mining	More than 6 months.	Up to 4 months, bituminous Up to 4 weeks, lignites
History of storage	Stored after initial heating and cooling	Freshly mined
Type of coal	Hards, cannels, anthracites, dry steam coals	Softs, brights, lignites. Dirty coals containing pyrites.
Site of store	Open positions on clean, firm ground	In contact with hot pipes, walls or surfaces. Enclosed stores. Contact with oily waste.

6. *Bulk Density of Stored Coals*

Air dried graded coal, with random packing
    —average   45 lb/ft^3
    —anthracite or dry steam coal   47–48 lb/ft^3
Air dried ungraded coal
    —average   46–48 lb/ft^3
    —anthracite   48–50 lb/ft^3

Notes:

    1. Moisture added to these increases the weight, *pro rata*.

    2. Coal at $47 \cdot 3$ lb/ft^3 occupies $47 \cdot 3$ ft^3/ton.

REFERENCE

1. FRANCIS, W. *Boiler House and Power Station Chemistry*, London, 1962.

COMBUSTION CALCULATIONS—COAL AND OIL

A. CHEMISTRY OF COMBUSTION

1. *Complete Combustion*

The combustion of a fuel may be represented as a series of chemical equations, which show the number of atoms of oxygen which combine with one or more atoms of each combustible element present, with the heat developed during combustion. Thus:

$$C + O_2 = CO_2 + 174,480 \text{ B.t.u.} \tag{1}$$

$$2H_2 + O_2 = 2H_2O + 245,950 \text{ B.t.u.} \tag{2}$$

$$S + O_2 = SO_2 + 12,600 \text{ B.t.u.} \tag{3}$$

Equation (1) means that 12 lb of carbon (the atomic weight in lb) combines with 32 lb of oxygen (the molecular weight $= 2 \times$ the atomic weight) to form 44 lb of carbon dioxide (the molecular weight of $CO_2 = 12$ lb $C + 32$ lb O_2) and liberates 174,480 B.t.u. Note that the heat liberated by the combustion of 1 lb of carbon $= 174,480/12 = 14,540$ B.t.u./lb, is the calorific value of amorphous carbon.

Similarly equation (2) means that 4 lb of hydrogen (the weight of 2 molecules of hydrogen expressed in lb) combines with 32 lb of oxygen and liberates 245,950 B.t.u. Hence the gross calorific value of hydrogen $= 245,950/4 = 61,490$ B.t.u./lb.

2. *Partial Combustion*

Combustion of part of the fuel represents a loss, in proportion to that portion of the fuel not burned to carbon dioxide, water, or sulphur dioxide. In the case of hydrogen and sulphur, that part not consumed will remain as hydrogen or sulphur. In the case of carbon, a lower oxide, carbon monoxide, may be formed, represented by:

$$2C + O_2 = 2CO + 104,880 \text{ B.t.u.} \tag{4}$$

or
$$C + \tfrac{1}{2}(O_2) = CO + 52,440 \text{ B.t.u.} \tag{5}$$

This represents a loss of 122,040 B.t.u. per 12 lb of carbon when burned to CO instead of to CO_2. This is recovered if the carbon monoxide is burned with more oxygen to form carbon dioxide, thus:

$$CO + \tfrac{1}{2}(O_2) = CO_2 + 122,040 \text{ B.t.u.} \tag{6}$$

This intermediate formation of carbon monoxide is applied usefully in the formation of producer gas (cf. Data Sheet No. 106), but any carbon monoxide formed during the direct combustion of a fuel represents a loss of heat equivalent to 70% of the calorific value of the carbon in the carbon monoxide.

3. Nitrogen in Air or Fuel

Air contains 79% by volume of nitrogen or 76·8% by weight. Solid and liquid fuels contain small, variable proportions, usually less than 2% by weight, of nitrogen. Nitrogen is non-combustible and acts as a diluent to the oxygen in air. In order to calculate the weight and volume of flue gases produced during combustion it is necessary to know the amounts of nitrogen present in the air and fuel.

Air consists of 79 volumes of nitrogen and 21 volumes of oxygen (small proportions of inert gases are included as nitrogen). The ratio of nitrogen to oxygen by volume = 79/21 = 3·76. Since the molecular weights of all gases occupy the same volume under the same conditions of temperature and pressure, the molecular ratio of nitrogen to oxygen in air is 3·76.

Equations (1) to (6) may be re-written on this basis to include the molecular proportion of nitrogen present during combustion, e.g.

$$C + O_2 + 3\text{·}76 \ N_2 = CO_2 + 3\text{·}76 \ N_2 + 174,480 \ \text{B.t.u.}$$

meaning that 12 lb carbon burn in 32 lb oxygen + 105·3 lb nitrogen to form 44 lb carbon dioxide + 105·3 lb nitrogen + 174,480 B.t.u. By dividing by 12 we get: 1 lb carbon burns in 2·66 lb oxygen + 8·82 lb nitrogen to form 3·66 lb carbon dioxide + 8·82 lb nitrogen + 14,540 B.t.u. Note that the presence of nitrogen does not affect the amount of heat liberated, though it reduces the flame and flue gas temperature. The ratio $N_2 : O_2 = 3·76 : 1$ is used only when calculating volumes of air or nitrogen.

The proportions of nitrogen and oxygen in air by weight are $76·8 : 23·2 = 3·31 : 1$.

∴ to obtain weight of air equivalent to the weight of oxygen used, multiply this by 100/23·3.

4. *Relationship between Volume and Temperature and Pressure of Gases*

Fundamental gas laws state that for any gas

$$\frac{pv}{T} = \text{constant}$$

where p = pressure
v = volume
T = absolute temperature $= t°C + 273$
$\qquad\qquad\qquad\qquad\quad = t°F + 460$

When conditions change from T_1 to T_2 and from p_1 to p_2

then $V_2 = V_1 \times \dfrac{T_2}{T_1} \times \dfrac{p_1}{p_2}$

5. *Relationship between Volume and Weight of Gases*

Avogadro's Hypothesis states that the molecular weight of any gas occupies 22·4 l. at N.T.P. N.T.P. (normal temperature and pressure) = 0°C and 760 mm Hg pressure. It is more convenient in combustion calculations in the English-speaking world to express weights and units in lb and ft^3 and to use S.T.P. in place of N.T.P. S.T.P. (standard temperature and pressure) = 60°F and 30 in. Hg. pressure. At S.T.P. the pound molecular weight of any gas occupies 379 ft^3 (or 385 ft^3 when saturated with water vapour at 60°F).

The *specific volume* of a gas at S.T.P. is the volume occupied by unit weight and for this purpose may be calculated by dividing 379 by the molecular weight of the gas in pounds. Thus the specific volume at S.T.P. of oxygen = 379/32 = 11·82. The molecular weights and specific volumes at S.T.P. of gases commonly used in combustion calculations are:

Gas Formula	Molecular Wt. (approx).	Specific Volume ft^3/lb at 60°F and 30 in. Hg
H$_2$	2	187·60
O$_2$	32	11·82
N$_2$*	28·3	13·43
CO$_2$	44	8·60
SO$_2$	64	5·79
H$_2$O	18	21·00
CO	28	13·51
CH$_4$	16	23·60
Air	—	13·06

* Including inert rare gases.

B. CALCULATION OF AIR REQUIRED FOR COMBUSTION: AND OF THE PRODUCTS OF COMBUSTION USING THEORETICAL AIR

These are best expressed as weight or volume per lb of fuel. From the previous data the following amounts of oxygen and air are required for the combustion of 1 lb of each combustible element of a fuel, with the products of combustion obtained:

Combustible Element	lb air components, or products of combustion, per lb of element							
	O_2	N_2	Air	CO_2	CO	N_2	H_2O	SO_2
*Carbon	2·66	8·82	11·48	3·66		8·82		
**Carbon	1·33	4·41	5·74		2·33	4·41		
Hydrogen	8	26·4	34·4			26·4	9	
Sulphur	1	3·3	4·3					2

* When burned to CO_2.   ** When burned to CO.

The volume of the products of combustion in ft^3 at S.T.P. are:

	CO_2	CO	N_2	H_2O	SO_2
From 1lb carbon to CO_2	31·52		118·5		
From 1lb carbon to CO		31·52	59·25		
From 1lb hydrogen as water vapour			352·8	187·7	
From 1lb sulphur			44·4		11·6

From these figures the weight and volumes of air required and weights and volumes of products of combustion using theoretical air may be calculated for any solid or liquid fuel, thus:

Example:

Coal Analysis	lb constituent/lb coal
C = 82%	C = 0·82
H_2 = 4%	H_2 = 0·04
O_2 = 5%	O_2 = 0·05
S = 1%	S = 0·01
N_2 = 1%	N_2 = 0·01
H_2O = 2%	H_2O = 0·02
Ash = 5%	Ash = 0·05

Using Theoretical Air

  0·82 lb carbon requires 0·82 × 2·66 lb O_2 = 2·18 lb O_2

  0·04 lb hydrogen ,, 0·04 × 8 lb O_2 = 0·32 lb O_2

  0·01 lb sulphur ,, 0·01 × 1 lb O_2 = 0·01

  Total wt. O_2 required   2·51 lb

  Wt. O_2 present in coal   0·05 lb

  ∴ O_2 to be supplied from air   2·46 lb

  ∴ Wt of air required = $2·46 \times \dfrac{100}{23·2}$ = 10·6 lb air

                                   = 138 ft³ at S.T.P.

  Nitrogen in coal = 0·01 lb   *Vol. at S.T.P.*

  Nitrogen in air = 10·6 − 2·46 = 8·14 lb

  ∴ nitrogen in flue gases = 8·15 lb   109·5 ft³

  Wt. of CO_2 produced = 0·82 × 3·66 = 3·00 lb   25·8 ft³

  Wt. of H_2O produced = 0·04 × 9 = 0·36 lb

  Wt. of H_2O in coal = 0·02 lb

  ∴ Total water vapour in flue gases = 0·38 lb   8·0 ft³

  Wt. of SO_2 produced = 0·01 × 2 = 0·02 lb   0·1 ft³

  ∴ Total products of combustion, wet = 11·55 lb   143·4 ft³

  ∴ Total products of combustion, dry = 11·17 lb   135·4 ft³

Percent CO_2 by volume in dry flue gases = $\dfrac{25·8}{135·4} \times 100 = 19·05\%$

C. SIGNIFICANCE OF PERCENTAGE OF CARBON DIOXIDE IN FLUE GASES

1. The flue gases obtained from any fuel when burned with the amount of air necessary for complete combustion, but without excess, contain a fixed and characteristic percentage of carbon dioxide. This is known as the "Theoretical percentage of carbon dioxide".

2. With pure, dry, carbon, the oxygen of the air is replaced

quantitatively by carbon dioxide, so that the theoretical percentage is 21.0% by volume.

3. Any air supplied in excess of that theoretically required for any fuel reduces the percentage of carbon dioxide in the flue gases proportionally.

4. In practice, the percentage of CO_2 in the flue gases is determined by some form of gas analysis apparatus, in which the gas is stored and analysed over solutions of reagents in water. Its water vapour content is small (1.3% at $60°F$) and is constant during the determination, so that the result obtained is the CO_2 percentage by volume on the "Dry basis". The theoretical CO_2 used in calculations is also the percentage by volume on the dry basis.

5. With fuels containing hydrogen, or hydrocarbon gases, the theoretical CO_2 is lower than that for carbon, because air supplied to burn the hydrogen forms water, which condenses, leaving nitrogen to dilute the flue gases formed from the carbon alone.

In the above example, the theoretical CO_2 for the coal considered is 19.0%. The range of theoretical CO_2 for bituminous coals is about 18.0% to 19.0%. For high temperature cokes it is above 20% and for petroleum oils between 14% and 15%.

6. Sulphur dioxide in the flue gases is analysed as carbon dioxide, but this introduces only a small error in low sulphur fuels.

7. Any carbon monoxide produced reduces the proportion of carbon dioxide formed and must be allowed for when the amount is known.

D. CALCULATION OF EXCESS AIR AND DRY FLUE GASES USING EXCESS AIR

1. *From the Basic Calculation as in para. B above*

Assume analysis of flue gases to be:

$$\left.\begin{array}{l} CO_2 = 12\% \\ CO \ = \ 1\% \\ O_2 = \ 7\% \\ N_2 = 80\% \end{array}\right\} \begin{array}{l} \text{by volume} \\ \text{dry basis} \end{array}$$

Actual volume of dry flue gases

$$= \frac{\text{Theory } CO_2}{\text{Actual } CO_2 + CO} \times \text{Theoretical Vol. of dry flue gases}$$

$$= \frac{19 \cdot 05}{12 + 1} \times 135 \cdot 4 \text{ ft}^3$$
$$= 197 \text{ ft}^3$$

Vol. of theoretical dry flue gases $= 135 \cdot 4 \text{ ft}^3$ (para. B)

But, the difference between these two volumes is the volume of excess air.

$\therefore$ vol. excess air $= 61 \cdot 6 \text{ ft}^3 = 4 \cdot 73 \text{ lb}$

Theory air $= 138 \text{ ft}^3$ (para. B)

$\therefore$ excess air $= \dfrac{61 \cdot 6}{138} \times 100$ $= 44 \cdot 6 \%$

Wt. of dry flue gases $=$ Theory wt. $+$ wt. excess air
$$= 11 \cdot 17 \text{ (from para. B)} + 4 \cdot 73$$
$$= 15 \cdot 9 \text{ lb} = 197 \text{ ft}^3 \text{ at S.T.P.}$$

Wt. of wet flue gases $= 15 \cdot 9 + 0 \cdot 38 = 16 \cdot 28 \text{ lb}$

2. Carbon Balance Method

In this method the weight of flue gases per pound of coal is obtained from the weights of carbon in 1 lb of coal and 1 lb of the resultant flue gases.

Analysis of Flue Gases by Volume

$$CO_2 = 12 \%$$
$$CO = 1 \%$$
$$O_2 = 7 \%$$
$$N_2 = 80 \%$$

Wt. of O_2 required per lb of fuel
$$= 0 \cdot 82 \times 2 \cdot 66 + 0 \cdot 04 \times 8 - 0 \cdot 05 + 0 \cdot 01$$
$$= 2 \cdot 46$$
$$= 2 \cdot 46 \times \frac{100}{23 \cdot 2} = 10 \cdot 6 \text{ lb air} = 138 \text{ ft}^3$$

Weight Analysis of Flue Gases

	% by vol.	Molecular weight (m.w.)	Weight product (vol. × m.w.)	% by wt.
CO_2	12 ×	44 =	528	$17 \cdot 48 \left(\text{e.g.} \dfrac{528}{30 \cdot 44} \right)$
CO	1 ×	28 =	28	$0 \cdot 93$
O_2	7 ×	32 =	224	$7 \cdot 4$
N_2	80 ×	28·3 =	2264	$74 \cdot 19$
		Total	3044	100·00 %

$\therefore$ Carbon as $CO_2 + CO$ in 1 lb flue gases

$$= 0 \cdot 1748 \times \frac{12}{44} + 0 \cdot 0093 \times \frac{12}{28}$$
$$= 0 \cdot 0515 \text{ lb}$$

Wt. of carbon in 1 lb coal = 0·82 lb

$\therefore$ wt. dry flue gases per lb coal $= \dfrac{0 \cdot 82}{0 \cdot 0515} = 15 \cdot 9$ lb

From the above table, the average molecular weight of the dry flue gases $= \dfrac{3044}{100} = 30 \cdot 44$; i.e. 30·44 lb occupy 379 ft³ at S.T.P.

$\therefore$ vol. dry flue gases at S.T.P. $= \dfrac{379 \times 15 \cdot 9}{30 \cdot 44}$
$$= 197 \text{ ft}^3$$

H_2O in gases from combustion
    of hydrogen in coal $= 0 \cdot 04 \times 9 = 0 \cdot 36$
H_2O in coal $= 0 \cdot 02$
            Total $= 0 \cdot 38$ lb/lb coal
$\therefore$ Total wt. flue gases/lb. carbon $= 15 \cdot 9 + 0 \cdot 38$
                        $= 16 \cdot 28$ lb/lb coal

The water occupies $\dfrac{379 \times 0{\cdot}38}{18}$ ft^3 $= 8$ft^3

∴ Volume of wet flue gases/lb coal $= 197 + 8$

                                              $= 205$ ft^3

But 1 lb coal contains only 0·95 lb of pure coal plus water.

∴ wt. of coal gasified $= 0{\cdot}95$ lb/lb coal burned

∴ wt. of air used $= 16{\cdot}28 - 0{\cdot}95$ lb

                                               $= 15{\cdot}33$ lb/lb coal

Theory air $= 10{\cdot}6$ lb/lb coal

∴ wt. excess air $= 4{\cdot}73$ lb/lb coal

                                               $= 61{\cdot}6$ ft$^3 = 44{\cdot}6\%$

E. UTILIZATION OF THESE DATA

(a) In the control of combustion. Excess air carries away sensible heat from the furnace, reducing the efficiency of the process proportionally.

(b) In the preparation of heat balances and the determination of the efficiency of heat utilization of the process. These matters are discussed in Data Sheets Nos. 160 and 170.

(c) Other examples of combustion calculations are given in Data Sheet No. 166.

F. SOURCE OF DATA FOR COMBUSTION CALCULATIONS

These calculations require the ultimate analysis of the fuel used and the analysis of the flue gases. Ultimate analysis is a difficult and time-consuming process and few industrial laboratories are equipped to undertake such determinations. In contrast, proximate analysis of coal by standard methods is relatively easy, as is simple gas analysis. In cases where ultimate analysis cannot be carried out, the best procedure is to determine the volatile matter and calorific value of the coal and then either to apply the Seyler relationships between V.M., C.V., C and H in Data Sheet No. 8, or to read from Seyler's

Fuel Chart (Data Sheet No. 5) the C and H percentages from the determined values of V.M. and C.V.   No such method is available for use with liquid fuels.

REFERENCES

The Efficient Use of Fuel, H.M.S.O., London, 1958.
FRANCIS, W. *Boiler House and Power Station Chemistry*, London, 1962.

COMBUSTION OF COAL ON GRATES

A. NATURE OF COMBUSTION PROCESS

Coal and air are brought together at a temperature sufficient to decompose the coal into "Fixed carbon" and "Volatile matter" and to cause the fixed carbon to ignite. Combustion then becomes self-supporting, i.e. sufficient heat is evolved to maintain these conditions.

B. COMBUSTION CONTROL

1. Air supply is controlled to provide sufficient to burn all combustible matter, without using undue excess. If too little air is supplied, some combustible products leave the furnace without burning, thus lowering the efficiency of the process. Such products are hydrogen, hydrocarbons, carbon monoxide, soot (entrained carbon) and carbon in the ashes. If too much air is supplied, the efficiency is reduced in proportion to the excess of air, because heat is required to raise the excess air to flue gas temperature.

2. Rate of combustion of coal on a grate is primarily determined by the rate of air supply.

3. Amount and rate of air supplied are controlled by the draught available in the furnace (cf. Data Sheet No. 20). This is, in turn, controlled by:

(a) The suction or pressure available from chimneys or fans.

(b) The resistance to the flow of air to the furnace (and of flue gases from the furnace) offered by the fuel on the grate and by the size and shape of the furnace, heating elements and flues.

4. Distribution of air in the furnace is determined by the rank of the coal.

Two air supplies are required to burn coal on a grate efficiently, viz.:

(a) Primary air—introduced under the grate and required to burn the fixed carbon of the coal.

(b) Secondary air—introduced over the grate and required to burn the volatile matter produced from the coal.

Since the ratio of fixed carbon to volatile matter increases with increase in rank, the ratio of primary air to secondary air increases with increase in rank of coal.

The caking characteristics of coal (related to rank) also influence the behaviour of coal on combustion, particularly the size of the aggregates of fixed carbon (coke with caking coals) formed on the grate and the resistance to the flow of primary air offered by the fuel bed. Special grates, or techniques, are required for coking coals (see paras. 2, 3(a) and (b).

5. *Time Factor.* Sufficient time is required for air to react with:

(a) Solid particles of fixed carbon on the grate.

(b) Gases in the combustion zone above the grate.

Item (a) depends upon the thickness of the fuel bed and the re-activity of the fixed carbon, which is high for low rank coals and low for high rank coals.

Item (b) depends upon the mixing of air with flue gases and upon the shape and size of the combustion chamber. Turbulence in the combustion chamber improves the mixing of air and gases. This may be achieved by directing jets of secondary air downwards, towards the gate, or by supplying this air with a rotary motion.

6. *Effect of Cooling Furnace Gases.* Cooling, before combustion is complete, causes black smoke or soot to be formed from hydrocarbon gases. Cooling may be due to:

(a) Heavy stoking at infrequent intervals.

(b) Excessive cold air supply.

(c) Contact with cold metal.

Preheated air supplied in controlled amounts, together with good design of furnace, prevents the formation of black smoke. The thermal value of black smoke is seldom more than 2 % of that of the coal, but the nuisance value is considerable (cf. Data Sheet No. 172).

High volatile, "fat", coals are particularly liable to produce black smoke. Low volatile, "lean", coals (or coke) do not easily produce smoke.

7. *Size Grading of Coals*—effect of free moisture.
(a) Small sized, uniformly graded, fuels (e.g. $>\frac{1}{2}$ in. <2 in.) provide best air distribution of primary air and optimum performance.
(b) High proportions of fines ($<\frac{1}{8}$ in.) or of large lumps (>2 in.) cause uneven distribution of air and patchy fires.
(c) Combustion of fines is improved by wetting until visible free moisture is present (usually from 6 to 10 %). This causes steam to be evolved on the grate, causing the fine coal to "float" and thus permit the free passage of air. The loss of efficiency due to water is about 0·1 % for each 1 % of water added. The overall increase in efficiency of the furnace due to wetting may be in excess of 10 % when using small, dirty, badly graded, coals.
(d) With some forms of mechanical stokers (q.v.) carefully sized and clean coal, free from dust, is almost essential.

C. METHODS OF FIRING

1. *Hand Firing—Non-coking Coals*

(a) *Spreading*

Coal is thrown over the whole grate area at regular intervals. The fuel bed is made thinner at the back to reduce smoke formation. This method gives the maximum rate of combustion with hand firing, but grate cleaning is difficult.

(b) *Wing, or Side, Method*

Alternate sides are cleaned and lightly spread with coal.
Advantages:
(i) One side is always in good condition.
(ii) Volatiles always burn efficiently without smoke production.

(c) *Requirements for Success*

(i) Firing at frequent, regular, intervals.

(ii) Thickness of bed is determined by grading of coal. Thin fires with slacks.

Thick fires are used with lump fuel.

(iii) Poking and raking during active combustion must be reduced to a minimum.

(iv) CO_2 content of flue gases maintained at 11% to 13%, i.e. excess air $\simeq 50\%$, gives maximum efficiency without visible smoke.

2. Hand Firing—Coking Coals

Each charge is coked at the front of the grate before pushing evenly over the grate. Smoke is a minimum with light fines. Fires require more frequent attention than with non-coking coals. Output of furnace is lower than with non-coking coals.

3. Mechanical Stokers, Overfeed Stokers

(a) *Sprinkler*

The sprinkler imitates hand firing by throwing small increments of coal by a shovel or rotor on to different parts of the grate in turn. Suitable for small furnaces only (cf. Fig. 16.1). In the shovel type, a cam compresses a spring to various degrees, thus varying the throw. In the rotor type, smaller increments are thrown more frequently by high speed rotating blades. This gives thinner fires and more flexible operation. The grate may be fixed or rocking. The latter breaks up clinker and permits longer runs without hand cleaning. Disadvantage of these stokers is that fine coal dust and grit, thrown into the gas stream, are carried forward into the chimney gases, causing grit emission nuisance. The remedy is to use closely graded, preferably washed, coal, free from fines. Maximum effective rate of combustion on grate = 30 $lb/ft^2/hr$.

(b) *Ram Feed, Coking Stoker*

This imitates the hand firing of coking coals. A ram pushes coal

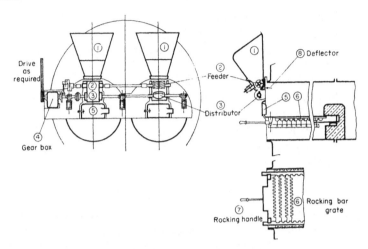

FIG. 16.1　Sprinkler Stoker in Lancashire Boiler.

from the hopper feed on to the front of the grate, where volatile matter is driven off and coke remains. A moving grate then imparts a forward motion to the coke (cf. Fig. 16.2). This stoker is often fitted to Lancashire or Cornish boilers. A type of moving grate coking stoker suitable for use in large water tube boilers is the Taylor Retort Stoker. Thick fires are carried with both stokers, from 1 ft with the ram type, to several feet with the retort stoker. Advantages are that coking coals can be burned efficiently and that combustion control is easy. High CO_2 can be maintained in the flue gases, with consequent high efficiency. Disadvantages are that sudden large fluctuations in demand cannot be met easily and that high draught is necessary to draw air through the thick fires.

(c) Chain Grate Stoker

This is an endless metal chain conveyor, through which primary air passes, which carries fuel into the furnace and ash from the furnace. Feed rates can be regulated accurately, at the front end, by control of the thickness of coal bed admitted and by the speed of the grate.

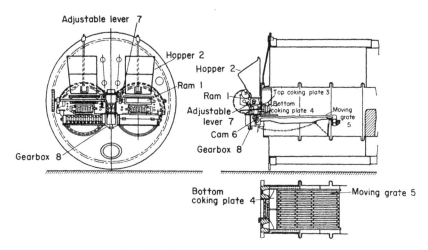

FIG. 16.2   Ram Type Coking Stoker.

Originally designed for large water tube boilers, small units can now be fitted to Lancashire or Cornish boilers (cf. Fig. 16.3). Any type of small coal can be burned effectively except: low ash coal (say $<5\%$) because of the necessity for protecting the grate from the furnace heat; slacks containing high proportions of fines ($>30\%$ $<\frac{1}{8}$ in.) which block the air passages in the grate; and coking coals. With Lancashire type boilers the full cross-section of the fire tubes cannot be used, but longer fires can be used to compensate. Best results are obtained by balanced draught, i.e. with primary and secondary air supplied under pressure at the front of the furnace and gaseous products of combustion removed under suction at the back (see Data Sheet No. 20).

(d) *Underfeed Stokers*

Coal is fed into channel A (Fig. 16.4) below the grate by a coarse Archimedean screw conveyor. Volatile matter distils through the fire and is burned smokelessly by secondary air passing over. The coke formed is forced up the channel A on to the terraced grate B, through which primary air passes.

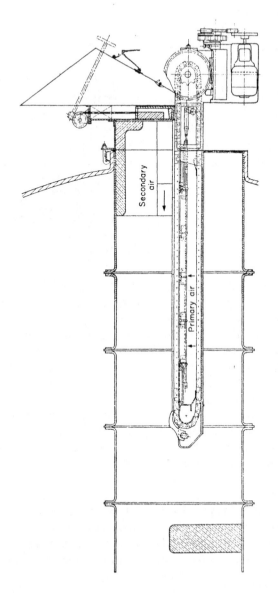

Fig. 16.3   Chain Grate Stoker in Lancashire Boiler.

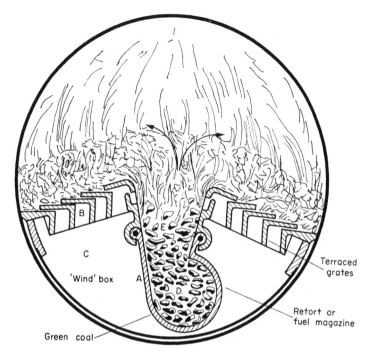

FIG. 16.4   Underfeed Coking Stoker in Lancashire Boiler.

Best grading of coal $<\frac{3}{4}$ in. for small stokers
$\qquad\qquad\qquad\quad >2$ in. for larger stokers
Maximum output of stoker $\simeq 1200$ lb fuel/hr.

(e) *Advantages of Mechanical Stokers over Hand Firing*
  (i) Operation is continuous if stoker is self-cleaning, therefore no loss of efficiency due to intermittent operation during charging and cleaning.
 (ii) Uniform feed rate and continuous operation make automatic control easy.
(iii) Higher CO_2 is possible in flue gases (12 to 14 % for mechanical stokers, 11 to 13 % with hand firing) with consequent higher efficiency (cf. Data Sheet No. 15).

(iv) Larger grates can be used, with higher outputs.

(v) Lower labour costs. One man can operate several furnaces fitted with mechanical stokers.

(f) *Characteristics of Good Mechanical Stoker*

(i) Must burn fuels of varying quality smokelessly and efficiently.

(ii) Must be self-cleaning.

(iii) Must be capable of ready adjustment to suit varying loads.

(iv) Maintenance costs must be low and replacements quickly available.

(v) Observation of fire in furnace must be possible.

(vi) Must be capable of automatic control.

(g) *Output of Mechanical Stokers*

Factors of grate area, rate of movement of grate, and reactivity of solid fuel, limit the maximum fuel consumption of a single mechanical stoker to about 20 ton/hr. For example, a chain grate stoker of 900 ft^2 grate area will burn a maximum of about 45,000 lb/hr.

For outputs greater than this, multiple stokers must be used, or the fuel burned in a cyclone stoker, or in pulverized form (see Data Sheet No. 17).

(h) *Banking*

Banking is a method of maintaining fires in furnaces during stand-by periods without undue consumption of fuel. Requirements of good banking practice are:

(i) Amount of fuel burned should be just sufficient to overcome the natural cooling of the furnace system plus any small requirements for process heat.

(ii) Fires should not be cleaned before banking, because any ash or clinker left on the grates reduces air flow to a minimum, and grates are easier to clean when cool than when hot.

(iii) Main dampers should be nearly closed, and the ash pit doors partially closed, during banking.

(iv) Secondary air openings should be closed.

(v) When restarting, main dampers are first opened, with small controlled openings in the fire doors. This purges the flue system from inflammable gases before active fires are started.

REFERENCES

FRANCIS, W. *Boiler House and Power Station Chemistry*, London, 1962.
The Efficient Use of Fuel, H.M.S.O., London, 1958.

COMBUSTION OF COAL WITHOUT GRATES

Two methods are available, viz.
A. As pulverized fuel.
B. As small coal in the cyclone furnace.

A. COAL AS PULVERIZED FUEL

1. *Advantages over Mechanical Stokers*

(a) Greater flexibility of control—banking and stand-by losses are minimum.
(b) Wide variety of coals can be used (including anthracite, under favourable conditions).
(c) Low grade coals can be used, provided special precautions are taken with high ash coals to avoid carrying fine dust and grit into the atmosphere.
(d) Combustion complete with low % excess air, therefore high flame temperature and high thermal efficiency. In power station practice 90% efficiency obtainable.
(e) Maximum efficiency also possible because of close regulation of rate of feed and supply of air by automatic control.
(f) Labour charges low and maintenance largely exterior to furnace.
(g) For metallurgical purposes, character of flame—i.e. oxidizing or reducing—can be controlled readily.

2. *Disadvantages*

(a) Relatively high cost of drying and grinding to fine particle size.
(b) Tendency for slagging on refractory walls and furnace linings.
(c) Discharge of fine dust and grit into atmosphere.

(d) Necessity for large combustion space to complete combustion and heat transfer and to avoid deposition of soot in tubes or flues.
(e) Contamination of product in furnace work by ash from coal.
(f) Difficulty of burning anthracites.
(g) Erosion of pressure boiler parts by fly ash entrained in flue gases—reduced availability and high maintenance costs.
(h) Erosion of I.D. fan blades and scrolls by entrained ash.

3. *Fineness of Grinding*

The higher the rank of the coal, the finer the grinding required. Grading usually required is 70% <240 B.S. sieve and all through 72 B.S. sieve. With anthracites, >80% must be <240 B.S. sieve and preheated air must be used to obtain good combustion.

4. *Preparation*

Use of air-swept mills reduces the necessity for drying before grinding, except in the case of very wet coals. Driers used are of cell-type: hot gas is the drying medium.

5. *Removal of Dust from Flue Gases*

It is necessary to remove dust before discharge to atmosphere—this is usually done by a series of cyclones near the base of the chimney.

Buell van Tongeren system—2 rows of 4 cyclones deal with 139,000 ft^3/min at 370°F at full load—99% dust >20 μ is removed. With <20 μ dust, efficiency decreases to 60% at 3 μ. If fine dust has to be removed, electrostatic precipitators are used after the cyclones. Note that 75 to 85% of the ash passes through the furnace in non-slagging types.

6. *Types of Burner*

(a) High V.M. coals—short flame with self-induced turbulence.
(b) Medium V.M. coals—short flame with externally induced turbulence.

(c) Low V.M. and anthracites—long flame—firing downwards into chamber (suitable for furnace work).

7. *Preparation of Fuel*

Drying. Surface moisture must permit easy flow to mill—say $<3\%$ free H_2O. Then additional drying takes place in the mill by passing through preheated air at 500–700°F. This can be the primary air for combustion. The dried air/coal mix leaves the mill at approx. 150°F.

8. *Systems of Conveying and Storing*

(a) *Unit or Direct System*
Each boiler is supplied with its own grinding plant in a self-contained system. The mill is preferably swept by air from forced draught fans.

(b) *Central or Bin System*
Pulverized fuel is removed from the air stream by cyclone separators. The powder can be delivered to outside users, or used locally, e.g. conveyed by screw type conveyors direct to primary air stream of burners. Condensation of water may occur during storage, causing trouble due to the clogging of the charge. Ring mains are used in some works, particularly in metallurgical applications. Pulverized fuel from the storage bins is fed to the ring main in an air stream—burners take off supply and excess is recovered by cyclones, and returned to store (cf. ring main system for oil firing, Data Sheet No. 70).

Choice of System
Unit system is preferred for large boilers and power stations. The advantages are:
(i) Individual control of all operations.
(ii) Maintenance and operational costs low.
(iii) Less danger of coal–air explosions, or of the combustion of powdered coal without explosion.
(iv) No tendency for pulverized fuel to clog.

Bin system—favoured for small, multiple, operations
       —favoured for metallurgical operations.

Equipment—Mills	*Speed*
(i) Ball or Tube Mill (Hardinge)	Slow—20–40 r.p.m.
(ii) Rollers on table or bowl (Lopulco)	
Ball and track (Babcock)	Medium—100–300 r.p.m.
(iii) Impact. Swinging Hammer (attritor, Impax, etc.)	High—1000–4000 r.p.m.

(a) Air swept—ratio length: diameter $= 1\frac{1}{2} : 2$. Raymond/Kennedy
    —occupies more floor space—little maintenance. Power
    40–50 kW/ton coal. May be fitted with classifier, returning
    coarse grit to mill—can be used for anthracites.
(b) Lopulco—fixed rolls—spring loaded and rotating table, or
    vice versa.
    —product to classifier—coarse returned to mill, fine to burner.
    —space required lower than (i)
    —less sensitive to H_2O than (i)
    —power consumption lower than (i)
    —does not grind anthracite effectively.
(c) High speed—Kramer—operated by impact against air or against
    screens. Quality of grinding and performance fall off as impellor
    and screens wear—higher maintenance—more power required
    —not suitable for anthracites, which are highly abrasive.
    Coal feed is passed through magnetic separator to remove
    tramp metal so as to prevent accidents.

Grindability of Coal
    Generally more difficult with high ash coals and anthracites.

Requirements—75–85 % < 200 B.S. sieve—bituminous coal
           —80–85 % < 200 B.S. sieve—anthracites

N.B. only the higher volatile matter anthracites can be burned
reasonably.

    The relationship between mill capacity, power, and cost of grinding are shown in Fig. 17.1. The output is also related to the grindability of the coal.

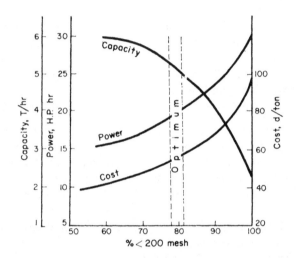

FIG. 17.1 Relationship between Capacity of Mill, Power, and Cost of Grinding.

Two indices for grindability are used, viz.

(i) *U.S. Ball Mill Index*—No. of revs. to produce $80\% < 200$ sieve under standard conditions.

$$\text{Index} = \frac{50,000}{\text{av. no. of revs. for 2 tests}}$$

(ii) *Hardgrove Index*—based on Rittinger's Law, which states that the power consumption is proportional to the new surface created. A prepared sample receives a definite amount of grinding energy in a laboratory ring–roll pulverizer. The sample is compared with a coal chosen as having 100 grindability (Pittsburgh Seam coal).

$$\text{Index} = 13 \times 6 \cdot 93 \, w$$

where w = wt. of material passing 200 B.S. sieve (obtained from orig. wt. of 50 g-wt. retained on sieve). Usual range of indices 25 to 75.

Comparison:

Hardgrove Index:	20	40	60	80	100
Ball Mill Index:	14	28	44	60	80

9. *Mechanism of Combustion of Pulverized Coal*

Three stages:

(a) Pre-ignition—some change of shape and size of particles with evolution of volatile matter.
(b) Ignition and combustion of volatile matter.
(c) Combustion of carbonaceous residue.

Caking coals form cenospheres—these are hollow, thin-walled spheres. Large ones are more difficult to burn than small ones. The higher the temperature of formation, the smaller the size and the more rapid the ignition.

Weakly caking or non-caking coals. N.C.B. groups 700–900 (high V.M.) and 100–200 (low V.M.) do not form cenospheres. Some fragmentation occurs (decrepitation) with high V.M. coals. The *solid residue* from high V.M. coals is much more reactive than that from low volatile coals (anthracites). Combustion of the solid residue requires more time than the volatile matter (gas + tar), therefore rate of combustion is determined by the reactivity of the solid residue. Above 800 to 1000°C, the rate depends more upon the rate of diffusion of oxygen to the surface. Higher rates can be obtained by increasing the relative motion between air and particle, i.e. by turbulence.

To burn anthracite requires:

(i) High pre-heat of air.
(ii) Fine grinding.
(iii) Low excess air.
(iv) Refractory walls backing ignition zone.

10. *Velocity of Propagation of Flame and Limiting Mixtures of Coal Dust and Air*

The approximate relationships between air/fuel ratios, coal volatile matter, inflammability limits, and flame speeds are shown in Table 17.1.

TABLE 17.1

RELATIONSHIP BETWEEN AIR/FUEL RATIO, COAL VOLATILE MATTER**, INFLAMMABILITY LIMITS* AND FLAME SPEEDS*

V.M. of coal %	*Inflammability limits lb air/lb coal*		*Max. flame speed ft/sec*	*Air/fuel ratio at max. speed lb air/lb coal*
	Upper	*Lower*		
15	1·8	2·7	13	2·3
20	1·7	7·0	23	3·8
30	1·5	14·0	43	4·5

* Cf. Data Sheet No. 116.   ** At 5% ash.
Increase in ash content decreases flame speeds and inflammability limits.

11. *Types of Burner*

Short flame requires turbulent flow.

Long flame requires parallel (stream-line) flow. These are used for corner firing in large boilers and for tilting burners, to permit controlled distribution of temperature.

Design must obtain correct coal/air ratio and velocity (cf. Table 17.1) to prevent blowing flame off burner or firing back.

12. *Air Preheat*

Reduces time for first 2 stages above.

Reduces heat loss in flue gases.

Temperature of preheat is limited by the temperature of initial decomposition of the coal, therefore lower temperature of preheat is used for low rank coals.

13. *Combustion Chamber Design*

(a) In large furnaces more than half the heat is absorbed by radiation to water-cooled walls.

(b) Size is mainly determined by the area of surface necessary for heat absorption.

(c) If too hot when leaving the furnace, fluid ash is deposited on exposed metal surfaces as slag.

(d) Therefore tall furnace is used for medium-large boilers and two or more water-cooled compartments in very large furnaces.

(e) Construction of walls:

    (i) Solid refractory—the limit is the softening point under load of the refractory. Maximum heat release $= 12,500$ B.t.u./ft^3/hr.

   (ii) Refractory cavity walled air cooled chambers. Maximum heat release $=15,000$ B.t.u./ft^3/hr. Air used is preheated and is used as primary air for combustion.

  (iii) Water walls backed by refractory bricks or cements. Maximum heat release $= 22,000$ B.t.u./ft^3/hr.

(f) Time required for combustion reduced by

    (i) Finer grinding (limit is economic).

   (ii) Air–gas–coal particles in turbulent motion—now achieved by multiple burners situated at corners of furnace and flames impinging on each other.

14. *Ash and Dust Disposal*

(a) *Dry Bottom Furnaces*

Ash particles are cooled by radiant heat exchange with walls; small particles pass forward with gases, larger particles fall to the bottom and are removed by hydraulic sluicing system (10–20% of ash). Flue gas may be recirculated in convector heat system to cool ash additionally.

(b) *Slag-tap Furnace*

Ash melts in furnace and flows down into a tank of water where it is granulated. It can be sold as concrete aggregate and for brick making. Low fusion ashes are preferred. The system permits:

(i) Higher furnace temperatures.

(ii) Higher combustion rates.

(iii) Higher outputs.

45–50 % of ash is removed as slag.

Grit Arrestors

These must be fitted to pulverized fuel furnaces. These may be either:

(i) Gas washers.

(ii) Mechanical separators—cyclone or multi-cyclones.

(iii) Electrostatic precipitators—the most efficient allow only 2 % to escape. These usually cannot handle overloads, as when water or steam lancing is operating.

15. Pulverized Fuel in Shell Type Boilers

Short fierce turbulent flame is required. Must not be chilled by cold surfaces, i.e. refractory firing cone is necessary (as with oil fuel). Heat release up to 150,000 B.t.u./ft^3/hr. Ash deposits moved by steam jets. Accumulated grit in settling chambers is removed by water spray.

16. Metallurgical Applications and Cement Manufacture

—Usually central or Bin and Feeder system.

—Oxidizing or reducing flames can be produced at will.

—Ash is detrimental in many metallurgical operations. Advantageous in cement manufacture because sold at cement prices.

(a) Annealing Furnaces

—Steel and malleable cast iron   —reduces scale losses

—consumption, 10–12 cwt   —improves output

    fuel/ton castings   —reduces cost.

(b) *Small Forge and Drop Forge Furnaces*
—Billets $2\frac{1}{2}$ in. sq. to 18 in. sq.—multiple burners.
—Fuel consumption 8–10 cwt/ton.
 To avoid contamination of billet, ash fusion temperature should
 be $>200°F$ more than maximum temperature of metal.

(c) *Heavy Forge Furnaces* (5–100 *ton ingots*)
—Avoid ash coming into contact with product (also in glass
 furnaces). Sulphur spoils surface, causes brittleness and bloom.
—Fuel is burned outside stock chamber in pre-combustion cham-
 bers.
—Fine grinding required to ensure ash entrained in flue gases.
 Fine grinding also permits more sulphur to pass into flue gases.

(d) *Melting Furnaces* (*Reverberatory*)
—Burners are placed at back of chamber. Fuel consumption
 10 cwt/ton alloy.
—Where molten metal is covered by a layer of slag, coal ash of
 low fusion point is not objectionable.

(e) *Copper Smelting*
 <20 ton/day in Great Britain.
 <750 ton/day in U.S.A.
 Multiple swivel type burners.
 Cycle takes 24 hr. Temperature 1100–1300°C.

(f) *Cement Manufacture*
 Rotary furnace 6–12 ft in diameter, 100–500 ft long. Slight angle
 to horizontal. Burner at lower end and feed towards burner, where
 clinker is discharged.
 Long flame required—ash in coal is generally similar in composition to Portland Cement therefore one of the few applications where
 high ash coal is welcomed, e.g. 20–30%.

(g) *Locomotives*
 Serious accumulation of ash in tubes.

(h) *Marine Boilers*
 Difficulties—slag and ash deposits
                —variability of fuels.

(i) *Colloidal Fuel*
 30–35% pulverized fuel is ground into fuel oil—powdered coal requires wetting. Firing as with heavy fuel oil. Reasonably stable—no attraction now, when coal and oil are approximately the same price on a calorific value basis.

B. THE BABCOCK CYCLONE FURNACE

This consists of a water-cooled cylinder, fitted at a small angle to the horizontal into the combustion chamber of a pulverized fuel furnace. Coal, ground $<\frac{1}{4}$ in. size, is fed tangentially to the outer end of the cylinder with primary air. The rotary movement is accentuated by the introduction of secondary air tangentially at high speed and surrounding the small coal and primary air. High temperatures develop rapidly, causing the coal ash to melt and run to the base of the combustion chamber. Unburned fuel (including volatiles) escaping immediate combustion in the cyclone burner are burned in the combustion chamber in a small proportion of tertiary air. Heat release is 500,000 to 600,000 B.t.u./ft^3/hr. Only 10% excess air is used, giving efficiencies up to 5% greater than with mechanical stoker firing and 20% greater output for the same sized combustion chamber.

 Fuel requirements are:
1. High volatile coal, for long flame and easy ignition.
2. Ash fusion point $<1430°C$ (2600°F) in reducing atmosphere, with slag viscosity 250 poises at 1480°C (2700°F).

Other advantages claimed over pulverized fuel operation are:
(a) Less fly ash on boiler heating surfaces, resulting in cleaner operation.
(b) Reduction in size of furnace.
(c) Reduction in amount of grit and dust in flue gases.

(d) Reduction in fuel preparation costs.

(e) Easy disposal of coarse, granulated, ash produced.

REFERENCES

The Efficient Use of Fuel, H.M.S.O., London, 1958.
SPIERS, H. M. *Technical Data on Fuel*, 5th Edition. London, 1952.

MINERAL IMPURITIES IN COAL — ASH AND CLINKER FORMATION

A. NATURE OF MINERAL IMPURITIES

Mineral matter may either be intimately mixed with the coal substance and impossible to remove by any washing process, or it may occur as bands or partings in coal seams, in which case partial separation occurs on breaking and much of the impurity may be removed by dry or wet cleaning processes.

The mineral impurities commonly found in coals are listed below:

COMMON MINERAL IMPURITIES IN COAL

Element	Usual state of combination	Usual amount of mineral as percentage of total mineral impurities
Silicon	Silica and silicates	The main mineral impurities of coal, from 50 to 90% of total
Aluminium	In combination with silica	
Iron	Pyrites and marcasite (sulphides) Ferrous carbonate Ferrous and ferric sulphate Ferrous and ferric silicates	In any proportion between the limits 0–20%. In ash of high fusing point it is usually below 10%
Calcium	Carbonate, sulphate, silicates	0–20%
Magnesium	Carbonate and silicates	0–8%
Sodium and Potassium	Chlorides, carbonate and silicates	0–4%
Titanium	Oxide or in combination as titanites	0–2%

128

Element	Usual state of combination	Usual amount of mineral as percentage of total mineral impurities
Manganese	Carbonate and silicate	Occasionally, in small proportions
Sulphur	In combination with the coal substance: as sulphides and sulphates	$0.5–10\%$
Phosphorus, Gallium, Germanium Nickel, Beryllium	As oxides, or in combination with above.	Occasionally found in small quantities, less than 1%.

B. CHANGE IN ORIGINAL MINERAL MATTER DURING COMBUSTION

The major proportion of the mineral matter in coal is usually a form of shale mixed with varying proportions of free silica, silicates and other compounds of iron, calcium, magnesium, titanium and the alkali materials. On combustion, some of the original compounds are decomposed and the residual materials may re-combine, or interact with other derivatives of the coal ash. For example, the sulphides, sulphates, and carbonates usually decompose, or oxidize, leaving their basic radicals free to combine with any excess of silica; whilst the shales lose water of hydration. The ash left on combustion is therefore not a true measure of the nature or amount of mineral matter originally present.

C. CORRECTION OF ANALYSES FOR MINERAL IMPURITIES

1. Parr Formula: $M = 1.08\ A + 0.55\ S$

where M = percentage of mineral impurity in coal

A = laboratory determination of percentage ash in coal by standard method of combustion

S = laboratory determination of percentage of sulphur in coal.

2. *King, Maries and Crossley Formula:*

$$M = 1\cdot09\ A + 0\cdot5\ \ S_{pyr} + 0\cdot84\ \ CO_2 - 1\cdot1\ \ SO_{3ash} + SO_{3coal} + 0\cdot5\ Cl.$$

The additional symbols in this formula represent the percentages found by analysis of the constituents of the coal or ash, viz.:

S_{pyr}	= pyritic sulphur in air dried coal
CO_2	= carbon dioxide, as carbonates, in coal
SO_{3ash}	= sulphate in ash
SO_{3coal}	= sulphate in coal
Cl	= chlorine in coal.

To calculate the proportion of mineral impurity present in a coal from the percentage of ash in the dry coal, multiply by the factor $\dfrac{100}{100 - M}$, where M is the percentage of mineral matter calculated by formula 1 or 2.

D. FUSION OF COAL ASH

When heated, coal ash does not melt sharply at any definite temperature but commences to soften at a substantially lower temperature than that at which it becomes molten. In laboratory determinations of the fusion point of ash (cf. B.S. 1016, Part 15, 1960) the following three points are recognized:

1. *Deformation temperature*—the temperature at which the top of the pile, cylinder, or cone, of ash first shows signs of deformation.

2. *Hemisphere temperature*—the temperature at which the material becomes fused into a roughly spherical lump.

3. *Flow temperature*—the temperature at which the ash becomes sufficiently molten to spread in a flat pool over the base.

The composition of the ash affects these temperatures as follows:

(a) The nearer the composition of coal ash approaches that of pure dehydrated china clay, of composition $Al_2O_3.2SiO_2$, the more refractory it will be.

(b) Lime and magnesia act as mild fluxes and lower the softening point, particularly when excess silica is present.

(c) Ferric oxide acts in a similar manner.

(d) Ferrous oxide, produced in the decomposition of ferrous carbonate and sulphate, or by the partial oxidation of iron sulphides, is particularly liable to form clinker and ranks with

(e) the oxides of sodium and potassium in having a marked capacity for lowering the fusion point of the ash.

(f) Coals producing a dark red ash, and containing a high proportion of sulphur, possess a low softening point and a wide temperature range between deformation and flow.

E. FORMATION OF CLINKER ON FURNACE GRATES

Clinker is a hard mass of refractory particles of ash, fine coal, and fused ash, that clogs a furnace grate, reducing the flow of air and, in severe cases, causes shut-down of the furnace or boiler. The formation of clinker is a complex process, but is caused, or accelerated, by the following factors:

1. Low softening point of ash. Minimum safe fusion point is 1300°C under normal operating conditions. Ashes with fusion points below 1100°C are extremely liable to form massive clinker.

2. Bad effects of low fusion point are accentuated by wide range of temperature between deformation and flow. Soft material in upper range binds solid particles more strongly than completely molten ash.

3. Low reactivity of carbonized residue, i.e. from low volatile steam coals and anthracites, requires high forced draught and fuel bed temperatures. These accentuate clinkering troubles.

4. Exposure of masses of ash and residual coal to furnace heat for long periods of time—called "Soaking"—is very bad practice.

5. Thick fire beds are more dangerous than thin beds, because reducing conditions prevail. Oxidizing conditions convert iron sulphides to ferric oxide, of relatively high fusion point. Reducing

conditions form ferrous sulphides and ferrous oxide, of low fusion point.

6. Molten or softened ash sticks more readily to hot surfaces than to cold ones. Water cooling prevents trouble of ash and clinker sticking to furnace side walls.

7. Preheated primary air accentuates clinkering troubles on grates.

8. Small, dirty coals, containing high proportions of iron and sulphur, are most liable to produce clinker in furnace practice.

REFERENCES

FRANCIS, W. *Boiler House and Power Station Chemistry*, London, 1962.
The Efficient Use of Fuel, H.M.S.O., London, 1958.

IMPURITIES IN COAL — BOILER AVAILABILITY

SMALL dirty coal, and mineral impurities, create other difficulties in furnace operation than clinker formation, particularly in the operation of large water tube boilers.

A. ARRANGEMENT OF PARTS OF LARGE WATER TUBE BOILER PLANT

A large water tube boiler consists of the following units that are affected by the grading and quality of the solid fuel used:
1. Equipment for the handling of the coal before reaching the boiler.
2. The grate and combustion chamber.
3. The boiler proper, consisting of steel drums and tubes through which water circulates during evaporation.
4. A super-heater for raising the temperature of the steam above that equivalent to the boiler pressure. This consists of a continuous small bore tube placed in the furnace, usually behind the first bank of boiler tubes.
5. An economizer for preheating the water to the boiler by sensible heat from the flue gases issuing from the boiler.
6. An air-heater for preheating the air for combustion from the residual sensible heat of the flue gases leaving the economizer.

B. EFFECT OF GRADING AND QUALITY OF FINE COAL ON BOILER OPERATION

Handling and Combustion Characteristics of Fine Slack

(a) *Rank of Coal*
Low rank coals are most liable to spontaneous combustion; they

133

ignite readily, burn with a long flame, and require a larger combustion space and more secondary air than high rank coals. Preheated air and a lower ratio of secondary air to primary air are required for high rank coals. Low rank (non-coking) coals sometimes decrepitate during combustion and cause excessive losses by falling through the grate without burning. Coking coals require special stokers.

(b) *Size Grading*

Size grading affects behaviour during handling, particularly the flow down hoppers and through chutes. Fine, wet, slacks are particularly difficult to handle in this way, causing sticking in hoppers and blockage of chutes. The effect of a high proportion of fines is balanced by adding an equal proportion of large grades, e.g. slacks containing $>40\%$ through $\frac{1}{8}$ in. material require $>40\%$ of material larger than $\frac{1}{4}$ in. for reasonable handling.

Size grading also affects behaviour during combustion. Fine, dirty, slacks cause uneven burning on grates, block air passages and form clinker easily. If dry, portions are blown from the grate and are deposited on tubes as "fly-ash" or "bird-nests", particularly when using high forced draught.

(c) *Moisture*

(i) During handling—particularly from grabs or when emptying wagons—dust nuisance is prevented by the presence of free moisture in excess of 5%.

(ii) Excessive free moisture accentuates sticking difficulties of fine slacks in hoppers and chutes.

(iii) On the grate, a high proportion of free moisture improves the combustion of fine slacks by preventing consolidation and the blockage of air passages.

(iv) Free moisture must be eliminated before grinding to pulverized fuel.

Retort stokers (coking stokers) are less sensitive to the effects of ash and size grading than chain grate stokers.

C. CLINKER FORMATION—see Data Sheet No. 18.

D. BOILER AVAILABILITY

Definition: The number of days per year that a boiler remains in service without shut down for cleaning or overhaul. The chief factor causing loss of service is the fouling and corrosion of external surfaces of tubes and brickwork by deposits formed from inorganic dusts (mineral matter) and sulphur oxides in the combustion gases.

Sulphur trioxide (SO_3), formed from the sulphur in coal and minerals, is a major factor.

1. By hydration sulphuric acid is formed, which corrodes metals at or below the dewpoint of the furnace gases, e.g. in economizers and air-heaters.

2. Chemical reaction with alkaline dusts forms readily fusible deposits, which stick to super-heaters, boiler tubes and economizers, collecting fly ash and unburned carbon from the coal.

Quality and grading of coal affect boiler availability as follows:

(a) Extremely fine ash and residual carbon are blown into the passes in the boiler tubes, causing "bird-nesting".

(b) High temperature deposits are formed on steam tubes nearest the combustion chamber and on super-heater tubes, consisting of:

(i) Re-fused ash, mainly spherical particles of the more-readily fusible portions of the coal ash.

(ii) Alkali-matrix deposits. These are whitish deposits, containing high proportions of sulphates and bisulphates, in which fly ash spheres are embedded.

(iii) Phosphate deposits. These consist of a hard outer shell, surrounding a soft core of fly ash. They are mainly due to the mineral fluorapatite, found in some coals.

(c) Low temperature deposits are formed in the cooler parts of the system; in the economizers and air-heaters. They are formed from alkali chlorides, sulphur compounds, and phosphates present in the mineral impurities of the coals.

E. FACTORS IN BOILER OPERATION AFFECTING BOILER AVAILABILITY

1. High temperature bonded deposits are associated with high fuel bed temperatures and smoke-free combustion at the rear of the furnace. Smoke formed at the rear of the furnace, e.g. by injecting pitch-creosote mixtures, materially reduces the formation of high temperature bonded deposits.
2. Stoker fired boilers, with high fuel bed temperatures, are much more liable to trouble from bonded deposits than pulverized fuel fired boilers, with their lower combustion temperatures and high solids burden in the gases.
3. Dry bottom pulverized fuel fired boilers are practically immune from bonded deposits and from back-end corrosion, except when the chlorine and sulphur in the coal are very high (chlorine $>0.6\%$).

F. FEATURES OF BOILER DESIGN FAVOURING INCREASED BOILER AVAILABILITY

1. Pulverized fuel firing in dry bottom furnaces.
2. Provision of wide gas lines in tube banks.
3. Limitation of gas temperature entering tube banks.
4. Provision of effective on-load cleaning devices, e.g. air, steam and water lancing.

REFERENCES

Boiler Availability Report, Bulletin No. MC/160, London, 1946.

FRANCIS, W. *Boiler House and Power Station Chemistry*, London, 1962.

MARSKELL, W. G. Boiler Availability Committee, Paper No. 6, *J. Inst. Fuel*, 1959.

NATURAL AND ARTIFICIAL DRAUGHT

THE pressure required to supply air to a furnace and to remove the flue gases from the furnace is called "Draught".

A. MEASUREMENT OF DRAUGHT

Since the pressure required is low, draught is usually expressed as inches of water gauge (in. w.g.), which is the height of water in a U-tube gauge equivalent to the pressure in the furnace, flue, or chimney.

Since 1 ft^3 of water weighs 62·4 lb, the weight of 1 in. of water operating over 1 ft^2 area is 5·2 lb; equivalent to a pressure of 5·2 lb/ft^2. Therefore 1 in. w.g. = 5·2 lb/ft^2.

Natural draught is produced by a chimney. The resultant flow of gas is controlled by dampers.

Artificial draught is produced by fans and is controlled by the speed of the fans, variation in the pitch of the fan blades, or by dampers.

1. *Design of Chimney*

The draught produced by a chimney is proportional to the height of the chimney and to the density of the chimney gases. The latter is determined by their composition and temperature. A chimney and furnace system is a thermo-syphon in which the difference in pressure at the base of the chimney due to the hot gases and that due to a column of air of equal dimensions determines the draught available (see Fig. 20.1). For example, if the density of the flue gases is 0·079 lb/ft^3 at 60°F and of air is 0·076 lb/ft^3 at 60°F, the weight of a column of flue gases occupying 100 ft³ at 350°F will be $7.9 \times 520/810 = 5.06$ lb. The weight of a similar column of air at 60°F is 7·6 lb. The draught available over a cross-section of 1 ft² is therefore $7.6 - 5.06 = 2.54$ lb/ft² = 0·49 in. w.g. Chimney height required for a given draught (and temperature) is calculated from the formula:

$$H = \frac{h}{\left(\dfrac{7.6}{t_a + 460} - \dfrac{7.9}{t_g + 460} \right)}$$

where H = height of chimney, ft.

h = draught required, in. w.g.

7·6 = wt. of 100 ft³ air at 60°F

7·9 = wt. of 100 ft³ flue gases at 60°F

t_a = air temperature, °F

t_g = mean flue gas temperature, °F

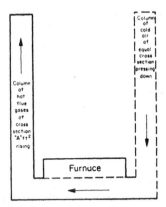

FIG. 20.1   Thermo-Syphon Effect creating Chimney Draught.

If the mean flue gas temperature is not known, it can be calculated, approximately, by deducting 2°F from that at the base of the chimney for every 3 ft of chimney height.

2. *Velocity of Air* (*or Gas*) *due to draught*

The basic equation for the velocity of gas in a chimney is

$$v = \sqrt{2 \, g \, l}$$

where v = velocity in ft/sec

g = acceleration due to gravity = 32·2

l = height in feet of a column of air (or gas) equivalent to a draught of h in w.g.

If the density of air is 0·076 lb/ft^3,

then $l = \dfrac{5 \cdot 2 \, h}{0 \cdot 076} = \dfrac{h}{0 \cdot 0146}$ ft.

$\therefore \; v = \sqrt{4410 \, h} = 66 \cdot 4 \, \sqrt{h}$, i.e. 1 in. w.g. produces a velocity of 66·4 ft/sec.

This is a maximum velocity. The value obtained in practice depends upon the dimensions and surface of the chimney, the effect of changes of section and other factors (cf. Data Sheet No. 163).

The chimney should be designed to give a maximum velocity of 15 ft/sec for small furnaces and 50 ft/sec for large furnaces.

Required chimney area $= \dfrac{\text{Volume of gas flowing, ft}^3/\text{sec}}{\text{Velocity of gas flowing, ft/sec}}$.

B. ARTIFICIAL DRAUGHT

The natural draught of a chimney is limited by practical considerations, so that draught for large furnaces is usually supplied by fans. Natural draught operates entirely by suction, that is the chimney sucks, or induces, the flow of air or gases through the furnace.

Artificial draught may be employed as:

1. Induced draught.
2. Forced draught.
3. Balanced draught.

1. *Induced Draught*

A fan is installed at the base of the chimney to augment the natural draught of the chimney. The draught from the fan overcomes the resistance of the fuel bed to the passage of primary air and the resistance of the furnace installation to the secondary air drawn over the fire bed. The furnace operates under suction.

2. *Forced Draught*

A fan is installed below, or in front of, the grate to force primary air through the fire bed and secondary air over the grate. The furnace operates under pressure.

3. *Balanced Draught*

One fan is installed at the base of the chimney and another at the front end of the furnace. The pressure and suction effects of the fans balance in the furnace, which operates at, or near, atmospheric pressure.

C. COST OF PRODUCING DRAUGHT

1. *Natural Draught*

Heat from fuel is required to produce draught.
Heat available per lb fuel $= (t_g - t_a) \times Vg \times$ sp.ht.

where t_g and t_a = temperature of flue gases and air, respectively, °F
$\qquad V_g$ = volume of flue gases, ft³/lb fuel
$\qquad$ sp.ht. = specific heat of flue gases, volume basis.

If $t_g = 300$°F, $t_a = 60$°F, $V_g = 200$ ft³ and sp.ht. $= 0.02$ then heat available $= 240 \times 200 \times 0.02$
$\qquad = 960$ B.t.u., say 8% of the heat of a typical coal.

$$\text{Fan h.p.} = \frac{5.2 \times h \times V}{33,000 \times E}$$

where E = fractional efficiency of fan (0·5 to 0·75)
V = volume of air or gas handled at the operating temperature, ft³/min.
h = draught, in w.g.

Example: If $E = 0.5$, $V = 6000$ ft³/min, $h = 3$ in.

$$\text{Fan h.p.} = \frac{5·2 \times 3 \times 6000}{33,000 \times 0·5}$$
$$= 5·7 \text{ h.p.}$$

In practice, a fan of 6 h.p. would be used.

2. *Relative Merits of Induced and Forced Draught Fans*

Induced Draught	*Forced Draught*
Furnace under suction—air leaks are increased and reduce efficiency	Furnace under pressure—leaks are outwards, therefore little loss of efficiency, but danger of blow-out through front fire doors.
Fan operates hot—liable to corrosion and out of balance due to accumulation of deposits. Radial blades reduce deposit formation.	Fan operates cold—no corrosion or deposits—long life. Blades made to slope backwards to prevent overloading.
Greater h.p. fan is required because of the larger volume of gas handled.	Gives better control of distribution of air and higher rates of combustion than induced draught.

The best features of both systems are obtained by balanced draught.

REFERENCE

The Efficient Use of Fuel, H.M.S.O., London, 1958.

SOLID FUELS MADE FROM COAL — BRIQUETTES

THE objects of briquetting coal are:

1. To convert cheap or waste fine coal into lump fuel.
2. To produce from coals which decrepitate on the grate solid fuels which behave satisfactorily during combustion.
3. To produce smokeless solid fuel from non-agglutinating fine coal.

Because of the present emphasis on smokeless combustion in all countries, and on the Clean Air Act in Great Britain (Data Sheet No. 30) briquetting is now only important in providing solid "smokeless" fuels from cheap or waste coals.

A. MANUFACTURE OF BRIQUETTES

Briquettes are formed by the application of pressure to small or powdered coals. Two types of uncarbonized briquettes are manufactured, namely:

1. Binderless briquettes
2. Briquettes containing a binder.

1. *Binderless Briquettes — Lignites*

As yet it is only possible to prepare binderless briquettes on a commercial basis with sub-bituminous coals, lignites, or peat. Bituminous coals, carbonaceous coals, and anthracites all require the use of a binder, such as pitch, for the production of satisfactory briquettes. The briquetting of brown coals without binder has been developed extensively in Germany, and in Victoria, Australia. In these places large scale plants have been in operation for some years to upgrade the brown coal deposits.

In order to form satisfactory briquettes from lignites the following conditions are necessary:

1. Drying to reach the equilibrium moisture content of the coal.
2. The application of pressure sufficient to make the particles deform under load.

The optimum moisture is found by determining the moisture in the coal after reaching equilibrium with the air. For German brown coals the optimum moisture content is between $12\frac{1}{2}\%$ and 15%; for the Victorian coals it is somewhat higher, and for Nigerian lignites and sub-bituminous coals somewhat lower. The pressure required for self-binding briquettes is relatively high; usually about 5 ton/in² for lignites and twice this value for bituminous coals. Two types of press are suitable for the manufacture of self-binding briquettes, namely:

1. Direct acting plunger type presses, preferably operating as extrusion presses.
2. Ring-roll presses.

The plunger type press makes briquettes of rectangular, circular, or dumb-bell shaped section; the ring-roll press makes briquettes of roughly rectangular shape.

2. *Carbonized Briquettes* (*Lurgi Process*)

It has been found in Germany that many types of lignite, although not forming cokes on carbonization at ordinary rates in coke-ovens or gas retorts, will form strong, coherent, residues if carbonized rapidly. Lignites that do not form a coherent residue on carbonization can usually be made to form a serviceable coke if carbonized after briquetting. Suitable pressures, varying from 2 tons/in² to 10 ton/in² may be applied by the reciprocating extrusion press or by the ring-roll press. Lignites that behave satisfactorily in this process are those from Central Germany, in the Helmstedt district, and the brown coal deposits of Victoria.

The Lurgi carbonization process for lignites, and lignite briquettes, was used for more than 80% of the lignite carbonized in pre-war Germany.

For the successful carbonization of lignites, the fuel must first be dried and then heated with careful temperature control over the required range. The heating may be carried out indirectly, i.e. by heating the walls of a chamber into which the fuel is charged, or directly, i.e. by circulating the heating gases through the fuel itself.

In low temperature carbonization plants employing indirect heating, the throughput of the plant is limited by the poor conductivity of the refractory walls of the chamber or retort and of the adjacent layers of fuel. In recent years, the conductivity of the chamber walls has been increased by substituting steel for refractory material.

B. THE LURGI SPÜLGAS PROCESS

In the preferred direct heating process, combustion gases are brought into direct contact with the fuel. The method permits a high rate of heat transfer to the fuel and imposes no limits on the size of the carbonizing chamber. In consequence, units with a very high throughput can be built. The high rate of heat transfer and the small heat loss also result in high thermal efficiency.

The retort, illustrated in Fig. 4.1 is open at the top and is closed at the bottom by the coke discharging mechanism. The fuel passes through three successive zones, viz. drying, carbonizing, and coke cooling. The fuel in both the drying and the carbonizing zones is heated by means of circulating gases, which also reduce the temperature of the coke in the coke cooling zone. The heat recovered by cooling the coke is utilized in the carbonization zone.

The circulating gases are mixed with the hot gaseous products of combustion from a separate chamber. The volume of burned gas is so small that only a slight dilution of the carbonization gas occurs. The mixed gas is a good fuel, with calorific value 140–200 B.t.u./ft³.

The coke cooling gases consist of products of combustion and steam (given off by the fuel) and contain but little free oxygen.

The Lurgi process is carried out in large ovens each with a throughput of 350–450 ton per day. When briquettes are carbonized in the Lurgi direct heating oven, they either retain their shape or break into a few large pieces. Some contraction in volume takes place at the same time. The resulting product is a dense lump fuel, resistant to abrasion, and possessing good combustion characteristics.

Operating Results Obtained with Lurgi Spülgas Plants

The Lurgi process is used for both the *extraction of oil* and the *production of coke* from all kinds of fuels. The special method of heating employed in the Lurgi ovens ensures the recovery of the hydrocarbons with a minimum of decomposition, the yield of tar and oil being 90–95% of that obtained in the Gray–King or Fischer assay.

C. BITUMINOUS COALS AND ANTHRACITES

Bituminous coals, carbonaceous coals, and anthracites, cannot normally be made into binderless briquettes, but briquetting with a binder is a very useful method of utilizing small waste high rank coals in a convenient solid form. The following are the principal types of binders that have been used in practice:

1. Inorganic binders: sodium silicate, sulphite lye, lime–silica, magnesium oxychloride, and cement.
2. Cereal binders: starches, or ground cereals, such as maize flour.
3. Heavy hydrocarbons or asphalts: coal tar pitch or bitumen.

Inorganic binders have the obvious disadvantage of increasing the ash content of the briquettes, but the simplicity of the briquetting process may sometimes offset this disadvantage.

Magnesium Oxychloride Briquettes

Coal dust is intimately mixed with 5% of magnesium oxide powder and this is wetted with a solution of magnesium chloride containing approximately 18% of magnesium chloride, controlled by adjusting the specific gravity to 1·16. Sufficient solution is added to just damp the coal–magnesium oxide mixture. After further mixing, the mixture is packed by hand into wooden moulds and compressed to form briquettes about 2 in. thick. The moulds containing the briquettes are allowed to stand for twelve hours and the moulds are then removed for use in the preparation of new briquettes. The process is cheap and the briquettes are sufficiently strong to withstand any reasonable amount of handling. They burn well and it is possible to recover magnesium oxide from the ash. If a low ash coal is used, the ash itself can be used instead of fresh magnesium oxide.

Cereal Binders and Mixed Binders

Cereal binders can be used in very small proportions, for example, $2\frac{1}{2}$ to 3% makes a satisfactory briquette. Unfortunately such briquettes disintegrate under moist or "tropical" conditions. The use of small additional proportions of a hydrocarbon type binder, such as pitch, or bitumen, improves the water-resisting properties, so that briquettes that are satisfactory in every way may be made by the addition of $2\frac{1}{2}$% of a ground cereal and $2\frac{1}{2}$% of pitch to the coal.

Pitch- or Bitumen-bound Briquettes

Of all materials tried as binders, the most generally used are pitch and bitumen. Two types of process are available for mixing the pitch or bitumen with the coal, namely:

(a) Cold powder process.
(b) Hot spray process.

Also, two types of press are generally used:

(a) Plunger type reciprocating press.
(b) Ovoid type press.

A typical coal-tar pitch should have the following properties:

Ash	not exceeding 0·5%
Softening pt. ring and ball	80–85°C
Solubility in aniline or pyridine	70–75%
Volatile matter	60–70%
Free carbon	18–30%

Suitable bitumens for use in briquetting have the following specification:

Penetration at 25°C	10/20	2/7
Softening pt., ring and ball, °C	63/73	110/120
Ductility at 25°C min.	5	—
Loss on heating, percentage wt., 5 hr. at 163°C max.	0·1	0·05
Drop in pen. after heating, max. percentage.	20	—
Flash pt. (Cleveland open cup) min. °C	250	320
Solubility in carbon disulphide, percentage wt. min.	99	99
Sp. gr. at 25°C	1·02/1·07	1·04/1·09

D. PROCESSES OF MANUFACTURE

Small coal is delivered to the feed hopper of a mixer, or measurer. The pitch is broken down below $\frac{1}{2}$ in. size in a pitch cracker and delivered into the pitch feed hopper of the coal and pitch mixer. In this apparatus the proportions of coal and pitch are regulated and the materials are subjected to a preliminary mixing. The mixed coal and pitch are then delivered into a disintegrator, via a magnetic separator. The materials are ground together, thoroughly mixed, and delivered into the vertical heater or pug of the briquette machine, where superheated steam softens the finely ground pitch and brings the blended materials to the correct degree of temperature and plasticity for the production of satisfactory briquettes. With the rectangular press, the hot semi-plastic material is fed under pressure into the mould table, where it is pressed at 2 ton/in². Various sizes of rectangular briquettes are made, the smallest briquette weighing $2\frac{1}{2}$ lb and the largest 28 lb.

Ovoid or egg-shaped briquettes are manufactured with the same method of preparation of the mixture. An ovoid press consists of two heavy rollers rotating so that the two rims just touch each other. These rims are completely filled with halves of egg-shaped moulds, and the rolls are mounted so that the opposite halves of each mould coincide in the nip of the rolls. The briquetting mix is introduced downwards into the nip and the briquettes are delivered on to a conveyor belt placed beneath the rolls. The ovoids produced vary in size, but are generally 2 to 4 in. long and weigh from 1 to 5 oz. By proper care in weighing and mixing the ingredients, it is possible to produce ovoids from carbonaceous or anthracitic coals containing as little pitch as 6% or as little bitumen as 5%.

E. CARBONIZED BONDED BRIQUETTES—THE PHURNACITE PROCESS

Carbonaceous coals and anthracites are often briquetted and sold in the uncarbonized condition. These briquettes can be carbonized to produce a fuel that is very superior in properties compared with the uncarbonized briquettes. In the Phurnacite process, ovoid briquettes are first made, as described above, and the ovoids are then carbonized at 750–850°C in narrow ovens, similar to coke ovens, except that they have an inclined floor to enable the briquettes to be discharged readily after firing. The ovens use a waste heat or recuperative system of fuel economy instead of the more general regenerative system of modern coke oven practice. Gas is removed in two stages, the first stage representing the initial distillation of the pitch, and the second stage being the main gas evolution from the residue. The pitch gas is scrubbed before use as fuel gas. The main gas supply, which consists of a gas of approximately 500 B.t.u./ft^3 calorific value, is cooled and used either for heating the ovens or for sale. The process of carbonization takes about four hours.

F. BINDERLESS BRIQUETTING BY SHEAR STRAIN

The National Coal Board at the Coal Research Establishment at Stoke Orchard are engaged upon a major project of briquetting bituminous coals without a binder for the production of low volatile briquettes. The main results published to date[1] are summarized below:

(1) The density and strength of a coal powder compact can be materially increased for a given applied pressure if it is subjected to shear strain whilst under load. Elastic recovery is also reduced.

(2) The full benefit is only obtained if shear strain is introduced under maximum load.

(3) The maximum increase in density, as measured by porosity, is ca. 15% at 10 ton/in^2 applied pressure, and the corresponding increase in strength is 5·5 fold (from 200 to 1100 lb/in^2).

(4) The optimum moisture for coals is between 50% and 100% of the "equilibrium" moisture content (cf. Data Sheets Nos. 1 and 28).

(5) Low rank coals are more sensitive to moisture than high rank coals. Deterioration is large with "over-dry" coals and small with moist coals.

(6) The strength of the briquettes is greater with low rank coals than with high rank coals (e.g. breaking loads: coal type 902 = 306 lb; coal type 204 = 130 lb).

(7) An optimum pressing temperature exists for all coals that is above the temperature of initial decomposition, for example 410 to 430°C for coals in the 800–900 groups. The coal is partially devolatilized during this process.

(8) Finer grinding is required with increase in the rank of the coal. Anthracites may be briquetted at high pressures following extremely fine grinding.

(9) Petrographic composition affects the results obtained. Durains form the best briquettes. Briquettes made from fusain are extremely weak.

(10) By carbonization, binderless briquettes can be converted into good quality coke, even when using 900 class coals (normally not coking).

Machines are being developed for the manufacture of binderless briquettes based on these principles, including the use of the chars obtained by the fluidized carbonization of low rank coals.

REFERENCES

1. GREGORY, H. R. *J. Inst. Fuel*, XXXIII, **236,** 447, 1962.
MARTIN, G. and FRANCIS, W. *Industrial and Manufacturing Chemistry*, Part II, Vol. I. London, 1954.
LOWRY, H. H. *Chemistry of Coal Utilization*, New York and London, 1945.

THE CARBONIZATION OF COAL IN LABORATORY APPARATUS

CARBONIZATION, sometimes called destructive distillation, is the decomposition of coal by heat in the absence of air or oxygen to produce a solid, coherent residue (coke) and liquid and gaseous products that may be sold as fuels or used as chemical intermediates. The useful liquids produced are benzole, oils and tar (cf. Data Sheets Nos. 63 and 64). The gaseous product is coal gas (cf. Data Sheet No. 104). The yields and chemical nature of these products depend mainly upon the rank and type of coal carbonized and upon the temperature and duration of carbonization. To understand the nature of the different commercial processes of carbonization it is necessary to study first the manner in which coking coals decompose by heat in laboratory apparatus.

A. DECOMPOSITION OF COKING COALS BY HEAT

Laboratory Test Apparatus used

Laboratory apparatus for studying the carbonization of coals includes the following:

1. Vacuum distillation—only used in fundamental studies and concerned mainly with studies of the yields and types of products obtained over a range of temperatures.
2. Gray–King assay—used mainly in Commonwealth countries for the assessment of yields and types of products obtained by heating in a small glass or silica retort for 1 hr at 600°C (sometimes also at 900°C). Coke type is used in the N.C.B. classification (see Data Sheet No. 6).

3. Fischer assay—used in Germany and the U.S.A. for similar purposes. A small aluminium retort is used at 500°C. Results somewhat resemble those obtained in the Gray–King assay at 600°C.

4. B.M.A.G.A. apparatus—used in the U.S.A. for obtaining additional information on the yields of coke, tar and gas that can be expected in high temperature practice. This is a vertical cylinder of mild steel holding up to 2 cwt of coal and operated at temperatures up to 1000°C.

5. Audibert–Arnu dilatometer—used for evaluating the development of plastic properties (softening and swelling under heat) of coal in the E.C.E. classification. This dilatometer method measures, *inter alia*, the softening temperature and the temperature of maximum dilatation (swelling) of a coal.

B. SUMMARY OF SEQUENCE OF EVENTS DURING PROGRESSIVE CARBONIZATION

The following is the sequence of events during the carbonization of a typical medium volatile coking coal by rapid heating in laboratory apparatus over a range of temperature up to 900°C (V.M. 27·6 to 32%, N.C.B. code number 301b, Gray–King Coke Type >G.4.

Tempera-ture	Effect	Nature of products		
		Carbonaceous residue	Tar and oil	Gas
300°C (572°F)	Initial decomposition temp.	Coal	nil	Some CO + CO_2 + H_2O
320°C (608°F)	First slight appearance of oil	Coal	Thin, light coloured oil	Above, plus some methane and unsaturateds
360°C (680°F)	Marked evolution of thick oils and hydrocarbon gases. Coal residue begins to soften	Coal, partially softened	Darker, red or brown, oil	More methane and higher paraffins; some hydrogen

		Nature of products		
Tempera-ture	Effect	Carbonaceous residue	Tar and oil	Gas
430°C (806°)F	Evolution of viscous oil and tar. Coal residue becomes softer and swells. Pronounced gas evolution causes bubble formation. Temp. or rapid decomp. of coal	Soft carbon-aceous mass, of max. volume and bubble structure	Oil becomes more viscous—very dark brown	Max. evolu-tion of para-ffin and unsaturated hydrocarbons with some CO, H_2O and hydrogen
460°C (860°F)	Oil and tar yield diminishing. Plastic expanded mass solidifies to semi-coke	Solid semi-coke, with max. bubble structure and weak cell walls	Nearly viscous oil or tar	As at 430°C. Calorific value of gases ca. 900 B.t.u./ft³
600°C (1112°F)	Oil and tar cease. Hard semi-coke starts to shrink	Semi-coke is harder and shrunken (colour still black)	None evolved	Diminishing yields of hydrocarbons and water; increase in CO and hydrogen
900°C (1652°F)	Continued shrinkage hardens the coke. Structure changes with commencement of formation of graphitic lattice	Hard, silvery grey appearance	None evolved	Gases mainly CO, H_2 and CH_4. C.V. ca. 400 B.t.u./ft³

C. CHANGES IN PRIMARY PRODUCTS BY PYROLYSIS

Note that if the temperature is raised suddenly to 900°C, the following changes take place, due to pyrolysis of the primary products formed at intermediate temperatures:

1. Coke formed is hard and grey in colour, with some lustre.

2. Light paraffin hydrocarbons in gas and oil are partly converted into aromatics, e.g. benzene and naphthalene.

3. Heavier paraffin hydrocarbons in the oil are converted into aromatic oils or solids, e.g. anthracene, creosote, carbon and pitch.

4. Paraffinic alcohols are converted into phenols.

5. The yield of tar and oils consequently decreases by about 25% and the density increases correspondingly.

6. The gas has the composition of towns gas, with calorific value ca. 500 B.t.u./ft^3.

D. VARIATION IN BEHAVIOUR WITH RANK OF COAL

1. Only a limited range of coals forms a reasonable coke. Range of volatile matter ca. 20 to 38%. Range of N.C.B. classes 301 to 602.

2. Coals forming maximum swelling cokes of maximum strength have V.M. 28 to 32% (N.C.B. class 30lb).

3. Temperatures in Table B, above, vary with the rank of coal by ca. ±20°C, increasing with increase in rank and vice versa.

4. Yields of products obtained vary with proximate analysis of coal, i.e. coke yields are proportional to fixed carbon in coal; oil and gas yields are proportional to volatile matter.

5. Tar production ceases in coals containing less than about 14% of volatile matter, i.e. 3·5% hydrogen.

E. TYPICAL RESULTS OBTAINED BY GRAY–KING ASSAY

Coal Analysis A.F.D. basis %			Gray–King Assay at 600°C		
C	H	V.M.	Coke Type	Tar and Oil %	Water evolved
82·2	5·6	41·0	G.3	16·0	5·0
83·4	5·2	35·0	G.5	12·1	4·1
86·0	5·2	34·0	G.8	11·7	2·1
89·0	5·0	32·0	G·9	10·0	1·8
90·5	4·7	24·0	G.8	7·0	1·3

F. RELATIONSHIP BETWEEN YIELDS AND COMPOSITION OF COAL

Attempts have been made to relate yield of products obtained by carbonization, particularly yields of tar and oils, to the proximate or ultimate analysis of coal, e.g.:

1. *Yield of Coke*

Gray–King assay coke at 900°C $\rightleftharpoons$ Fixed carbon in coal

,,   ,,   ,,   ,,   ,, 600°C $\rightleftharpoons$ Fixed carbon × 10/9

2. *Yield of Tar and Oil at 600°C*

Yield of tar and oil $= (H - 3·5)^{1·5} \times 5·48\%$

where $H = \%$ of hydrogen in the coal

e.g. $H = 3·5$ tar and oil yield $= 0\%$

       $H = 4·5$,, ,, ,,   ,, $= 5·48\%$

       $H = 5·0$,, ,, ,,   ,, $= 10·05\%$

       $H = 5·5$,, ,, ,,   ,, $= 15·5\%$

It follows that the type of coal determines the tar yield more than its rank, i.e. the presence of substances rich in hydrogen, such as spore exines, cuticles or resins in durains; or of spores in cannel coals, increases both hydrogen level and tar yields proportionally.

G. RELATIONSHIP BETWEEN LABORATORY RESULTS AND COMMERCIAL PRACTICE

1. Laboratory studies show that the nature of the coke produced at ca. 600°C is fundamentally different from that produced at temperatures above ca. 900°C.
2. All tar is evolved at temperatures below 600°C.
3. The nature of the tar at 600°C is fundamentally different from that produced at temperatures above 900°C and is aliphatic, rather than aromatic, in type.
4. Hence two basically different commercial carbonization processes are possible, viz:
   (a) Low temperature carbonization at temperatures ca 600°C.
   (b) High temperature carbonization at temperatures > ca. 900°C.

These are discussed in Data Sheets Nos. 23 and 24.

REFERENCE

FRANCIS, W. *Coal, Its Formation and Composition*, London, 1961.

SOLID FUELS DERIVED FROM COAL—
LOW TEMPERATURE COKE

As SHOWN in Data Sheet No. 22, low temperature coke can be made in the laboratory at a temperature of ca. 600°C to yield also maximum yields of tar and oil (of an aliphatic character) and gas of high calorific value (900–1000 B.t.u./ft^3).

In practice the process of low temperature carbonization is difficult, and not attractive commercially, for the following reasons:

1. Coal is a poor conductor of heat. Low temperature coke is worse: so that a high temperature gradient is necessary to carbonize even a thin layer of coal in reasonable time. To achieve 600°C in the centre of a charge the outer layers become overheated, resulting in a variable product and uneven operation. For example, a temperature gradient of 250°C may be required to carbonize at a rate of only 1 in./hr.

2. The complex, aliphatic, character of the tar and oil, and its readiness to form emulsions, make processing difficult and there is not a ready market for the refined products. Aromatic tar from high temperature carbonization is more readily separated into well-established, saleable, products.

3. Industrial gases of high calorific value are not readily saleable because most appliances are designed to burn gas of lower calorific value (e.g. 500 B.t.u./ft^3 for towns gas; 300 B.t.u./ft^3 for water gas and 150 B.t.u./ft^3 for producer gas). Richer gases must be diluted, or degraded, before use in such appliances.

During the last 50 years some 300 low temperature carbonization processes, designed to overcome these difficulties, have been tried and failed, either on technical or commercial grounds. Only one process, based on the original Parker "Coalite" process, has survived over these 50 years of trial and error.

Since the last war, the Clean Air Act of 1956, with the establishment of smokeless zones, which require large quantities of solid

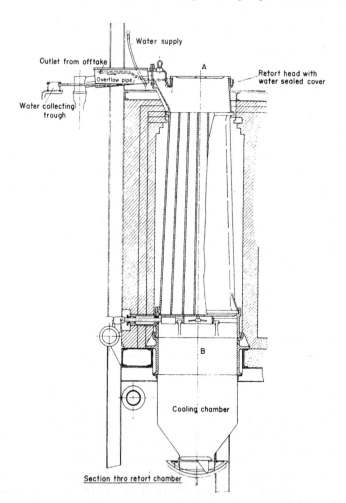

FIG. 23.1   Coalite Process — Retort (Low Temperature Carbonization Ltd.)

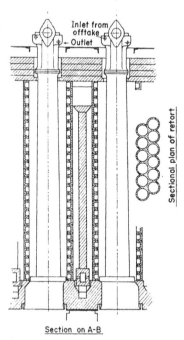

Section on A-B

fuels capable of being burned without visible smoke (as is the case with cokes of all types) has given an impetus to the industry. Several low temperature carbonization processes are now operating commercially in Great Britain with reasonable success.

COMMERCIAL PRODUCTION OF LOW TEMPERATURE COKE

For successful technical operation, difficulty 1, above, must be overcome. This has been achieved, in varying degree, by:

1. Carbonization in thin layers in externally heated, vertical, metal retorts—the "Parker" or "Coalite" process.
2. Internal heating by the heat from the products of combustion of part of the gas yield—"Rexco" process.

G

3. Carbonizing in continuous vertical gas retorts at temperatures some 250°C lower than those used in town gas manufacture.

1. *Parker or Coalite Process* (Fig. 23.1)

Each retort is a monobloc iron casting 9 ft high, containing 12 tubes, which taper from $4\frac{1}{2}$ in. at the top to $5\frac{1}{4}$ in. at the bottom. A battery contains 36 retorts in two rows of 18. Retorts and combustion chambers are arranged alternately, so that each retort is located in a radiation chamber formed by the walls of adjacent combustion chambers. The retorts are heated only by radiation from these walls, so that there is no overheating and the inside temperature of the retorts can be maintained accurately at 600°C (1112°F). A cooling chamber is fitted below each pair of retorts, of size sufficient to hold the coke from both. The pairs of retorts are charged and discharged every 4 hr.

The coal used is washed smalls of moderate coking power; Gray–King coke types F to G.1. Careful control of this ensures freedom from sticking and a properly sized product. Typical yields per ton are:

"Coalite"	15 cwt
Low temperature tar	16·5 gal
Motor spirit	3·5 gal
Gas	4000 ft^3
Calorific value of gas	= 700 B.t.u./ft^3
	≡ 28 therms.

2. *"Rexco" Process*

The retort is a brick-lined cylinder, 10 ft in diameter and 25 ft high. A charge of 34 ton of coal is carbonized downwards by burning gas at the top, passing the combustion products through the charge. Carbonization takes 6 hr, and cooling, by recirculation of combustion gases, a further 7 hr.

The process requires careful selection of type and grading of the coal, which is a blend of 33% of doubles and 67% of cobbles of low caking power, Gray–King types B to E, to reduce resistance to the flow of gases through the charge. Typical yields per ton are:

Coke	12·5 cwt
Low temperature tar	15 gal
Motor spirit	1 gal
Surplus gas	= 24,500 ft^3
Calorific value of gas	= 140 B.t.u./ft^3
	≡ 35 therms.

3. *Modified Gas Works Coke* (*Seabrite, Sunglow, etc.*)

Ordinary gas manufacturing retorts are used, but are operated at lower temperatures than normal, e.g. about 850°C instead of > 1000°C.

Care is taken in the selection of the coal, which is low in ash and "activated" by the addition of small proportions of peat (5%) or by impregnation with 0·5 to 1·0% of sodium carbonate.

This smokeless fuel is available in greater quantities than normal low temperature coke, but is not so reactive (cf. Data Sheet No. 25). Therefore it is more difficult to ignite and cannot be burned at the same low rates.

The tar and gas can be blended with normal gas works products, which makes the process economical.

SOLID FUELS DERIVED FROM COAL— HIGH TEMPERATURE COKE

THE manufacture of high temperature coke may be considered under two main headings:
A. Gas works practice—coke is a by-product of the coal gas industry —quality and yield of gas is the major consideration.
B. Metallurgical practice—quality and yield of coke is the first consideration—gas and other by-products are secondary.

A. GAS WORKS PRACTICE

1. *Horizontal Retorts*

The earliest type of retort; still used in small works. Modern type is oval or ⌂ shaped section, 20 ft long, 23 in. wide and made of fireclay. The ends are fitted with cast iron doors and ascension pipes to carry gas and volatile matter to a hydraulic main. The retorts are arranged in tiers, three or four deep, and many tiers are grouped to form a battery. They are heated by producer gas, made directly from hot coke in step-grate producers placed below the retorts. Air for combustion is preheated to 800°C (1472°F) by waste flue gases in a recuperator. Heat required for the process is ca. 42 therms per ton of coal carbonized. Waste heat boiler raises 850 lb steam/ton of coal or 2·8 lb/lb coke used in the producer. The process is intermittent; 12–14 cwt of coal is carbonized in 10 to 12 hr at a temperature of ca. 1000°C (1832°F). The hot coke is pushed out by a ram and quenched with water.

The coke produced is partially graphitized and is less reactive and more difficult to ignite than low temperature coke.

2. Intermittent Vertical Chamber Ovens

An oven consists of a vertical refractory chamber of dimensions up to 21 ft high, 10 ft long and tapering from about 8 in. at the top to 12 in. at the bottom. A number of ovens, with heating flues between, form a battery, which is heated by burning producer gas from a centrally placed unit. Air for combustion is heated by recuperators. The temperature may be 1350°C (2462°F) at the bottom of the oven and 1050°C (1922°F) at the top. The charge of about 4 ton of coal takes 12 hr for carbonization. Steam is passed up through the charge during the last two hours to increase the yield of gas. Fuel consumption is 38 therms/ton of coal. A waste heat boiler recovers 550 lb steam/ton of coal, or 1·9 lb/lb coke used in the producer. The coal charge is admitted through the top of the oven and the coke is discharged through the base into a metal truck, and is quenched with water in a central tower. The coke is dense, unreactive, and difficult to ignite.

3. Continuous Vertical Retorts

These are narrow vertical refractory ovens, about 25 ft high, tapering from 10 in. at the top to 18 in. at the base and of length up to 108 in. The largest size oven will carbonize about 12 ton of coal per day. The principle of operation is that the coal descends continuously through the retort, which is heated through the sides, at such a rate that it is fully carbonized when it is discharged through the base into a sealed coke cooling chamber. The rate of travel is governed by the operation of the coke extractor mechanism. Steam is admitted continuously in controlled amounts below the extractor, cooling the coke and forming water gas, which dilutes the coal gas. The amount of steam used varies from about 5 to 20%, giving mixed gases of calorific value varying from 510 B.t.u./ft³ to 460 B.t.u./ft³, respectively. Fuel consumption at 10% steam is ca. 36 therms per ton of coal carbonized. Steam raised in a waste heat boiler is 1600 lb/ton of coal or 6·3 lb/lb coke used in the producer. Maximum flue temperature is ca. 1350°C (2462°F). The ash content of the coke is higher than that of coke made from the same coal by other means because of the conversion of additional carbon to water gas by steaming. The continuous action of the steam upon the coke somewhat spoils the appearance and increases the ash content. The coke is also made more reactive, so that continuous vertical retort coke is the easiest of the high temperature cokes to ignite and burn.

4. Medium Temperature Coke

As described in Data Sheet No. 23, any of the above processes can be used for the manufacture of medium temperature coke, for use as smokeless fuel, by operating at a lower temperature and by adding some ingredient such as peat or soda to activate the coke.

5. Type of Coals used in Gas-Works Practice

Requirements:
(a) High volatile matter—with bituminous coals, within the range 32 to 40%; with cannel coals, no upper limit.
(b) Moderate caking power—horizontal retorts and intermittent chamber ovens can use fairly high swelling coals—Gray–King coke types G.3 to G.6, N.C.B. groups 500 and 600. Continuous vertical retorts require less swelling coals—Gray–King types G.1 to G.3, N.C.B. groups 600 to 800.

6. Yields of Products

	Horizontal Retort	Intermittent Vertical Ovens	Continuous Vertical Retorts 5% Steam
Coke cwt/ton	14 to 15	13 to 14	12 to 13
Tar and oils gal/ton.	12 to 14	11 to 13	14 to 16
Gas ft³/ton	12,000	15,000	16,500
Gas C.V. B.t.u./ft³	550	520	490
Gas therms/ton	66	78	80·6

B. METALLURGICAL PRACTICE

1. *Beehive Coke*

This was the first form of oven used in the manufacture of metallurgical coke. The quality of the coke was good, but the process was wasteful in fuel and by-products were not recovered. The process is obsolete, or obsolescent, in most countries.

2. *By-product Coke Ovens*

(a) Waste heat ovens.
(b) Regenerative ovens.

Both types are similar in operation and differ only in the proportion of gas available for sale. The regenerative ovens, in which heat is recovered from the furnace gases by transfer to combustion air in regenerators, requires much less gas for heating the ovens than waste heat ovens. When producer gas is the heating medium, two regenerators are used, one for air, the other for producer gas. In this case all the coke-oven gas is available for sale. The modern coke oven is a rectangular refractory chamber, of length 40 ft, height 14 ft and width 12 in. to 17 in., with removeable doors at both ends to enable the hot coke to be pushed out with a ram. Two ascension pipes, leading to hydraulic mains, are fitted. The coal is usually introduced by gravity through several charging holes in the oven top. In some ovens a stamped charge of moist coal is pushed into the oven with the same ram used to discharge the coke. A large number of ovens, with heating flues between, is arranged in a battery, with regenerative chambers for heat exchange between hot flue gases and combustion air (or gas) placed below. Flue temperature is usually 1350°C (2462°F). Carbonization time for a 22 ton charge varies from 12 to 18 hr, with the width of the oven. The walls are made of silica brick (96 % SiO_2). The temperature along the wall face is made even by reversing the flow of combustion gases through the flues and regenerators every 30 min. A section through the flues of a regenerative coke oven is shown in Fig. 24.1.

If coke oven gas is used for heating, up to 60% of surplus gas is available for sale. The heat required for carbonizing is ca. 1000 B.t.u. per ton of coal.

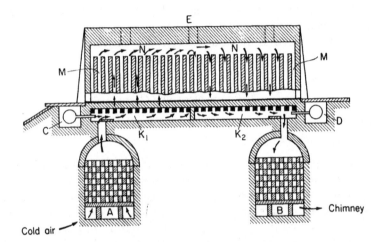

FIG. 24.1   Section through Flues and Regenerator of Regenerative Coke Oven.

Typical yields per ton are:

Coke	14 cwt
Tar	10 gal
Benzole	3 gal
Ammonium sulphate	25 lb
Gas—yield	12,500 ft^3
—C.V.	525 B.t.u./ft^3
—therms	66

3. Type and Grade of Coal Required
(see also Data Sheet No. 26)

Volatile matter	22 to 36%—optimum 22–32%
Gray–King coke type	G.1 to G.9 ,, G.4 to G.9

N.C.B. code groups	300 to 600	,,	301a, b, 401
Ash content	$<7\frac{1}{2}\%$	,,	$<5\%$; with low sulphur and phosphorus
Size grading	$<\frac{1}{2}$ in.	,,	$<\frac{1}{4}$ in.
Free moisture	5 to 10%	,,	5% for top charging 10% for stamped cake charging

4. Related Data

The following Data Sheets provide further information on gasworks and coke-oven practice:

Data Sheet Nos.	Subject
25	Physical and Chemical Properties of Cokes.
26	Effect of Coal and Process Variables on Coke Properties.
63 and 64	Liquid Fuels derived from Coal.
105	By-products of Carbonization Processes.
103 and 104	Gaseous Fuels derived from Coal.

REFERENCE

BRAME, J. S. S. and KING, J. G. *Fuel—Solid, Liquid and Gaseous*, London, 1956.

PHYSICAL AND CHEMICAL PROPERTIES OF COKES

(1) Low H_2O and ash are desirable.

Gas coke: H_2O variable (a source of frequent complaints from users).

Metallurgical coke should contain $<1.5\% H_2O$.

Each additional $1\% H_2O$ in blast furnace coke increases fuel consumption by 1.2%.

Each additional 1% ash in blast furnace coke increases fuel consumption by 2%.

Maximum desirable ash is $7\frac{1}{2}\%$.

(2) Low phosphorus required in coke for steel works, i.e. $< 0.012\%$ for acid process.

Low sulphur required for steel works—$< 1.0\%$.

(3) *Absolute Density*—increases by shrinkage in ovens during partial graphitization—proportional to temperature reached. Maximum absolute $D = 2.3$ (graphite) is not reached in practice.

Method of determination—The coke is ground <72 B.S. sieve and dispersed in water. The density is calculated from the weight of water displaced by 1 g of powdered coke. (Organic solutions give high values due to adsorbed layers.) The higher the rank of the coal carbonized, the higher the D of the coke under the same conditions, viz.

C % in coal	D g/ml ash-free coke
89	1·95
87	1·87
85	1·83
83	1·71
81	1·70

The results obtained are corrected for ash content as follows: (specific gravity of ash is taken as 2·5)

$$\text{True } D = 100d - \frac{2 \cdot 5\ a}{100 - a}$$

where d = observed value, a = ash %

(4) *Apparent Density*—varies from 0·95 to 0·85 for oven coke, and down to 0·75 for low temperature coke.
Method: Immerse lumps of coke in boiling water.
Cool and weigh the water displaced per gramme.

$$Porosity = 100\ \frac{\text{Diff. between true and apparent densities}}{\text{True density}}$$

Range: 50 to 55% for high temperature coke
　　　　60% for low temperature coke.

High porosity, with interconnecting pores, is desirable in furnace cokes to obtain high rates of combustion. In the blast furnace, high strength, that is good resistance to size breakdown, is considered more important.

(5) *Bulk Density—Method:* a box of 2 ft^3 capacity, i.e. with a $15\frac{1}{8}$ in. edge, is filled with coke pieces, of size $\frac{1}{2}$ in. to 1 in. and is weighed.

Typical Results:

Coke Type	lb per ft³—dry
Coke oven	27–33
Horiz. retort	24–27
Cont. vert. retort	21–22
Low temp. retort	18–22

(6) *Hardness and Strength*

Shatter Test—50 lb of coke >2 in. size is placed in a box of dimensions 28 in. × 18 in. × 15 in., placed 6 ft above a steel base plate $\frac{1}{2}$ in. thick. The hinged base of the box is released suddenly, when the contents drop on to the base plate. The operation is repeated several times and the coke is then screened through a series of sieves. The sieves are made of square stamped sheet.

Typical Results:

Shatter Indices of Industrial Cokes (3 *drops*)

	Metallurgical cokes			Gas retort cokes		Low temp. coke
	S. Wales	Durham	Yorkshire	Horiz.	Vert.	
Percentage > 2 in.	85	80	70	60	55	65
Percentage > 1½ in.	92	90	80	74	76	80
Percentage > 1 in.	98	98	96	88	85	88
Percentage < ½ in.	2	2	4	5	8	7

Desirable Values:

Blast furnace coke: 80% > 2 in., 90% > 1½ in., 97% > ½ in. Foundry coke (requires higher resistance to shatter) >85% on 2 in. sieve.

(7) *Abradability* by modified Cochrane method: 28 lb of $+3$ in. coke is rotated in a welded steel drum 18 in. D, fitted with $2\frac{1}{2}$ in. angle iron plates at 17° to axis, at 18 r.p.m. for 1000 revs. The percentage of material remaining on $\frac{1}{8}$ in. screen is called the "Abrasion index".

Results: with modern blast furnace cokes, index varies from 77 to 82%. Index is increased by the ash content, or by the use of coal of low swelling power. Gas retort coke varies from 60 to 65%. Index for low temperature coke $\simeq 50\%$. There is a rough correlation between shatter and abrasion indices for oven coke: the abrasion index increases by 1·0% for an increase of 0·2% in the half-inch shatter index.

(8) *Reactivity*—This is a function of density, i.e. reactivity is inversely proportional to absolute density.

Definition: ability to react with O_2, CO_2 or H_2O. For industrial fuels, reactivity to oxygen is most important. For domestic fuels, ease of ignition and high reactivity are important (see Critical Air Blast test, q.v.).

Blast furnace—High reactivity is important to promote the formation of CO on the hearth.

Cupola—The high temperature oxidation zone is large, and unreactive coke in large pieces is preferred.

Producer Gas—High reactivity is favoured to increase CO in the reduction zone.

Water Gas—High reactivity is desirable in "make" but undesirable in "blow"—on the whole unreactive coke is preferred.

F.R.S. Method of Determining Reactivity

Reactivity is measured in terms of the completion of the reaction $CO_2 + C = 2CO$, under standard conditions at 950°C. The equilibrium concentration of $CO = 98\cdot7\%$ under these conditions. A 7 ml column of 10 to 20 I.M.M. screened coke is maintained at 950°C. A current of CO_2 is passed through at 5 ml/min and the CO produced is measured.

Three reactivities are measured at different times:

R.I. The number of ml CO formed per 100 ml CO_2 at the start of the reaction. This is the initial reactivity, with a limit at the equilibrium concentration of 197·4 ml.

R.II. A constant value is reached after the expulsion of V.M.

R.III. A lower constant value is reached after the continued action of CO_2.

TYPICAL REACTIVITY VALUES OF INDUSTRIAL
COKES
(Max. value = 197·4)

	R.I.	R.II.	R.III.
1. Beech charcoal	180	—	160
2. Gas-retort coke	120	72	59
3. By-product coke	98	72	57
4. S. Wales met. coke	73	67	42
5. Beehive coke	43	40	42

Critical Air Blast Method

The C.A.B. value is the minimum rate of flow of air, in ft^3/min., necessary to maintain combustion in a column of closely graded material (14 to 25 B.S.) which is 25 mm deep and 40 mm in diameter.

Typical Values:

Wood charcoal	0·005
Low-temperature coke	0·015
Anthracite	0·035
Gas retort coke, static	0·060
Gas retort coke, continuous vertical	0·050
Oven coke	0·065

The lower the C.A.B. value, the more reactive the coke.

(9) *Effect of Iron on Reactivity* (*F.R.S. Method*)

Reactivity is affected by the presence of easily reduced iron compounds.

R.I—ash exerts full effect, iron being in metallic state.

R.II—iron is present as ferrous oxide and is almost inactive.

R.III—corresponds to the ash-free reactivity of the coke. Metallurgical coke contains little iron and gives flat reactivity curves. In cokes containing much iron, e.g. vertical retort cokes using Yorkshire coals, approximate equivalence to R.III can be obtained by

(a) extracting soluble Fe by mineral acids or

(b) adding to the coke the requisite proportion of SiO_2 and Al_2O_3 to combine with the iron.

(10) *Effect of sodium carbonate on reactivity*—decreases the reactivity to oxygen but increases the reactivity to CO_2 and steam.

(11) *Mott and Wheeler*[1]—*U.S. Bureau of Mines method*—a fuel bed of 1 in. to $1\frac{1}{2}$ in. coke, 14 in. deep, is used in a laboratory furnace of grate area 1 ft^2 and with a controlled air blast. The composition of the gases is determined at a series of 8 points in the fuel bed at $1\frac{1}{2}$ in. intervals above the grate. Temperatures are also measured at these points with an optical pyrometer. Results are expressed as "Reactivity with O_2" and measure the distance from the grate at which O_2 is not present in the gases. "Reactivity with carbon dioxide" is the distance at which the gases contain $> 20\%$ CO. The maximum temperature of the fuel bed is also recorded.

REACTIVITIES OF METALLURGICAL COKES (MOTT AND WHEELER)

Coke type	O_2 disappears at	20% CO at	Max. temp. of fuel bed $°C$
Charcoal	3 in.	5 in.	1560
Beehive	6 in.	> 12 in.	1800
Blend of coking and non-coking coal	4 in.	7 in.	1685
Yorkshire coking coal	4 in.	11 in.	1700

The size of the furnace was later increased to 2 ft in diameter and of the bed to 24 in. depth to treat different grades of coke.

EFFECT OF SIZE GRADING

	$3\frac{1}{2}$–3	$2\frac{1}{2}$–2	$1\frac{1}{2}$–1
Size, inches			
Rate of combustion lb/ft²	15	14	18
O_2 disappears, inches	7·5	6	4
CO % at 12 in. above grate	10·5	21	30
Max. temp. °C	1620	1590	1610
Height above grate, inches, for max. temp.	4	6	3

(12) *Effect of Coal on Reactivity*

    (a) Cokes of high reactivity are obtained from weakly caking coals or blends.

    (b) Cokes of low reactivity are obtained from strongly caking, high rank, coal.

(13) *Blast Furnace Requirements* (*Mott and Wheeler*)

    (a) Size and hardness are more important than reactivity.

    (b) Satisfactory hearth temperature is best obtained with unreactive coke containing little breeze.

(14) *Sarjant*[2]. Reactivity is expressed best as capacity of coke to burn to CO_2 rather than to CO at high temperatures.

Method used: preheated air is passed through a small bed of coke maintained at 1300°C and the resultant gas is analysed.

Reactivity = ratio of the weight of carbon in the gas (CO_2 + CO) produced from unit vol. of air; to the weight at complete conversion to CO, i.e. CO_2 + CO/2 CO_2 + CO.
Within the range 1200 to 1400°C there is a correlation between reactivity and coke bed temperature (T_c), viz.

$$R = \frac{T_c - 719\cdot4}{1000}$$

Values vary from 0·5 to 0·75 for cokes. These values can be used to interpret cupola conditions and the economic attainment of the required melting conditions.

(15) *Ignition Temperature*

This varies primarily with the percentage of residual volatile matter in the coke. The percentage of residual volatile matter varies with the coking temperature and with the residual hydrogen.

Typical Results:

IGNITION TEMPERATURES IN AIR OF INDUSTRIAL COKES

Source of Coke	Ignition Temp. °C	Volatile Matter %	Hydrogen %
Beehive	625	1·0	0·2
Coke ovens	605	1·2	0·3
Gas works—continuous vertical	585	1·4	0·3
Gas works horizontal	560	2·0	0·5
Low temperature	460	8·0	3·0

(16) *Analyses of Cokes*

Methods are described in detail in B.S. 1016 *Analysis and Testing of Coal and Coke*, Parts 2, 4, 5, 7, 9, 10, 13, 14 and 15 (1957 to 1960). Some of these methods are described briefly in Data Sheet No. 28. Methods for the sampling of coke are described in B.S. 1017 *Sampling of Coke*, Part 2 (1960).

REFERENCES

1. MOTT, R. A. and WHEELER, R. V. *The Quality of Coke*, London, 1939.
2. SARJANT, R. J. *Coke and Gas*, **15**, 89, 129 (1953).
BRAME, J. S. S. and KING, J. G. *Fuel—Solid, Liquid and Gaseous*, London, 1956.

EFFECT OF COAL AND PROCESS VARIABLES ON COKE PROPERTIES

A. COAL RANK, COAL TYPE AND BLENDING

The first property required of coal for coke making is that the rank and type should lie within close limits, i.e. volatile matter 22 to 36%; Gray–King Coke Type G1 to G9; Crucible Swelling Index 4 to 9; N.C.B. Code Groups 300 to 600. If a coal lies outside these limits, but still possesses coking properties, it may be used for lower grade metallurgical cokes, or for making high or low temperature cokes for furnace use.

The most highly swelling coals within the good coking range may produce weak cokes, because of excessive after shrinkage, with the formation of cracks, or may create sufficient pressure during the swelling process to damage coke oven walls. Such adverse effects are overcome by blending with non-swelling coals or coal products such as anthracite, steam coal, coke breeze, or fusain.

The four components of banded bituminous coal, vitrain, clarain, durain and fusain, behave differently on carbonization. Fusain is invariably non-swelling. Durains and splint coals are usually non-swelling, or less swelling than the associated vitrain and clarain. Clarain is usually the most high swelling component of any given coal.

Fusain, when available, i.e. from dry screening processes, or by the separate mining of thick bands, is perhaps the best material to use for blending with highly swelling coals. The optimum addition is 3%. Finely ground coke, or anthracite dusts, are satisfactory substitutes. These additions improve the density and hardness of the cokes produced from high swelling coals and decrease the reactivity.

B. SIZE GRADING

The more finely the coal carbonized is crushed, the more uniform, and the denser, is the resultant coke. The practical economical limit is to crush the coal through a $\frac{1}{4}$ in. mesh screen, with $>80\%$ through a $\frac{1}{8}$ in. screen.

C. MOISTURE

1. *Inherent or Equilibrium Moisture*

This is a measure of the micro-pore volume of the coal, which is a characteristic of rank and type. There is a fairly well defined relationship between equilibrium moisture of coal and swelling power. This is the equilibrium moisture swelling index curve of Berkowitz, shown as Fig. 26.1.

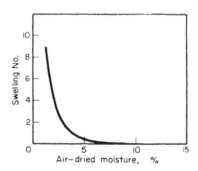

FIG. 26.1   Relationship between Equilibrium Moisture and Swelling Index Curve of Coals (Berkowitz).

2. *Free Moisture*

This is an accidental variable, determined by the mode of preparation of the coal and storage conditions. Free moisture affects the behaviour on coking as follows:

(a) Free moisture retards the coking process, lengthening the process by ca. $\frac{1}{4}$ to $\frac{3}{4}$ hr per 1% of free moisture.

(b) Free moisture protects the volatile products from pyrolysis in the presence of hot coke and hot oven walls. The water gas reaction also takes place, an effect similar to the action of steaming in vertical gas retorts (cf. Data Sheet No. 24). The final effect is a slight, but measurable, increase in tar, ammonia and gas yields.

(c) Free moisture also assists in preventing loss of fine coal dust from the ovens when charging. Optimum free moisture content under these headings is 5%.

(d) Free moisture is necessary to bind the coal mass together in a stamped cake, when this method of charging the ovens is used. Optimum free moisture for this is ca. 10%.

D. ASH CONTENT

The effect of high ash on the physical properties of coke is to decrease the hardness and abrasion resistance. Maximum desirable percentage of ash on this count is $7\frac{1}{2}$%. Sulphur and phosphorus in coke ash cause brittleness, or "shortness", in steels. Sulphur is partly removed in the blast furnace, but should not exceed 1% in the coke. Phosphorus is removed during steel making by the basic hearth process, but not in the acid process. For the latter the upper limit for phosphorus in coke should be 0·012%.

E. STORAGE

The swelling index of coal falls rapidly with low temperature oxidation. i.e. by storing finely ground coal. The quality of coke produced from the weakly caking coals of North Staffs, South Yorkshire and Lancashire is greatly reduced by storing for a few days after preparation. High swelling coals are not greatly affected by a few days storage, but longer storage decreases the swelling index. This may be advantageous with some dangerously swelling coals, as an alternative to blending with non-swelling compounds (cf. Section C. 1 above).

F. METHOD OF CHARGING OVENS

Top charging (by gravity) gives less dense charges and cokes than stamped charges. Dry slacks may be used with top charging. Stamped charges are to be preferred for coals of low swelling index.

G. RATE OF HEATING OF CHARGE

Rate of heating of coal has a profound effect upon the coking process. High rates of heating cause maximum swelling, excessive in the case of strongly caking coals, but improving the coke formed from low swelling coals. With modern, narrow ovens, ca. 12 in. wide and flue temperatures $\simeq 1350°C$, rates of carbonization up to 0·95 in./hr are obtained. At such rates, strongly caking coals require blending with non-swelling, finely divided materials such as fusain, coke breeze, or non-coking, high rank, coals. This, in turn, requires more uniformly mixed and graded charges and produces harder, less reactive, and more uniform cokes, as are required for blast furnace practice.

H. QUENCHING

The hot coke discharged from the ovens must be quenched quickly without leaving moisture in the coke in excess of ca. 1·0 %. This is best achieved in central quenching towers, using controlled amounts of water. Inert gas quenching may be used, but corrosion problems are acute.

REFERENCES

BRAME, J. S. S. and KING, J. D. *Fuel—Solid, Liquid and Gaseous*, London, 1956.
MOTT, R. A. and WHEELER, R. V. *The Quality of Coke*, London, 1939.

CHOICE OF SOLID FUELS FOR SPECIFIC PURPOSES

A. DOMESTIC APPLIANCES

Types are restricted by necessity to conform to requirements of the Clean Air Act (cf. Data Sheet No. 30).

1. *Open fires*

House coal—doubles and trebles—any rank except anthracites —high V.M. coal ($>20\%$) is not now permitted in Smokeless Zones.

Low temperature cokes—e.g. Coalite, Rexco etc.—sizes $1\frac{3}{4}$ in. to 4 in.—these are easily ignited and burned.

Medium temperature cokes—e.g. Cleanglow, Seabrite etc.— sizes $> 1\frac{3}{4}$ in.— require more draught than L.T.C. and ignite less easily.

High temperature cokes—not really suitable, except when high draught is available—sizes 1 in. to 3 in.—continuous vertical retort coke ignites and burns most easily of these cokes, with highest efficiency of all solid fuels.

2. *Openable Stoves*

Anthracites $1\frac{1}{4}$ in. to 2 in., Phurnacite, Welsh boiler nuts, low and medium temperature cokes, are most suitable.

3. *Closed Stoves of all Types*

Coking coals are not suitable. Requirements generally are as for openable stoves, but particularly suitable are: Gas coke—$\frac{1}{2}$ in. to $1\frac{1}{4}$ in. Welsh nuts—$\frac{3}{4}$ in. to $1\frac{1}{2}$ in. Anthracites—$\frac{5}{8}$ in. to $1\frac{1}{4}$ in.

$$\left.\begin{array}{l}\text{Coalite, Rexco}\\ \text{Seabrite,}\\ \text{Cleanglow}\end{array}\right\} \quad \frac{3}{4}\text{ in. to } 1\frac{3}{4}\text{ in.}$$

4. *Boilers*

Medium and high temperature cokes, anthracites and Phurnacite are most suitable. Fuel size is determined mainly by draught available and fire-box size, e.g. < 0.8 ft^3 capacity—$\frac{1}{2}$ in. to $1\frac{1}{4}$ in. coke (Size No. 3), > 1.0 ft^3 capacity—1 in. to 2 in. (Size No. 2). Equivalent sizes of other fuels may be used.

5. *Greenhouse Heaters*

Anthracite peas, with automatic hopper feed.

B. INDUSTRIAL—INCLUDING POWER STATIONS

1. *Hand Fired Boilers*

Size grading varies with ash content. With $1\frac{1}{2}$ in. slacks, upper limit of ash = 10%. With $> 1\frac{1}{2}$ in. size, singles or nuts, upper limit of ash = 20%.

Coal types, N.C.B. 200 to 202; 602 to 902 with side firing or spreading method: 202 to 204; 401 to 601 with coking method. Coke grade 1 in. to 2 in. (Size No. 2).

2. *Stoker Fired Boilers*

(a) Sprinkler stokers—Size grading: Doubles, singles, 1 in. smalls. Max. ash content 10%. Ash fusion temperature $> 1200°C$. N.C.B. groups: 100 to 200; 600 to 900.

(b) Chain grate stokers—Size grading: Singles, peas, 1 in. smalls. Minimum ash content 5%. Ash fusion temperature $> 1300°C$. Crucible swelling index < 3. N.C.B. groups 600 to 900.

(c) Coking (Retort) stokers—Size grading: Doubles, singles, 1 in. smalls.

Max. ash content 20%. Ash fusion temperature > 1300°C.

Crucible swelling index 2 to 5. N.C.B. types 202 to 204; 501 to 701.

(d) Underfeed stokers—Size grading: Doubles, singles.

Max. ash content 10%. Ash fusion temperature 1200°C. Crucible swelling index 2 to 4. N.C.B. types 203, 601 to 801.

3. *Pulverized Fuel*

Size grading to mill is not important.

(a) Boilers and General—After grinding: Bituminous coals; 70% < 240 B.S. sieve, all through 72 B.S. sieve. Anthracites; 85% < 200 B.S. sieve, all through 72 B.S. sieve. Ash content and ash fusion points depend upon applications—see Data Sheet No. 17.

(b) Gas turbines—After grinding, 90% < 200 B.S. sieve. Ash content as low as possible. Separator before turbine removes particles of ash > 20μ size.

(c) Metallurgical—See Data Sheet No. 17.

4. *Metallurgical*

Composition of ash is important when combustion products come into contact with metal charge—see Data Sheet No. 17.

(a) Hand fired—Size grading > 1$\frac{1}{2}$ in.

Max. ash content 10%.

(b) Stoker fired—as for boilers, items 2(a) and (b) above.

(c) Crucible and Cupola furnace—high calorific intensity required —obtained with hard cokes of low reactivity, burned with high draught. Size 2–3 in., free from breeze.

Maximum ash 8%

Maximum sulphur 1%

Maximum moisture 1%

Shatter index > 90% over 1$\frac{1}{2}$ in.

5. *Gas Producers*

First essential is that the fuel should not stick in the gas chamber. With static producers only non-coking coals, or coke, may be used. Close size grading, to permit uniform flow of gas, is equally important.

(a) Static—Size grading $\frac{1}{2}$ in. to $1\frac{1}{4}$ in. for small outputs or $\frac{3}{4}$ in. to 2 in. for larger outputs.
Max. ash content 10%. Ash fusion temperature > 1350°C.
Maximum crucible swelling No. $2\frac{1}{2}$.
Maximum Gray–King coke type D.
N.C.B. Coal types 100 to 201; 801 to 902.

(b) Mechanical—Size grading $\frac{3}{4}$ in. to 2 in. for medium outputs. 1 in. to 2 in. for max. outputs.
Max. ash content 10%. Ash fusion temperature > 1350°C.
Max. crucible swelling No. 3.
Max. Gray–King Coke Type E.
N.C.B. Coal types 100 to 201; 702 to 902.

6. *Rotary Cement Kilns*

Pulverized fuel only. The amount and composition of ash is most important here. Low sulphur preferred, but high ash, of composition similar to that of Portland cement, desirable, since ash enters the product and is sold at cement prices.

7. *Brickworks and Pottery Kilns*

(a) Hand (top) firing—Size grading: $1\frac{1}{2}$ in. slacks. Closer size grading for some kilns, e.g. Doubles, singles.
Max. ash content 10%, 5% for high final temperatures.
Coal type—long flame, non-coking. N.C.B. groups 800 and 900.
Sulphur < 1% for pottery ware.

(b) Mechanical firing—As above, but close graded singles preferred.

C. TRANSPORT

1. *Railways*

(a) Hand fired—Lump coal with low ash and some caking properties preferred. N.C.B. groups 500 to 700; 202 to 205. Ash content < 10%.

(b) Stoker fired—Size grading: Doubles, singles, $1\frac{1}{2}$ in. smalls. Max. ash content 10%. N.C.B. groups 700 to 900; 201 to 205.

2. *Ships' Bunkers*

(a) Hand fired—Lump coal 3 in. to $1\frac{1}{2}$ in. preferred. Ash content < 10%. High rank, non-caking coals. N.C.B. types 201 to 205.

(b) Stoker-fired W.T. boilers—Close graded, doubles or singles preferred, or $1\frac{1}{2}$ in. smalls. Ash content < 10%. N.C.B. types 201 to 205.

D. CARBONIZATION

1. *Gasworks*

High volatile, coking, coals are essential.

(a) Horizontal and Intermittent—Good caking index, Gray–King coke types G3 to G9. N.C.B. groups 500 to 600. Sulphur < 1%, ash < 10% preferably < 5%. Washed slacks preferred.

(b) Continuous Vertical—as above, but with lower caking index, i.e. Gray–King coke types G1 to G3. N.C.B. groups 600 to 800.

2. *Coke Ovens*

Strongly caking coals, with low ash, sulphur, and phosphorus preferred. N.C.B. types 301 to 401. Gray–King coke types G4 to G9. Ash < 5%, sulphur < 1%, phosphorus < 0·012%. Size grading < $\frac{1}{4}$ in., 80% < $\frac{1}{8}$in. H_2O 5% top charging, 10% stamper charging.

3. *Low Temperature Coke*

(a) Coalite—Gray–King coke type F to G1. Ash $< 5\%$. N.C.B. groups 600 to 800. Grading—washed slacks.

(b) Rexco—Ash $< 5\%$. N.C.B. groups 700 to 900. Size: 33% 2 in. × 1 in. + 67% 4 in. × 2 in. Gray–King coke types B to E.

E. BRIQUETTING

(a) Uncarbonized—before grinding, 1 in. smalls. After grinding $< \frac{1}{8}$ in. Ash content $> 5\%$. N.C.B. group No. 100.

(b) Carbonized (Phurnacite)—before grinding, anthracite Duff. N.C.B. group No. 100. Blended with low volatile steam—1 in. smalls, N.C.B. types 201 to 203. After grinding < 30 B.S. sieve. Ash content $< 10\%$.

F. DRYING

Drying by direct contact with hot gases (e.g. foodstuffs). Anthracites with low sulphur, ash, and arsenic. Sizing: Peas or pearls, with automatic feed to furnace.

METHODS FOR THE EXAMINATION OF COAL AND COKE

PROXIMATE ANALYSIS OF COAL

B.S. 1016, Pt. 3, 1957

Free Moisture

Spread a 2 lb sample passing through a $\frac{1}{4}$ in. sieve on to a tared copper, tin, or enamel, tray, about 12 in. square, and weigh. Allow to dry for 24 hr at the laboratory temperature and re-weigh.

$$\frac{\text{Loss in weight}}{\text{Weight of sample}} \times 100 = \text{percentage of free moisture.}$$

Equilibrium Moisture

Grind the air-dried coal from the free-moisture determination to pass through a 14-mesh sieve. Weigh approximately 5 g into a tared, covered, watch-glass. Remove the cover and dry for 1 hr at 105°C in an air oven. Cool in a desiccator and re-weigh covered.

$$\frac{\text{Loss in weight}}{\text{Weight of air-dried coal}} \times (100 - \text{percentage of free moisture})$$

$$= \text{Percentage of equilibrium moisture.}$$

Total Moisture

Total moisture = Free moisture plus equilibrium moisture.

Ash Determination

Weigh approximately 1 g of the analysis sample into a tared silica dish, 10–15 mm deep and of diameter 5 cm. Place the dish and coal in a cold muffle furnace and raise the temperature to 500°C in 30 min. Then raise the temperature to 800°C in 1 hr, and maintain at 800°C for a further hour.

$$\text{Percentage of ash in analysis sample} = \frac{\text{Weight of ash}}{\text{Weight of coal taken}} \times 100$$

Volatile Matter Determination

The volatile matter determination is carried out in a standard type silica crucible, supported during heating so that the base of the crucible does not rest on the floor of the muffle furnace used. The edge of the crucible and the underside of the lid flange should be ground flat in each matched set. The muffle, which is closed during the determination, is maintained at a temperature of 925°C.

Percentage of volatile matter in analysis sample = (loss in wt × 100) − percentage of moisture in sample.

Fixed Carbon

The fixed carbon is calculated as follows:

(a) *Dry Coal*

Fixed carbon = 100 − (V.M. + ash)

(b) *Coal containing moisture*

Fixed carbon = 100 − (V.M. + H_2O + ash)

Sulphur

The sulphur in coal is best determined by heating with Eschka mixture. After ignition at 800°C, the sulphates are estimated gravimetrically by precipitation as barium sulphate. Eschka mixture consists of 2 parts by weight of pure, light calcined, magnesium oxide and 1 part by weight of pure, anhydrous, sodium carbonate.

Wt. of $BaSO_4$ × 0·1374 = weight of sulphur.

Determination of Nitrogen in Coal — Macro-Method

B.S. 1016, Pt. 6, 1958

The nitrogen is converted into ammonium sulphate by heating with concentrated sulphuric acid in the presence of a catalyst. The catalyst used is either selenium powder or mercuric sulphate plus potassium sulphate. The ammonia formed is determined by steam distillation into a standard acid solution after adding excess of sodium hydroxide. A blank determination is carried out on the reagents above.

$$\text{Nitrogen } \% = \frac{V_1 - V_2}{W} \times 0\cdot14$$

W = wt of coal used (g)
V_1 = volume of N/10 H_2SO_4 neutralized in blank (ml)
V_2 = volume of N/10 H_2SO_4 in determination (ml).

CRUCIBLE SWELLING TEST FOR COALS

B.S. 1016, Pt. 12, 1959

The property of swelling is usually measured by the crucible swelling test. In this test, one gram of air-dried coal, freshly ground to pass a 72-mesh sieve, is heated above a Teclu burner flame so that the temperature of the inner surface of the base of the crucible reaches 800°C within $1\frac{1}{2}$ min and 820°C within $2\frac{1}{2}$ min of lighting the burner. After the flame from the burning volatile matter has died out, or for $2\frac{1}{2}$ min, whichever is the greater period of time, the crucible is cooled and the coke button removed and compared with standard numbered profiles from 1 to 9 in half units.

The result is recorded as a *swelling number*, which is the number of the standard profile most nearly corresponding to the coke button obtained under test taking the average of five determinations.

GRAY–KING ASSAY

B.S. 1016, Pt. 12, 1959

The retort consists of a closed silica tube, approximately 30 cm long and diameter 2 cm, with a short side tube of about 1 cm diameter, sealed in at right angles about 2 cm from the open end, which is closed by a rubber stopper. The tube is heated in a close fitting cylindrical horizontal furnace, capable of accurate regulation so that the temperature rises from 300 to 600°C in 1 hr. The side tube is connected to a short tube containing a wide glass cork, or a rubber tube fitted with a pinch-coke, and dips under water.

During an assay, the furnace is first heated to a temperature of 325°C. 20 g of the dry sample, ground to pass a 72-mesh B.S. sieve, is placed inside the retort and held in the lower 6 in. with an asbestos plug. The retort is then placed inside the furnace. The resistance of the furnace is adjusted so that the temperature rises uniformly from 325 to 600°C in 1 hr. The temperature remains at 600°C for a further 15 min. After cooling, the coke is compared with standard profiles numbered A to G.3.

Types G.4 to G.10 cannot be defined accurately by the degree of swelling, but may be defined accurately by repeating the test with increasing amounts of electrode carbon, ground to pass through a 72-mesh B.S. sieve, until a standard coke of type G is obtained. The subscript is the minimum number of grams of electrode carbon present in the 20 g test sample to give a standard "G-type" coke.

METHOD OF REPORTING

The following is a convenient method of reporting the normal examination of a delivery of coal:

Analysis of Incoming Coal

Date ....

Name of Coal..

No. of Sample ....

Name of Contractor   ....

ANALYSIS:

		As received.	As dried.
Moisture: Free		%	
Hygroscopic		%	
			Nil
Total		%	
Volatile Matter		%	%
Fixed Carbon		%	%
Ash		%	%
Total		100·0	100·0
Sulphur		%	%
Calorific Value		............B.t.u./lb............B.t.u./lb	

GRADING:

Size	Over 1 in.	1–½ in.	¾–½ in.	⅜–¼ in.	¼–⅛ in.	Thro' ⅛ in.
Percentage						

Nature of Ash { Colour.
{ Fusion Point.
Nature of Coke.
Combustion Characteristics.
Remarks.

Signed ....

METHODS FOR THE ANALYSIS OF COKE

The methods used for the analysis of coke are generally similar to those described for coal, with the exceptions given below. Full details of methods of analyses and physical tests will be found in B.S. 1016, Parts 5, 9, 10, 13, 14 and 15.

Determination of Total Moisture

Place a 2 lb sample of coke, crushed to pass a ½ in. mesh sieve, in tared shallow metal trays in layers not deeper than 1½ in. and heat to a temperature not exceeding 200°C until constant in weight.

Preparation of Sample for Analysis

After the determination of moisture, crush the sample through a 14-mesh B.S. sieve. After quartering twice, take a sample of 4 oz and crush to pass a 72-mesh B.S. sieve. Spread out into a uniform layer for 24 hr, so as to reach an air-dry condition.

Moisture in Air-Dried Sample

Heat 1–3 g of the sample in a shallow layer on tared watch-glasses for 1 hr at 105–110°C. Cool in a desiccator and weigh.

Volatile Matter

Weigh out 1 g of the sample into the standard volatile matter crucible used for coal. Add 2–4 drops of benzene, to displace air from the crucible during heating. Then proceed as for coal.

REFERENCES

B.S. 1017, Part 1. *Sampling of Coal*, 1960.
          Part 2. *Sampling of Coke*, 1960.
B.S. 1016, Part 3. *Proximate Analysis of Coal*, 1957.
          Part 4. *Proximate Analysis of Coke*, 1957.
          Part 6. *Ultimate Analysis of Coal*, 1958.
          Part 12. *Caking and Swelling Properties of Coal*.
          Part 13. *Tests special to Coke*.
FRANCIS, W. *Boiler House and Power Station Chemistry*, London, 1962.

H

DETERMINATION OF THE CALORIFIC VALUE OF COAL, COKE AND OIL

THIS determination is best carried out in the bomb calorimeter.

BOMB

A sectional drawing of a suitable bomb is shown in Fig. 29.1.

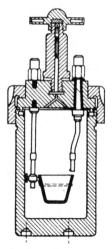

FIG. 29.1   Section of Bomb Calorimeter.

This is made of Austenitic Cr–Ni–Mo steel (resistant to corrosion) of capacity 250 to 300 ml and of sufficient strength to withstand the combustion of 1 g of coal or oil in oxygen at an initial pressure of 30 atm.

Calorimeter Vessel

During the determination, the bomb is immersed in 2 l. of water in a calorimeter vessel, surrounded first by an air space, approximately 1 cm thick, and then by a lagged water jacket containing 10 l. of water. The calorimeter vessel is fitted with an adequate stirring device and a carefully calibrated thermometer, with a range of 5 or 6°C by intervals of 0·01°C, capable of being read, with a travelling lens, to 0·001°C.

Water Equivalent of Apparatus

The water equivalent of the apparatus is determined by burning 1 g of pure, dry, benzoic acid in the bomb calorimeter under the exact conditions of test. The calorific value of benzoic acid is 6319 cal/g.

Method of Ignition

The charge in the bomb is ignited by passing a low voltage current momentarily through a thin platinum wire, to which is attached a short length of cotton thread dipping into the coal, coke or oil in the containing crucible.

Pressure of Oxygen

The initial pressure of oxygen in the bomb is 25 atm for bituminous coals and oil; 30 atm for anthracites and coke.

Determination

Approximately 1 g of coal or oil is placed in the crucible and the apparatus assembled in the standard manner described in B.S. 1016, Part 5 (1957). After standing for some 5 min, the temperature is read and recorded at intervals of 1 min. These readings are logged as the "Preliminary period".

The coal or oil is then ignited by momentarily closing the firing circuit. Readings are taken at intervals of 1 min until the temperature rise first stops and then begins to fall. This is called the "Chief period". Temperature readings are continued at minute intervals for 5 min. This is called the "After period".

From these readings a graph may be drawn, from which the true temperature rise may be deduced; or the cooling correction may be calculated on empirical lines by formulae such as the Regnault and Pfaundler or the Dickinson, which is simpler.

Regnault and Pfaundler Formula

$$\text{Cooling correction} = nv + \frac{v' - v}{t' - t}\left\{ \sum_1^{n-1}(t) + \tfrac{1}{2}(t_0 + t_n) - nt \right\}$$
$$= nv + kS$$

where

S = expression within the brackets

n = number of minutes in the chief period

v = rate of fall of temperature per minute in the preliminary period. If the temp. in this period is rising, then v is negative

v' = rate of fall of temperature per minute in the after period

t and t' are average temperatures during preliminary and after periods respectively.

$\sum_1^{n-1}(t)$ = sum of the readings (t_1, t_2, $t_3 \ldots t_{n-1}$) during the chief period

$\tfrac{1}{2}(t_0 + t_n)$ = mean of firing temperature, t_0, and first temperature, t_n, after which the rate of change is constant.

$k = \dfrac{v' - v}{t' - t}$ and is the "cooling constant" of the calorimeter.

Dickinson Formula

$$\text{Cooling correction} = v(T_a - T_0) + v'(T_n - T_a)$$

where T_0 = the time at temperature t_0 (min.)

T_n =　,,　　,,　,,　　　　　,,　　　t_n
T_a =　,,　　,,　,,　　　　　,,　　　$t_0 + 0{\cdot}6(t_n - t_0)$ min.

v, v', t_0, t_n, are as in the Regnault and Pfaundler formula. The cooling correction is added to the apparent temperature rise, viz.: $(t_n - t_0)$

Other Corrections

1. Correction for the Cotton Thread

This is calculated from the weight of the length of cotton, and the heat of combustion of cotton, which is a pure form of cellulose.

The calorific value of cellulose, dried at 110°C = 4180 cal/g.

2. Correction for Firing Wire

This is calculated from the known weight of firing wire, i.e. 100 cal/g for platinum wire.

3. Correction for Nitrogen and Sulphur

When coal is burned in a calorimeter bomb both sulphuric and nitric acids are formed and heat is evolved due to the formation and solution of these acids. The nitric and sulphuric acids formed can be determined by titration of the acids condensed in the bomb. Alternatively the sulphur may be determined by the Eschka method (cf. Data Sheet No. 28).

Nitric acid: Deduct 1·43 cal/ml N/10 HNO_3 formed.
Sulphuric acid: Deduct 22·5 cal/ml N/10 H_2SO_4 formed.

Alternatively:

Sulphur: Deduct 2·26 cal/mg sulphur present in fuel.

Calculation of the Water Equivalent of Bomb

Let the weight of benzoic acid be a grammes	
Then the heat liberated from the benzoic acid	$= a \times 6319$ cal
Let the titration of the nitric acid formed	$= c$ ml
Then heat due to formation and solution of nitric acid	$= c \times 1·43$ cal
Let the weight of cotton used	$= d$ g
Then the heat due to the combustion of cotton	$= d \times 4140$ cal
Let the *corrected* temperature rise	$= t°C$
Let wt of platinum firing wire be l g	
Then heat release from firing wire	$= l \times 100$ cal.

Then the *Water Equivalent* $= \dfrac{6319a + 1·43c + 4140d + 100l}{t}$

Calculation of Calorific Value of Fuel Sample

Calorific value cal/g

$$= \frac{\text{Corrected rise} \times \text{water equivalent} - \text{sum of corrections}}{\text{weight of fuel}}$$

Calorific value in B.t.u./lb = C.V. in cal/g × 1·8

REFERENCES

B.S. 1016, Part 5 (1957). *Gross calorific value of coal and coke.*
FRANCIS, W. *Boiler House and Power Station Chemistry,* London, 1962.

THE CLEAN AIR ACT, 1956

THIS Act implemented the main recommendations of the Beaver Committee's Report on air pollution, published in 1953.

A. CONTROL OF INDUSTRIAL SMOKE

1. *Dark Smoke Emission is an Offence*

The definition of dark smoke is Shade No. 2, or over, on the Ringelmann Chart (Fig. 30.1). The maximum permissible duration of dark smoke is not specified, but that used by most local authorities is a maximum of 2 minutes in any period of 30 min.

Defences in the act include:

  (i) Lighting up.

 (ii) Mechanical breakdown that could not be foreseen, provided against, or prevented, by action taken after the failure occurred.

(iii) Unsuitable fuel.

 (iv) Insufficient time to alter existing appliances to conform with the Act, which allows for this purpose a period of 7 years from the date of passing the Act.

  (v) The grant of a certificate from the Local Authority that it has not been practicable to carry out the necessary alterations. This is valid for one year.

 (vi) Local Authorities must be informed of the installation of new furnaces, which must, as far as is practicable, be capable of continuous operation without the emission of smoke.

2. Control of Grit

(i) All furnaces burning solid fuel shall use any practicable means for minimizing the emission of grit and dust. A simple expansion chamber, which enables the heavier particles only to separate, will not satisfy this requirement.

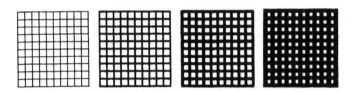

FIG. 30.1   Ringelmann Chart.

(ii) New furnaces burning pulverized fuel, or new solid fuel furnaces burning over one ton per hour, must be fitted with suitable and efficient grit arrestors which are approved by the Local Authority. Suitable grit arrestors include the electrostatic precipitator, cyclones and multi-cyclones, wet filters, sleeve and bag filters.

(iii) The Local Authority can ask for dust emission measurements of any pulverized fuel furnace, or any furnace burning one or more tons per hour of solid fuel and for information on fuel consumption of such furnaces.

3. Chimney Heights

The Act provides powers for controlling the height of new industrial chimneys. Plans for new chimneys must be approved by the Local Authority.

4. Special Industrial Premises

Special industrial premises, including power stations, gas works and coke ovens, are placed under the supervision of the Alkali Inspectors (instead of the Local Authority) under the provisions of the Alkali, etc., Works Regulation Act, 1906.

5. Transport Pollution

Smoke and fumes from road vehicles are not controlled under the Clean Air Act, but are controlled under the Road Traffic Act, which is administered by the police. Railway locomotives and ships (within defined navigable waters) are subject to the same control of dark smoke as applies to the chimneys of buildings. In the case of ships, the permissible limits range from 10 min in 2 hr to 20 min in 1 hr.

6. Sulphur Oxides

The emission of sulphur oxides from flue gases is not controlled by the Clean Air Act, except indirectly, because some measure of limitation of concentration at ground level is exercised by control of chimney height.

B. CONTROL OF DOMESTIC POLLUTION

This is provided for by the creation of "Smoke control areas". Any local authority, with the approval and confirmation of the Minister of Housing and Local Government, may declare a smoke control area. In such an area an offence is committed if smoke is emitted from any chimney unless:

(i) An "authorized fuel" is used. Authorized fuels include anthracite, carbonized briquettes, coke, steam coals containing less than 20% of volatile matter, low temperature coke, gas and electricity. Oil is not an authorized fuel because it can, if improperly burned, create a heavy black smoke.

(ii) An appliance is used that is exempted on the grounds that it can be used for burning smokelessly non-authorized fuels.

Local Authorities are authorized to repay 70% of the reasonable necessary expense of converting existing coal-burning appliances into appliances capable of burning smokelessly authorized fuels.

The main objections to the Act are:

(a) The inadequate supply of "authorized fuels" if smokeless control areas are to be declared extensively.

(b) The exclusion of paraffin, gas and diesel oils from the list of "authorized fuels".

(c) The substantial absence of control over pollution by sulphur oxides.

REFERENCE

FRANCIS, W. *Boiler House and Power Station Chemistry*, London, 1962.

A NATIONAL FUELS POLICY

The four basic considerations that should determine the fuels policy of a nation are:
(A) Cost of heat per useful therm.
(B) Atmospheric pollution per useful therm.
(C) Capital costs and conservation of natural resources.
(D) Relative merits of fuels and electricity as sources of heat.

A. COST OF HEAT SUPPLIED

1. *Cost per Useful Therm (domestic heating)*

Source of heat	Cost to consumer	Efficiency %	Cost per useful therm (in pence)
Electricity	1¾d. per unit*	100	40·3
Gas	1/6d. per therm*	80	21·2
Anthracite	£15 per ton	65	19·7
Coke	£11 per ton	60	17·1
Gas oil	1/6d. per gal	75	14·7

* Plus standing charge, not included in costs.

2. *Quantity of Basic Fuel to Give* 1 *Therm of Useful Heat (industrial)*

Basic fuel	Form of heat	Efficiency, overall %	lb basic fuel per therm useful heat
Coal	Town gas*	85	11·75 (235 ft³ gas)
Coal	Coal	89	9·0
Coke	Coke	89	9·8
Coal	Electricity	25	32·0
Residual fuel oil	Electricity	25	21·8

* Yield depends on process used. By complete gasification, one useful therm is obtained from 11·75 lb of coal.

B. ATMOSPHERIC POLLUTION BY SULPHUR OXIDES, PER THERM USEFUL HEAT

Form of heat	Sulphur in basic fuel %	lb sulphur in basic fuel/useful therm	lb sulphur (as sulphuric acid) per useful therm
Town gas	(Coal) 1·0	0·1175	0·02*
Gas oil	0·5	0·029	0·087
Coal	1·0	0·090	0·270
Res. fuel oil	3·0	0·183	0·549
Electricity			
—from coal	1·0	0·320	0·960
—from res. fuel oil	3·0	0·654	1·960

* Sulphur in town gas is reduced < 20 g/100 ft³ before sale

C. CAPITAL COSTS AND CONSERVATION OF NATURAL RESOURCES

1. *Capital Cost of Gasification and Electrical Generation*

Gasification	Lurgi plant	£45/therm/day
	Carburetted W.G. plant	£15/therm/day
	Catalytic gas reformer	£10/therm/day
Electricity	Thermal station	£75/therm/day

2. *Conservation of Fuel Resources*

The present rate of increase in electricity generation in Great Britain is ca. 5% per annum, i.e. fuel consumption is doubled every 14 years.

The coal burned in Central Electricity Generating stations in 1961 was ca. 50×10^6 tons out of a total coal production of ca. 200×10^6 tons.

At the present rate of increase in electricity the whole of our yearly output of coal will be required in 1990, or its equivalent in oil, water, or atomic power.

Therefore unless oil is imported on a considerable scale, or the development of atomic power is greatly accelerated, the growth of electricity must be restricted, and a fuels policy developed that will make the best use of our national resources of capital, industry and fuel.

D. PROS AND CONS OF ELECTRICITY AND FUELS FOR HEATING

1. *Electricity*

(a) Electricity is nearly twice as dear as gas, more than twice as dear as coal and nearly three times as dear as oil, on an equal thermal basis.

(b) The generation of one therm of electricity consumes more than three times as much coal as when this fuel is burned directly. Other forms of fuel are also much more efficient producers of heat than electricity (cf. Table A.2).

(c) The atmospheric pollution resulting from the generation of one useful therm of electricity (in terms of H_2SO_4 emitted) is nearly four times as great as that from coal or oil (used directly) and between 70 and 140 times that produced from one useful therm of gas (Table B).

(d) The capital cost of generating plant per useful therm is several times that of the production of gas by modern gasification processes (cf. C.1).

(e) The annual coal production and the coal reserves of Great Britain are insufficient to permit the growth of electricity at present rates.

(f) In the further development of electricity in Great Britain, alternative sources of energy should be used, e.g. water power, atomic power, and imported low sulphur oils.

2. *Gas* (see Section C, Vol. II)

(a) Gas is the cleanest and most readily controlled source of heat. Its development by new and improved processes should be encouraged.

(b) In other countries, prosperity and atmospheric cleanliness have followed the widespread use of methane and natural gas. These gases are now being made available in England. This trend should be accelerated.

(c) Gas can be stored underground in large quantities. A progressive national fuels policy would include the large scale manufacture of gas at a uniform economic load, storing summer surplus for winter use.

(d) Sulphur compounds in all gases can be removed easily and cheaply. No practical process exists for the removal of sulphur from other fuels.

3. *Oil* (see Section B, Vol. 1)

(a) Low sulphur oils are next to gases in cleanliness and controlability.

(b) They are more readily available and more economical than solid fuels.

(c) They can be stored easily, economically, and cleanly. They do not deteriorate during storage.

(d) The cost to the consumer is relatively low, but is increased by a protective tariff.

(e) This tariff should be removed, for oil is the only fuel likely to be available in sufficient quantities for our requirements in the near future.

(f) High sulphur oils should not be used as fuels, but should be gasified and the sulphur removed from the gas before sale.

4. *Coal*

(a) Raw coal containing high proportions of volatile matter and sulphur should not be used, but should be gasified by the methods described in Section C, Vol. II, and the gases purified before use.

(b) Coals containing more than 15% of volatile matter should not be used for domestic use because they produce appreciable smoke and they are not suitable for domestic boilers (cf. "The Clean Air Act", Data Sheet No. 30).

(c) Coal should be sold to a guaranteed specification, with redress in the case of unsatisfactory deliveries.

(d) Coke should be sold on a volume basis because of its high capacity for absorbing and retaining moisture.

E. CONCLUSION

The above constitutes the framework of a practical and progressive National Fuels Policy. If adopted, the atmosphere would be cleaner, better use would be made of our coal resources, and labour and industry would be deployed more effectively.

SECTION B
LIQUID FUELS

DEFINITIONS — UNITS — NOMENCLATURE OF ORGANIC CHEMISTRY

LIQUID FUELS — TYPES

Liquid fuels may be divided into two main classes, based on their utilization viz.:

1. Light oils or spirits; suitable for use with internal combustion engines and jet engines.
2. Heavy oils; suitable mainly or exclusively for burning in furnaces.

1. *Oils or Spirits*

Suitable for use in engines include:

(a) The lighter, more volatile, fractions obtained by distilling or cracking natural petroleum oils, shale oils, and related natural deposits.

(b) The light fractions obtained by the hydrogenation of coal, or coal tar, or heavy oil residues.

(c) The light fractions obtained by the synthesis of hydrocarbons by the Fischer–Tropsch process.

(d) Alcohols, particularly methyl and ethyl alcohol, obtained by synthesis, or by fermentation processes.

(e) Benzole, obtained by the distillation of coal tar or by extraction from coal gas.

Of these, only the most volatile and cleanest products, gasoline or petrol (natural or synthetic), benzole, and alcohol, are suitable for the spark ignition engine. The next higher fractions of petroleum oil, shale oil, and synthetic oil, generally included in the class of oils known as paraffin, kerosine, or naphtha, are suitable for jet turbines. The remainder of the lighter fractions of the distillation of petroleum oil, shale oil, and synthetic oil are suitable for Diesel engines. They are also suitable for combustion in small furnaces or combustion appliances.

2. *Furnace Oils*

These include the heaviest grades of natural petroleum oils, or cracked oils, from which the more valuable engine oil and lubricating oil fractions and the bitumen have been removed by distillation, together with the less valuable heavier products of distillation, or hydrogenation, of coal, or of synthetic oils. In other words, a furnace oil is a heavy oil product, natural or synthetic, for which no more valuable use can be found.

PHYSICAL UNITS

1. Some units, such as density, specific heat and calorific value, have been defined in Data Sheet No. 1.
2. Viscosity—the most important new item, used in relation to liquid fuels, is viscosity, or resistance to flow. This property determines the behaviour of an oil in practical appliances such as atomization, flow, and pumping.

(a) Absolute Viscosity

This is the force required to move a plane surface of area 1 cm² over another parallel plane surface 1 cm away at a rate of 1 cm/sec when both surfaces are immersed in the fluid. This force (the unit of absolute viscosity) is called the poise; its symbol is η (eta). A smaller unit, the centipoise, is often used:

$$1 \text{ Poise} = 100 \text{ Centipoise}$$

(b) Kinematic Viscosity

This is the ratio of absolute viscosity to density; both measured at the same temperature. Unit of kinematic viscosity is the Stoke, symbol v (nu). This is the usual term used in the petroleum industry, though the centi-Stoke is also used.

$$1 \text{ Stoke} = 100 \text{ centi-Stoke}$$

$$\text{Kinematic viscosity } v = \frac{\text{absolute viscosity}}{\text{density}}$$

$$= \frac{\eta}{\rho}$$

Absolute and kinematic viscosity are measured in some form of U-tube viscometer (cf. Data Sheet No. 62).

(c) Arbitrary Units

In many countries, arbitrary units of viscosity are also used, based on the number of seconds taken for an oil to flow through a fixed orifice at a known temperature. Instruments used for this purpose are:

Redwood Viscometers Nos. 1 and 2—In Great Britain and the Commonwealth.

Engler Viscometer—In Europe

Saybolt Viscometer—In the U.S.A.

These units, e.g. Redwood seconds, cannot be correlated exactly with the fundamental units of viscosity, though approximate correlations are available in most cases.

NOMENCLATURE OF ORGANIC CHEMISTRY

Hydrocarbons—contain only carbon and hydrogen.

In **saturated aliphatic hydrocarbons**, carbon utilizes its full combining power (valency) of 4. The valency of hydrogen is invariably 1. The simplest aliphatic saturated hydrocarbon is methane, CH_4.

In **unsaturated aliphatic hydrocarbons**, 1 atom of carbon is combined with fewer than 4 hydrogen atoms, for example ethylene, C_2H_4; acetylene C_2H_2. Some large hydrocarbons contain both saturated and unsaturated groups, based upon the above key hydrocarbons.

Cyclic hydrocarbons—In these hydrocarbons the valency bonds of some carbon atoms are sufficiently close for the structure to form closed chains. Two classes of cyclic hydrocarbons are known, viz.

Alicyclic or naphthenic hydrocarbons, in which a repeating group of $-CH_2$ forms a ring of from 4 to 9 carbon atoms. The simplest member of this series is cyclobutane, C_4H_8.

Aromatic hydrocarbons; in these a repeating group of $-CH$ forms a closed ring of six carbon atoms. The simplest member of this series is benzene, C_6H_6. Multiple rings, each of six carbon atoms, are present in more complex aromatic hydrocarbons, e.g. naphthalene and anthracene.

STRUCTURAL REPRESENTATION OF HYDROCARBON FORMULAE

Hydrocarbon molecules may be represented conveniently by structural formulae, showing the direction and number of valency bonds between the atoms present. On this basis the above series of hydrocarbons may be represented as follows:

1. *Aliphatic, or Paraffin, Hydrocarbon Series*

These are called paraffin hydrocarbons because they are constituents of paraffin oil, the highest members of the series forming the white solids known as paraffin wax. All names for the paraffins terminate in -ane, e.g. methane, ethane, propane, butane. From five carbon members, upwards, the first part of the name is based on Greek numerology, e.g. *pen*tane, *hex*ane, *hep*tane, etc.

Basic formula for the series is C_nH_{2n+2}.

(a) Straight chain, e.g.
    for Butane C_4H_{10}

$$H-\overset{\displaystyle H}{\underset{\displaystyle H}{\overset{|}{\underset{|}{C}}}}-\overset{\displaystyle H}{\underset{\displaystyle H}{\overset{|}{\underset{|}{C}}}}-\overset{\displaystyle H}{\underset{\displaystyle H}{\overset{|}{\underset{|}{C}}}}-\overset{\displaystyle H}{\underset{\displaystyle H}{\overset{|}{\underset{|}{C}}}}-H$$

Characteristic—each carbon is attached to only one or two other carbon atoms.

(b) Isomers of paraffins—these have the same basic formulae as the paraffins, but have branched chains, i.e. at least 1 carbon is attached to 3 or 4 other carbon atoms.

Iso-paraffins contain 1 carbon attached to 3 others, viz.

iso-butane, C_4H_{10},

$$\begin{array}{ccccc}
 & & H & & \\
 & & | & & \\
 & H & H-C-H & H & \\
 & | & | & | & \\
H-C & - & C & - & C-H \\
 & | & | & | & \\
 & H & H & H &
\end{array}$$

Neo-paraffins contain 1 carbon attached to 4 others, viz.

iso-pentane, C_5H_{12},

$$\begin{array}{ccccc}
 & & H & & \\
 & & | & & \\
 & & H-C-H & & \\
 & H & | & H & \\
 & | & | & | & \\
H-C & - & C & - & C-H \\
 & | & | & | & \\
 & H & | & H & \\
 & & H-C-H & & \\
 & & | & & \\
 & & H & &
\end{array}$$

These formulae may also be written in a manner indicating the various groups present, e.g. CH_3 = methyl, $CH_3 . CH_2$ = ethyl; $CH_3 . CH_2 . CH_2$ = propyl.

Such groups have the general title "alkyl groups".

2. *Unsaturated Hydrocarbons*

(a) **Olefines**—The names for the olefines are based upon those of the corresponding paraffins, but the termination is -ene. They contain 2 hydrogen atoms less than the corresponding paraffins. Basic formula C_nH_{2n}.

Straight chain—ethylene, C_2H_4 or $CH_2 : CH_2$

Structural formula

Other important straight chain olefines are:

Propylene C_3H_6 ($CH_3 . CH : CH_2$)

Butylene C_4H_8 ($CH_3 . CH_2 . CH : CH_2$ α butylene

or $CH_3 . CH : CH : CH_3$ β butylene)

Branched chain—iso-butylene

C_4H_8 or

When formulae are written in the above form, two dots (:), or two lines (=), represent a double bond, typical of the olefine structure.

(b) **Acetylenes**—contain two hydrogen atoms less than the corresponding olefines. Basic formula C_nH_{2n-2}.

Structural formula

Most important are: Acetylene, C_2H_2 (i.e. $CH : CH$)

Methyl acetylene, C_3H_4 (i.e. $CH_3 . C : CH$)

Ethyl acetylene, C_4H_6 (i.e. $CH_3 . CH_2 : CH$)

In written formulae, three dots ($\vdots$), or three lines ($\equiv$), represent the triple (acetylene) bond.

3. *Polymethylene or Naphthene Series*

Members of this series are isomeric with the olefines (i.e. contain corresponding numbers of carbon and hydrogen atoms per molecule) but they are saturated, and possess cyclic or ring structures. Basic formula C_nH_{2n}. Important members and structure:

Cyclo-butane C_4H_8, i.e.

$$\begin{array}{cc} CH_2 & CH_2 \\ & \\ CH_2 & CH_2 \end{array}$$

Cyclo-pentane C_5H_{10}, i.e.

$$\begin{array}{ccc} & CH_2 & \\ CH_2 & & CH_2 \\ CH_2 & & CH_2 \end{array}$$

Cyclo-hexane, C_5H_{12}, i.e.

$$\begin{array}{ccc} CH_2 & & CH_2 \\ CH_2 & & CH_2 \\ CH_2 & & CH_2 \end{array}$$

Highest member of this series is cyclo-nonane, C_9H_{18}.

4. *Aromatic Hydrocarbons*

These contain 6 carbon atoms in the form of a hexagon shaped ring. Alkyl (aliphatic) groups may be attached to some carbon atoms. Basic formula C_6H_{2n-6} ($n \geqslant 6$). First member of series is benzene C_6H_6.

(a) *Single rings*

Benzene C_6H_6

Toluene C_7H_8
(methyl-benzene)

Xylene C_8H_{10}
(di-methyl-benzene)

In the case of xylene, the two methyl groups may be attached in three different positions, giving the three isomeric xylenes, called *ortho*, *meta*, and *para*-xylene, respectively.

(b) *Multiple rings*

Important examples:

Diphenyl $C_{12}H_{10}$

Naphthalene $C_{10}H_8$

Anthracene $C_{14}H_{10}$

ORGANIC DERIVATIVES OF HYDROCARBONS

Hydrocarbons react with chemical reagents to form the following important types of organic compounds:

1. *With Oxidizing Agents*

Products: alcohols, aldehydes, ketones, acids, ethers, phenols, resins, waxes, sugars, celluloses, plastics.

2. *With Halogens*

Products: fluorides, chlorides, bromides and iodides of corresponding hydrocarbons; plastics.

3. *With Nitrogen and Sulphur*

Products: nitro-paraffins, amino-compounds, pyridines, proteins, plastics.

4. *With Each Other* (*particularly unsaturateds*)

Products: polymeric plastics, e.g. poly-ethylene, poly-propylene.

PETROLEUM OILS — THE ORIGIN AND NATURE OF CRUDE PETROLEUM

A. ORIGIN

Petroleum oil is generally considered to be formed from animal and vegetables debris accumulating in sea basins or estuaries and buried there by sand and silt. The debris may have been decomposed by anaerobic bacteria under reducing conditions, so that most of the oxygen has been removed, or oil may have been distilled from the partially decayed debris by heat generated by earth movements or by depth of burial.

The final result is a black viscous product of composition:

Carbon	80 to 89%
Hydrogen	12 to 14%
Nitrogen	0·3 to 1%
Sulphur	0·3 to 3%
Oxygen	2 to 3%

An alternative mode of formation by synthesis, on the lines of the Fischer–Tropsch process (see Data Sheet No. 66), has been suggested by Robinson[1], but the bio-chemical view expressed above is accepted by most authorities.

The main differences between the origins of oil and of coal (cf. Data Sheet No. 5) are:

(1) Coal was formed mainly from land plants, decaying under mildly reducing conditions.

(2) Oil was formed mainly from sea plants and animals decaying under strongly reducing conditions.

(3) Coal seams remained where deposited.

(4) Oil can migrate under the effects of temperature and pressure, so that the location of existing deposits may not be the location of the initial accumulation of oil-forming debris.

(5) The source rock is sedimentary in nature and mainly or entirely of marine origin.

B. FORMATION OF EXISTING DEPOSITS

Temperature changes, earth movements, and differences in density between oil and salt water, caused the oil to migrate from the source rock to accumulate in favourable geological formations. Favourable locations mean a porous sedimentary rock, called a "Reservoir rock" in which oil and gas can accumulate in the upper layers, capped by an impermeable rock, or rock formation, which prevents escape of the oil and gas. Reservoir rocks are usually coarse grained sandstones, grit, limestones or dolomite. Cap rocks are fine grained clays and shales, marls and dense limestones. The strata in an oilfield form a trap and the following types are commonly found:

(a) *Anticlinal dome*, under which the oil can form a reservoir. In time the deposit separates into three layers, gas, oil and water.

(b) *Fault trap*, in which a fracture in the strata brings an impervious, sealing layer above the reservoir rock.

(c) *Stratigraphic trap*, in which inclined layers of oil containing rock are overlain by a cap of impervious rock.

(d) *Anticline formed by a salt dome*, which has been thrust through strata, sealing off the oil-bearing layers.

In cases (b) to (d) the gas has escaped and the deposit consists only of oil and salt water.

C. DETECTION OF OIL DEPOSITS

Oil deposits are detected by visual, geological, and geophysical methods.

(a) Visual methods include observations of oil seepages at the surface and fossils occurring in the strata.

(b) Geological methods include mapping the age of rocks, their nature, and the types of formations present. These may be assisted by aerial photography.

(c) Geophysical methods. These include:

    (1) *Gravimetric*—measuring with sensitive instruments the variations in density of the earth's crust.

    (2) *Seismic*—measuring the reflectance of shock waves passed through the earth's crust. This gives the depth of hard, reflecting, layers, such as limestone.

    (3) *Magnetic*—local variations in the intensity and direction of the earth's magnetic field show the distribution of the various rocks in the earth's crust.

(d) Drilling. The final test for oil-bearing strata is drilling. Cores from the drill are examined for fossil formation and evidence of porous or non-porous rocks. When oil has been proved, drilling with mud cooling is continued until the depth of the oil or oil-bearing strata has been ascertained.

D. NATURE OF PETROLEUM CRUDES

Petroleum oils are commonly classified into the following three main groups, depending upon the type of the hydrocarbons which predominate in the oil:

    (1) Paraffinic
    (2) Naphthenic
    (3) Asphaltic (aromatic).

Most crudes contain a variety of hydrocarbons, ranging from the simplest hydrocarbon gas, methane, to the most complex solid paraffin wax or bitumen. In the heavier hydrocarbons many different groupings may exist, for example a heavy hydrocarbon containing 35 carbon atoms may exist as any of the types:

(1) Paraffinic—containing 4 aliphatid, 1 naphthenic and 1 aromatic groups.

(2) Naphthenic—containing 3 naphthenic, 2 aliphatic and 1 aromatic grouping.

(3) Asphaltic—containing 3 aromatic, 2 aliphatic and 1 naphthenic grouping.

A possible structural formula for an oil of the 3rd class would be as shown in Fig. 52.1.

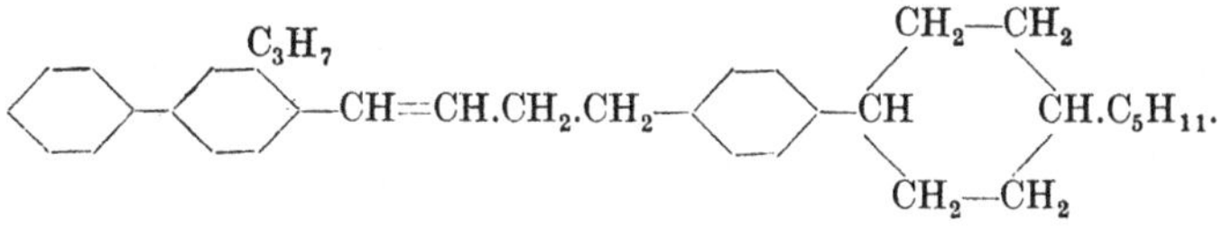

FIG. 52.1   Possible Structural Formula, Asphaltic Oil.

An alternative classification of oil types is:

(1) Paraffinic—if aliphatic groupings are > 75% of the whole.

(2) Naphthenic—if naphthenic rings are > 70% of the whole.

(3) Asphaltic—if aromatic rings are > 60% of the whole.

Many intermediate types of petroleum crude also exist.

The main differences in chemical and physical properties of the crude oil types are shown below.

CHARACTERISTICS OF PARAFFINIC AND ASPHALTIC CRUDES

Naphthenic crudes are intermediate in properties.

	Paraffinic	Asphaltic
Density	Low	High
Yield of gasoline	High	Low
*Octane number of gasoline	High	Low
Sulphur content	Low	High
Ratio of hydrogen to carbon	High	Low
*Smoke point of kerosine	High	Low
*Cetane value of gas oil	High	Low
*Pour point of gas oil	High	Low
Yield of lubricants	High	Low
Solid product	Wax	Bitumen

* These terms relate to the value of the products for use as motor spirit, lamp oil and/or Diesel fuel. Details are given in the appropriate data sheets, q.v. Nos. 56, 59 and 57.

TYPICAL FUEL OIL ANALYSES DERIVED FROM THESE CRUDE OIL TYPES ARE:

	Carbon %	Hydrogen %	Sulphur %	Density @ 60°F	C.V. B.t.u./lb	Viscosity Redwood seconds at 100°F
Paraffinic (Pennsylvania)	84·0	13·8	1·0	0·820	19,400	200
Naphthenic (Texas)	86·3	12·2	1·3	0·860	19,200	180
Asphaltic (Borneo)	86·7	10·7	2·1	0·960	18,900	40

YIELDS OF PRODUCTS OBTAINED BY DISTILLATION OF CRUDE TYPES

Temperature Range °C	Nature of product	Type of Crude		
		Paraffin	Naphthene	Asphalt
40–200	Petrol and naphtha	45·2	38·6	1·1
140–290	Kerosine	17·7	4·9	—
250–340	Gas oil	8·3	17·3	55·5
Over 340	Light lubricating oils	9·8	9·4	14·2
	Medium lubricating oils	3·4	6·3	4·7
	Viscous lubricating oils	—	—	11·6
	Residuum	14·7	22·1	12·7
	Distillation loss	0·9	1·4	0·2

REFERENCES

1. ROBINSON, Sir R. *The Origins of Petroleum, Catalyst*, **6** (1961). Industrial Journal of Shell Chemicals Co. London.
2. *Modern Petroleum Technology*, 3rd Edition, Institute of Petroleum, London, 1962.

PETROLEUM OILS—PRELIMINARY TREATMENT AND DISTILLATION

PRELIMINARY TREATMENT

Crude petroleum issuing from a well contains as impurities water, solids (including sand, bitumen or wax) and gas, consisting mainly of methane and ethane. These separate partially in storage tanks.

The crude oil may be passed to the storage tanks via a centrifugal separator, which effects, or assists, the separation of the crude oil from the water, wet gas, and solids. The crude oil is then either distilled on site, or is sent to refineries for distillation and further processing.

WET GAS TREATMENT

The wet gas consists of the hydrocarbon gases methane and ethane, with impurities or diluents such as nitrogen, helium, hydrogen, hydrogen sulphide, or carbon dioxide. Condensible vapours are water and low boiling hydrocarbons from propane to hexane. These are separated by processes of compression and cooling into dry gas (methane and ethane), water, and "wild" natural gasoline (i.e. containing propane and butane). The latter is distilled in a fractionating column at 100 to 200 lb/in^2 to remove propane and butane, with the formation of "stabilized natural gasoline". Stabilized natural gasoline has the following properties:

Composition: 40 to 50% butane and pentane
Distillation range: 30 to 160°C
Anti-knock properties: good.

I

DISTILLATION — THEORY

1. *Fractional Distillation at Atmospheric Pressure*

(a) *Introduction*

Fractional distillation is a series of processes of evaporation and condensation at a number of points in a vertical column.

Pure liquids boil at a fixed temperature at atmospheric pressure, when the vapour pressure of the liquid equals this pressure. Mixed liquids boil over a range of temperatures, when the sum of the partial pressures of the constituents equals atmospheric pressure.

At the boiling point of any mixture, the vapour and liquid phases are in equilibrium. If the pressure is reduced, or if the temperature is raised, evaporation follows. In the reverse case, condensation occurs. Vapour pressures are used to calculate the vapour and liquid phase compositions of mixtures when these are in equilibrium.

When the components of a mixture are separated continuously in a column, vapour passing upwards is enriched in the more volatile components by contact with the liquid stream (reflux) flowing downwards.

This process of *enrichment*, on which fractional distillation depends, requires a study of

    (i) Vapour–liquid equilibrium data.

   (ii) Number of theoretical separation stages (trays or plates) required.

  (iii) Evaluation of actual tray or plate efficiency (to relate practical to theoretical performance).

(b) *Vapour-liquid Equilibrium Data*

(i) *Pure "known liquids"*

The relation between vapour pressure and temperature, even for a pure compound, is extremely complex. It can be represented approximately by the linear equation

$$\log p = A - \frac{B}{T}$$

where A and B are constants and T = absolute temperature.

From this relationship, Duhring's Rule is derived: "If the temperatures at which two similar liquids exert the same vapour pressure are plotted against each other, a straight line relationship is obtained." Hence, if a suitable reference liquid has a known vapour pressure/temperature relationship, and two points on the vapour pressure curve of a second liquid are known, the vapour pressure curve of the second substance may be drawn parallel to that of the known substance.

The Othmer method is based on the *Clausius–Clapeyron* equation, viz.

$$\frac{d \log. p}{d \log. pR} = \frac{L}{L_R} \tag{1}$$

where p and pR are the vapour pressures of the unknown and reference liquids, and L and L_R are their molar latent heats, respectively.

Alternatively,

$$\log. p = \frac{L}{L_R} \log. pR + C \tag{2}$$

If the differential form of the equation (1) is plotted ($d \log p$ against $d \log pR$), the lines go through the origin, so that the complete relationship between vapour pressure and temperature for an unknown liquid is obtained by making only one determination.

The integral form of the equation (2) is more convenient to plot and use.

Cox chart. This is a convenient form of the log p/temperature relationship that is particularly suitable for petroleum hydrocarbons. The scales of vapour pressure (logarithmic) and temperature are first determined for a reference liquid, such as water. The V.P./temperature curves, which are straight lines with a common point of intersection, are then drawn in from one determination for each hydrocarbon, e.g. the boiling point at atmospheric pressure.

For mixtures of known hydrocarbons of decreasing V.P. at the same temperature, e.g. the series ethane to heptane, "key" components can be chosen for the volatile (overhead stream) and nonvolatile (bottom stream) products of a separation at a given point in a column. In the above case, butane would be the light "key" component chosen and pentane the heavy "key" component. The multi-component system is then considered as a binary system. This method may be used in the application of the McCabe–Thiele diagram (q.v.) to distillation problems.

(ii) *Mixtures of Unknown Composition*

The usual procedure is to define the fractions by means of standard distillation curves. For example, the fractions gasoline to gas oil by A.S.T.M. curves (Fig. 53.1).

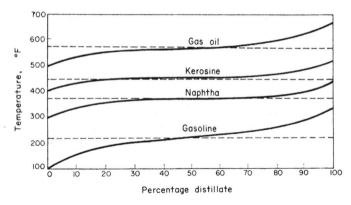

Fig. 53.1　A.S.T.M. Distillation Curves.

From such curves Packie[1] correlated the "Degree of fractionation" with the product of the internal reflux ratio and the number of trays in the column. "Degree of fractionation" = distance apart of curves (°F at 50% distilled point). "Slope of curves" = degree of overlap (°F) between the 5% distilled temperature on one curve and the 95% distilled temperature on the next upper curve.

(iii) *Raoult's Law*

In an ideal homogeneous solution, the partial pressure of a component at a given temperature is proportional to the molar fraction of the pure component in the mixture,

i.e. $pa = Ax_a$ (where A is a proportionality constant)   (3)

For the limiting value $x_a = 1.0$, A is the vapour pressue of the pure component.

For "non-ideal" solutions

$$P_a = \lambda_a A x_a \qquad (4)$$

where λ_a is an "Activity coefficient" ($>$ or < 1.0) Raoult's Law may be used to calculate the initial vapour composition of any mixture of known miscible liquids, e.g. heptane (C_7H_{16}), octane (C_8H_{18}), benzene (C_6H_6) and toluene (C_7H_8) in equal proportions by weight. (M.W. $= 100:114:78$ and 92, respectively.)

Assuming $\lambda_0 = 1.0$

100 g of mixture contains:

$\dfrac{25}{100} = 0.25$ mol. $C_7H_{16} \rightarrow 0.236$ molar fraction

$\dfrac{25}{114} = 0.219$ mol. $C_8H_{18} \rightarrow 0.206$ molar fraction

$\dfrac{25}{78} = 0.321$ mol. $C_6H_6 \rightarrow 0.302$ molar fraction

$\dfrac{25}{92} = 0.272$ mol. $C_7H_8 \rightarrow 0.256$ molar fraction

$\overline{\text{1·062 mol.}} \qquad \overline{\text{1·000}}$

Assume that the B.P. is 99°C and obtain the V.P. of the pure substances from tables:

	V.P. of pure subs. (a) mm	Molar fraction liquid (b)	Partial pressure (c) mm	Molar fraction vapour (d)
C_7H_{16}	770	0·236	183	0·236
C_8H_{18}	320	0·206	66	0·086
C_6H_6	1300	0·302	393	0·512
C_7H_8	500	0·256	128	0·166
			770	1·000

The total pressure 770 is near enough to 760 mm to accept 99°C as the B.P.

$$\text{Column } (d) = \frac{\text{Col. } (c)}{770}$$

If this first trial had not been successful, a second temperature would have been chosen, e.g. 98°C, and the calculation repeated.

(c) Tray Separation and Reflux Ratio

The internal reflux ratio at any tray is the ratio:

$$\frac{\text{moles liquid leaving}}{\text{moles vapour entering}} = \frac{O}{V}$$

For any given vapour/liquid equilibrium, a minimum reflux ratio is necessary for separation. At minimum reflux ratio, an infinite number of trays is necessary.

The optimum reflux ratio is obtained by balancing the number of trays in a column against capital costs.

The required degree of separation is calculated in terms of the reflux ratio and the number of theoretical trays in the column.

(d) *Calculation of Number of Stages Required*

At a given tray n in the upper, rectifying, part of the column, the vapour (Y_{n-1}) entering from the tray below is dispersed through the edges of the bubble caps as a stream of bubbles in the liquid (x_{n+1}) entering from the tray above, and leaving as composition x_n.

In a theoretical tray, the vapour is in equilibrium with the liquid, i.e. $Y_n = Kx_n$.

The relationship between the liquid and vapour streams passing in the column, e.g. V, Y_{n-1} and O, x_n (the "Operating line relationship") is calculated from heat and material balances.

Assuming constant overflow, and constant vaporization, on each tray:

$$Y_{n-1} = \frac{O}{D}x_n + \frac{D}{V}x_D \tag{5}$$

where D = the amount of distillate obtained in unit time and x_D = the molecular fraction of the more volatile component in D

x_n is obtained by equilibrium calculations

and $Y_{n-1} = Kx_{n-1}$. $\tag{6}$

The theoretical tray to tray analysis is carried out by the alternative application of equilibrium and operating line relationships. This gives the number of theoretical plates required to effect the required separation in the upper, rectifying, part of the column. Similar methods give the number of plates required for the lower, stripping, part of the column. The complete analysis for multi-component systems is laborious, but may be simplified by use of the McCabe–Thiele graphical method.

(e) *McCabe–Thiele*[2] *Graphical Method*

This is based on a binary mixture, making the following assumptions:

(i) Sensible heat changes are negligible compared with latent heat changes.

(ii) The molar latent heats of all components are equal.

(iii) The heat of mixing is negligible.

(iv) The leat losses from the column are negligible.

A materials balance at plate n on the vapour (Y_n) shows:

$$Y_n = \left(\frac{L_{n+1}}{L_{n+1} + D}\right)x_{n+1} + \left(\frac{D}{L_{n+1} + D}\right)xD \tag{7}$$

where L_{n+1} = moles of liquid overflow from plate $n + 1$ to n in unit time.

Similarly, for a plate m in the stripping section:

$$Y_m = \left(\frac{L_{m+1}}{L_{m+1} - W}\right)x_{m+1} - \left(\frac{W}{L_{m+1} - W}\right)x_w \tag{8}$$

where W = moles of bottom liquid flowing in unit time, and

$\quad x_w$ = the molecular fraction of the more volatile component in W.

In the McCabe–Thiele Diagram, the straight lines represented by equations (7) and (8) are plotted (as in Fig. 53.2) using values of y as ordinates and of x as abscissae (AC and CD, respectively). On the same diagram, the equilibrium vapour curve for the given binary mixture is also plotted (curved line).

The point $x4$ on line CD represents the composition of liquid on plate 4, with vapour composition represented by point $Y4$. The liquid composition on the plate above (No. 3) is represented by point $x3$.

The vapour entering plate 4 is given by point $Y5$. The changes in the column, starting with the overhead distillate x_D, may be traced by going stepwise from the line AC, first horizontally and then vertically, as shown.

Point C, the intersection of AC and CD, represents the theoretical feed plate composition. In practice, the feed plate corresponds to the first vertical step to the left of C. The number of theoretical plates corresponds to the number of intersections of vapour and liquid lines on AC and CD required to effect the fractionation.

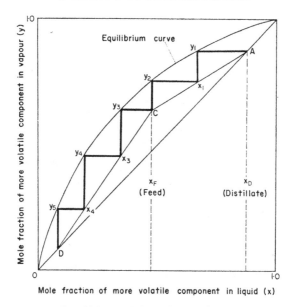

FIG. 53.2   McCabe–Thiele[2] Diagram.

(f) *Plate Efficiency, Number of Plates, and Spacing*

Equilibrium is not reached on each plate in practice. The plate efficiency, or partial equilibrium attained, must be known to design a practical column. The overall efficiency is defined as the number of theoretical plates required for a given separation, divided by the number used. For light hydrocarbon fraction, overall plate efficiencies between 0·6 and 0·9 are usual.

> e.g.   No. of theoretical plates   =   35
> Plate efficiency   =   0·7
> No. of plates used = 35/0·7   =   50

The normal plate spacing in fractionating columns used in oil refineries is between 18 in. and 30 in. This is partly to reduce entrainment at normal vapour velocities (1 to 4 ft/sec), and partly to allow space for inspection manholes between plates.

(g) *Heat Supply and Control*

(i) *Pipe or tube stills—Flash vaporization*

Normal procedure is to pump feed oil at high velocities (Reynolds Number > 10,000) through an oil or gas fired furnace, with radiation and convection sections. Heat release in pipe stills varies from 2000 to 5000 B.t.u./ft^3. furnace volume/hr. The heat flow range is from 5000 to 15,000 B.t.u./ft^2 tube area/hr.

The heating capacity of pipe stills varies from 20×10^6 to 100×10^6 B.t.u /hr, of which 55 to 60% is supplied by radiation.

As the oil flows through the pipe, it receives heat progressively. Vapour and oil remain in contact with each other as a foam until this enters the fractionating column, where the vapour "flashes off" and separation occurs, as outlined above. The pipe still supplies most, or all, of the sensible and latent heat required for vaporization.

(ii) *Heat to fractionating column*

Any additional heat required is supplied by steam (q.v.), in external reboilers, or in a reboiler situated at the base of the fractionating column. This reboiler counts as an additional plate.

(iii) *Control of heat by reflux*

(a) *Cold reflux*

This is reflux liquid returned to the top plate at a temperature below the equilibrium B.P. of the top product. This is an effective method of cooling, since it removes its quota of sensible and latent heat from the distillate. The composition of the reflux liquid is the same as that of the distillate and is obtained from the storage tanks.

(b) *Hot reflux*

This is supplied to the top of the column at the boiling temperature and is variable in composition. This is not a satisfactory method, because hot reflux can only exchange latent heat with the rising vapour and ca. 5 volumes are required per volume of overhead product.

(c) *Circulating reflux*

This is liquid withdrawn from the column and cooled before

returning. The quantity of heat removed is sensible heat only, and is relatively small. However, it permits heat to be drawn from any point in the fractionating column.

2. Steam Distillation

(a) When distillation is carried out in the presence of a vapour of an immiscible substance, the vapour pressure of one is not influenced by the other, and the mixture distils at the temperature at which the sum of the partial pressures equals that of the atmosphere.

(b) Steam is used for this purpose because
  (i) It is cheap.
  (ii) It is readily available at refineries.
  (iii) It has a low molecular weight, therefore a small weight of water produces a large volume of steam.
  (iv) It has a high latent heat, therefore brings into the system enough heat to vaporize nearly twice its weight of oil.
  (v) Water and light spirits are not miscible, therefore separation of distillates from water is easy.

(c) If, for example, an oil has a vapour pressure of 76 mm (1/10 atm) at 250°F: by distilling with steam the mixed steam/oil vapour has the composition 9 parts by volume of steam: 1 part by volume of oil vapour.

(d) Assuming that the oil vapour has a mean molecular weight of 180, its vapour density will be $180/18 = 10$ times as high as that of steam therefore on condensation the weight of liquid products will be $180/18 \times 10/90 = 1\cdot1/1$ oil/water by weight.

(e) Since the density of the oil is less than that of water, e.g. 0·8, the volume of oil distilled $= 1\cdot1/0\cdot8 = 1\cdot4$ times the volume of the water condensed from the steam.

3. Vacuum Distillation

(a) Liquids boil when the sum of their vapour pressures equals that of the surrounding pressure.

(b) If the vapour pressure of an oil is 10 mm at 100°C then the liquid will boil, and distillation will proceed at 100°C, if the pressure is reduced to 10 mm by external means.

(c) Distillation will be continuous if heat is supplied equivalent to the latent heat of evaporation of the oil and if the vacuum is maintained at the vapour pressure of the oil at the temperature of distillation.

4. *Vacuum — Steam Distillation*

(a) This is a method for supplying heat and a carrier in the form of steam, at the same time using a vacuum pump to reduce the total pressure.

(b) It is not a very practical solution to the problem and in most modern distillation plants it is not used.

5. *Pressure Distillation*

(a) This is the opposite of vacuum distillation, and causes distillation to take place at a higher temperature than at atmospheric pressure.

(b) The higher temperature causes cracking of the oil and changes in the composition of the distillate.

6. *Modern Distillation Technique*

(a) This usually consists of 1 or 2 stages of distillation at atmospheric pressure, assisted by steam distillation.

(b) The atmospheric pressure stages are usually followed by 1 stage of vacuum distillation.

7. *Industrial Fractionating Columns*

Industrial fractionating columns vary considerably in height, diameter, and number of trays. Typical dimensions are:

	Height ft	Diameter ft	No. of trays
Primary crude column	85	14	35
Light fractions column	120	12	45
Vacuum column	135	18	50

8. Trays and Plates

The oldest and most commonly used tray in large scale fractionation columns is the bubble-cap tray. Its great advantage is flexibility and nearly constant efficiency under varying conditions of operation. Figure 53.3 shows the principle of operation of the bubble cap unit.

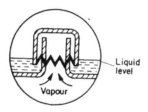

Fɪɢ. 53.3   Principle of Operation of Bubble Cap Unit.

Other trays commonly used are the "Shell" Turbogrid plate, consisting of parallel strips of metal on a circular frame, and the "Ripple" tray, made by corrugating a perforated plate into sinusoidal waves.

9. Superfractionation

See Data Sheet No. 55.

DISTILLATION IN PRACTICE

Modern distillation plants operate continuously, using pipe stills as heating units and with 2 atmospheric stages and 1 vacuum stage of distillation. Maximum temperature of operation is 400°C. A vacuum of 40 mm mercury is maintained in the columns of the vacuum distillation stage.

An atmospheric stage distillation unit is illustrated in Fig. 53.4.

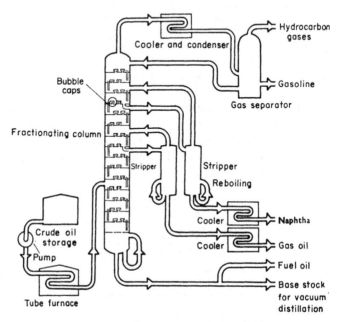

FIG. 53.4 Atmospheric Distillation Unit.

Fractions separated are:

        (1) Light gasoline
        (2) Heavy gasoline
        (3) White spirit
        (4) Kerosine
        (5) Light gas oil
        (6) Heavy gas oil
        (7) Lubricating oil distillates
        (8) Heavy fuel oils

Fractionation is obtained by multiple bubble-cap columns with "overhead" and "side-stream" products.

Side-stream products are sent through "strippers", which are also bubble-cap columns, where light ends are removed by steam.

The degree of fractionation is good, and some fractions are suitable for commercial outlets without further refining.

Heat exchangers are used wherever possible to economize on heat.

Complete instrumentation is generally practised to save labour. A plant distilling 5000 ton/day requires only 4 control men.

In the vacuum stage, the heavy oils from the atmospheric plant are fractionated into:

(1) Gas oil
(2) Lubricating oils (in 3 stages)
(3) Bitumen.

Yields of straight run distillation products from typical crudes have been given in Data Sheet No. 52.

REFERENCES

1. PACKIE, J. W. *Trans. Am. Inst. Chem. Eng.*, **37**, 51 (1941).
2. McCABE and THIELE E. W. *Ind. Eng. Chem.* **17**, 605 (1925).
Modern Petroleum Technology, 3rd Edition, Institute of Petroleum, London, 1962.
PERRY, J. H. *Chemical Engineers Handbook*, New York, 1953.

PETROLEUM OILS—CRACKING AND REFINING PROCESSES

THE NECESSITY FOR CRACKING

An average grade crude petroleum oil yields by distillation 20 to 30% gasoline, 30 to 45% intermediate oils and 25 to 50% residual fuel oil. Increasing demands for high quality gasolines (petrols) for high compression ratio spark ignition engines greatly exceed availability by distillation. Many processes have been developed for cracking the products obtained by distillation to obtain greater yields of improved gasolines at the expense of the gas and heavy fuel oil fractions. The heavy requirement for aviation gasoline during the 1939–1945 war was an additional incentive to develop highly refined products for aircraft. The basic technical requirement for spark ignition engines is a high anti-knock rating (see Data Sheet No. 56). The basic economic requirement is to produce the maximum yield of the most highly priced product.

Important cracking processes developed during the past three decades include the following:

1. Thermal cracking
2. Thermal reforming
3. Catalytic cracking.

1. *Thermal Cracking* (*Dubbs Process*)

When heavy petroleum oil is heated above the decomposition temperature, the molecules are broken down and rearranged. The result is an increase in the yield of gasoline and an increase in the proportion of ring compounds present. The gas formed contains high proportions of olefines and the residue obtained is petroleum coke. The principal and characteristic reaction taking place with paraffin type oils may be represented by the equation:

$$R.CH_2.CH_2.CH_2.R' \rightarrow R.CH : CH_2 + CH_3.R'$$

This process was used up to about 1939 on gas oil and fuel oil stocks in a plant similar to that illustrated in Fig. 54.1.

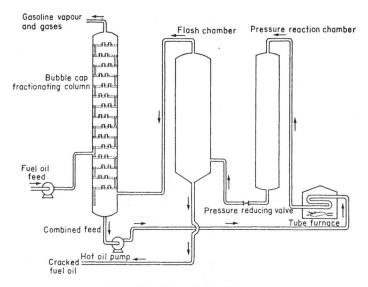

FIG. 54.1   Thermal Cracking.

Heavy oil was pumped into a bubble-cap fractionating column, where it was preheated and mixed with heavy cracked oil from the process. The mixed feed, at pressures up to 1000 lb/in², was passed through a tube furnace, where it was heated to a maximum temperature of 540°C (1004°F) before passing to the reaction chamber. This permitted a time dwell during which a controlled amount of cracking could take place. Pressure was reduced before passing into a flash chamber, where heavy cracked fuel oil separated, and then to the base of the bubble cap tower, from which the cracked gasoline and gas passed out at the top.

Yield of gasoline was from 50 to 70%, of octane number ca. 65 to 70 (cf. Data Sheet No. 56). This, after the addition of lead tetra-ethyl, was sufficient for most car engines at that time.

2. *Thermal Reforming*

This is essentially the same process as thermal cracking, except that the feed stock has roughly the same boiling range as the product and the temperatures and pressures used are generally higher. A reduced yield of product is obtained, with better anti-knock properties. The maximum unleaded octane number obtainable at a reforming temperature of 560°C (1040°F) is about 80. Yield at this temperature $\simeq 70\%$. The gas is rich in C_3 and C_4 olefines and forms a suitable charge for catalytic polymerization (q.v.).

3. *Catalytic Cracking*

By use of catalysts such as natural or artificial clays (e.g. bentonite and montmorillonite activated by sulphuric acid, or synthetic aluminium silicates) better yields of gasoline, of much higher anti-knock properties, could be obtained than by thermal cracking and reforming.

The main effect of the catalyst is to direct the cracking of paraffin towards the centre of the molecule and to convert olefines into the corresponding iso-paraffins. Naphthenes are cracked to olefines and paraffins. Aromatics are largely inert, but a small proportion forms coke on the catalyst. Three main types of catalytic cracking processes have been used, viz.:

(a) Fixed bed (Houdry—first used in 1936)
(b) Moving bed (Thermofor and Houdriflow)
(c) Fluidized bed.

(a) *Fixed Bed Catalyst*
Catalyst, in the form of compressed pellets, is contained in reactors which are normally arranged in groups of three. The reactors are,

in effect, tubular heat exchangers designed to supply the heat necessary to break down the heavier molecules and to remove the heat evolved when burning off the carbon on the catalyst during the regeneration cycle.

Operation of the process is cyclic, in four stages of total time ca. 30 min, e.g. (1) Reaction: 10 min at 30 lb/in^2 and 900°F (480°C); (2) Purge: 5 min; (3) Regeneration: 10 min, temperature 950°F (510°C); (4) Purge: 5 min. The temperature of the catalyst bed is controlled by circulating a molten mixture of alkali metal salts through vertical tubes within the reactor core. Overall catalyst life is about 18 months, but the yield of gasoline falls from about 52 to 40% during this period.

(b) *Thermofor Moving Bed Process* (*introduced in* 1942)

Beaded catalyst is used, of composition similar to that in the Houdry process. The beads flow downward by gravity through a tall reactor, at 950°F (510°C), with hot vapours of the oil to be cracked. Additional oil is obtained by steaming the catalyst at the base of the reactor. The hot, carbon-coated, catalyst falls into a kiln, where the carbon is burned off at a temperature of 1050°F (565°C). The regenerated catalyst is then transferred by elevator to the feed hopper of the reaction chamber. Catalyst consumption is about 0·2 lb/ barrel of oil processed (35 Imp. gallons).

Typical results:

Gasoline yield	43 to 56%
Light cycle stock	15 to 27%
Heavy cycle stock	17 to 19%
Coke ca.	5
Octane number (with 3 ml. lead tetra-ethyl/gal)	96 to 97

(c) *Fluidized Catalytic Cracking*

The most modern and most used process (80% of world catalytic cracking capacity).

The catalyst consists of closely graded powder, which is recirculated between two vertical vessels operating as reactor and regenerator. (The principle of operation is illustrated in Fig. 54.2.)

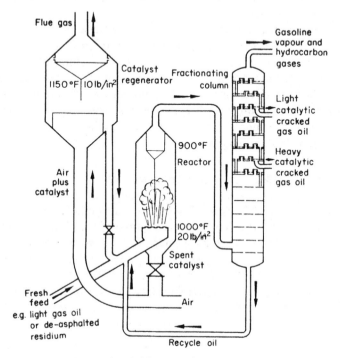

FIG. 54.2 Fluidized Catalytic Cracking.

Fluidized beds of powders are obtained by forcing gas through columns of powder until the "Minimum fluidized velocity" is reached. At this point the particles are arranged as a loose packing in the gas stream, so that they will flow as a fluid. A slight increase in gas velocity causes gas bubbles to flow through a zone of low solids concentration, in which high mass transfer rates between catalyst surface and gas enable high reaction rates and high heat transfer to be maintained.

A catalyst stand-pipe, with control valve, projects from the bottom of each vessel, the outlet of which is connected by pipe line to the base of the other vessel. The sequence of events is as follows:

(1) The feed (a fraction from vacuum distillation) is heated and vaporized by a stream of hot catalyst, passing into the reactor at about 1000°F (540°C). The catalyst separates from the vapour and sinks to the base of the reactor, from which it flows, with air, into the regenerator.

(2) In the regenerator the temperature rises to about 1150°F (620°C) due to the combustion of carbon on the catalyst. The regenerated catalyst flows down the stand-pipe into the fresh oil feed.

(3) The cracked vapours pass from the top of the reactor to the fractionating column, from which the heavier fractions are recycled through the reactor.

The catalyst to oil weight ratio varies from 5 to 15% and the reactor space velocity varies from 1 lb to 3 lb oil/hr/lb catalyst.

Large catalytic cracking plants will process up to 40,000 barrels per day of feed stock, with yields of 50 to 60% of gasoline of octane number ca. 90. A large C_4 fraction is obtained, in addition, which is a valuable feed stock for alkylation (q.v.).

Typical results:

Gasoline yield	53 to 59%
Light cycle gas oil	18 to 25%
Heavy cycle gas oil	2 to 3%
Coke	5 to 8 %
Octane number (unleaded)	92 to 94%

REFINING CRACKED GASOLINE

Straight run and cracked gasoline require to be refined chemically, before sale, to remove sulphur and gum-forming compounds (polyolefines). Refining processes include:

(a) Washing with a dilute solution of caustic soda, to remove hydrogen sulphide, carbon dioxide, carbonyl sulphide and lower mercaptans. The caustic soda is converted to NaHS and cannot easily be recovered. Where sulphide is high, the Girbotol process is preferred. With caustic soda, mercaptans form mercaptides, e.g.

$$RSH + NaOH \rightleftharpoons RSNa + H_2O$$

The process is only effective up to C_5.

The solution is regenerated by steam stripping, the distilled mercaptans being burned or recovered for sale.

Girbotol process. H_2S and CO_2 react with aliphatic amines in 15 to 30% aqueous solutions at ordinary temperatures and are removed from solution by heating to 100°C. Diethanolamine is the preferred amine used, e.g.

$$(CH_2OH.CH_2)_2NH + H_2S \rightleftharpoons [(CH_2OH.CH_2)_2NH_2]HS$$

(b) Washing with cold 80% sulphuric acid. This converts mercaptans and organic hydrosulphides to disulphides (soluble in gasoline and odourless). Olefines are converted into tar, which separates out. The gasoline is then washed with caustic soda solution and redistilled. Some sulphuric acid is produced during distillation by hydrolysis of esters. Therefore a further wash with dilute soda is necessary, followed by water.

(c) A sweetening process using copper chloride, or "Doctor" solution, for removal of mercaptans. Doctor solution (sodium plumbate) is made by dissolving litharge in caustic soda

$$PbO + 2NaOH = Na_2PbO_2 + H_2O$$

This solution, plus a little sulphur, reacts to form oil soluble mercaptides, e.g.

$$2RSH + Na_2PbO_2 \rightarrow (RS)_2Pb + 2NaOH$$

The free sulphur converts the lead mercaptides to disulphides, which are sweet smelling and oil soluble. The lead is precipitated as lead sulphide.

$$(RS)_2Pb + S = R_2S_2 + PbS$$

The spent solution is regenerated by blowing air through at 80 to 110°C.

(d) *Inhibitor sweetening.* Anti-oxidation inhibitors of the phenylene diamine type "sweeten" olefine gasolines containing small proportions of mercaptans in the presence of traces of caustic soda and oxygen. Traces of caustic soda and dissolved oxygen are present after caustic soda washing. The anti-oxidant may be added to storage tanks. The sweetening process takes some 24 hr to complete.

REFERENCE

Modern Petroleum Technology, 3rd Edition, Institute of Petroleum, London, 1962.

PETROLEUM OILS — REFORMING PROCESSES

THE NECESSITY FOR REFORMING

During the 1939–1945 war, new processes were developed for the production of high octane number gasoline for aircraft engines. With the advent of the jet engine, such fuels were no longer required, but the increase in compression ratio in motor car engines since the war maintained the trend. The processes, developed during the past two decades for these purposes, include:

1. Polymerization
2. Alkylation
3. Isomerization
4. Hydroforming
5. Platforming.

1. *Polymerization and Polyforming*

Polymerization

Catalytic polymerization is a method of converting the C_3 and C_4 olefines produced in thermal and catalytic cracking processes into high octane gasolines. The catalyst may be 60% sulphuric acid, or a solid made by impregnating Kieselguhr with phosphoric acid.

The gases are first water washed to remove hydrogen sulphide, and are then passed, whilst wet, over the solid catalyst at 420°F (220°C) and 900 lb/in^2. Propane and butane are removed in separating columns for sale as bottled gas. Unconverted olefines are recycled. Typical reaction is:

2 moles
isobutylene

$$CH_3{\diagdown}{\diagup}C{=}CH_2 \rightarrow CH_3{-}\underset{\underset{CH_3}{|}}{\overset{\overset{CH_3}{|}}{C}}{-}CH_2{-}\overset{\overset{CH_3}{|}}{C}{=}CH_2$$

1 mole di-isobutylene

The polymer may be used directly in high octane motor spirit, but for aviation spirit it must be hydrogenated to a saturated product.

2. Alkylation

This is a process for reacting an iso-paraffin with an olefine to produce a branched chain iso-paraffin, with molecular weight equal to the sum of the reactants. Catalysts are sulphuric acid (original) and hydrogen fluoride (recent). For example:

$$CH_3{-}\underset{\underset{CH_3}{|}}{\overset{\overset{CH_3}{|}}{CH}} + CH_2{=}CH{-}CH_2CH_3 \rightarrow CH_3{-}\underset{\underset{CH_3}{|}}{\overset{\overset{CH_3}{|}}{C}}{-}CH_2{-}\overset{\overset{CH_3}{|}}{CH}{-}CH_3$$

iso-butane   iso-octane

The process is continuous and feed rates are adjusted to give a reaction time of 10 to 20 min. The mixture of iso-paraffins and olefines is first dried over bauxite and then fed into the lower section of the reactor. Recycled hydrogen fluoride enters through the base and the products go first to a separating vessel, and then to fractionating columns to remove propane and butane from the alkylate product. Temperature 125°F (52°C) and optimum iso-butane–olefine ratio is 7:1.

3. Isomerization

Isomerization has been developed recently for two main purposes: (1) to convert n-butane into iso-butane for alkylation.

(2) to convert *n*-pentane and *n*-hexane into iso-paraffins to improve the knock rating of high volatile gasolines. A typical reaction is:

$$CH_3.CH_2.CH_2.CH_3 \rightarrow \begin{matrix} CH_3 \\ \diagdown \\ CH_3 \diagup \end{matrix} CH.CH_2$$

n-butane   iso-butane

The first development was the conversion of *n*-butane to *i*-butane, using aluminium chloride activated by anhydrous hydrogen chloride as catalyst. The aluminium chloride is supported on silica gel. Dry butane, containing a little HCl and hydrogen, is passed over at 230°F (110°C) and 300 lb/in². The products are fractionated, the iso-butane being removed for alkylation and the unconverted *n*-butane and hydrogen recycled. Conversion per passage is up to 60%. The isomerization of pentane and hexane proceeds on similar lines, but temperatures and pressures are higher, viz. 500°F (260°C) to 900°F (480°C) and 300 lb/in² to 1000 lb/in².

Octane ratings between 95 and 107 are obtained with 95% pure iso-paraffins.

4. *Hydroforming*

This is a process for reforming low octane gasoline or naphtha by reaction with hydrogen in the presence of a catalyst. As with catalytic cracking, fixed bed and fluidized bed hydroforming may be used.

(a) *Fixed Bed Cyclic Hydroforming*

The process uses a catalyst containing 8 to 10% of molybdena on an alumina support. Temperatures of 900 to 1000°F (480 to 540°C) and pressures from 200 to 300 lb/in² are used. The catalyst beds are regenerated after 4 to 8hr operation. Both upflow and downflow regeneration is practised so as to hold the temperature between 1050 and 1100°F. A high partial pressure of hydrogen is maintained during the hydroforming process by recycling the hydrogen produced by the dehydrogenation of naphthenes and the cyclization of paraffins, for example:

Dehydrogenation of naphthenes

$$
\begin{array}{ccc}
\text{CH}_2 & & \text{CH} \\
\text{CH}_2 \quad \text{CH}_2 & & \text{CH} \quad \text{CH} \\
\text{CH}_2 \quad \text{CH}_2 & \rightarrow & \text{CH} \quad \text{CH} \quad + 3\text{H}_2 \\
\text{CH}_2 & & \text{CH} \\
\text{cyclo-hexane} & & \text{benzene}
\end{array}
$$

Cyclization

$$
\begin{array}{ccc}
\text{CH}_2\text{—CH}_2 & & \text{CH} \\
\text{CH}_2 \qquad \text{CH}_2 & & \text{CH} \quad \text{CH} \\
\text{CH}_3\text{—CH}_2 . \text{CH}_3 & & \text{CH} \quad \text{C} . \text{CH}_3 \quad + 4\text{H}_2 \\
& & \text{CH} \\
n\text{-heptane} & & \text{toluene}
\end{array}
$$

Desulphurization also takes place, most of the sulphur present being removed as hydrogen sulphide, e.g.

$$\text{Amyl mercaptan} + \text{H}_2 \rightarrow \text{pentane} + \text{H}_2\text{S}$$
$$\text{Thiophene} \qquad + \text{H}_2 \rightarrow \text{butane} \ + \text{H}_2\text{S}$$

Unleaded octane numbers of 80 to 85 are obtained from low-octane gasolines in yields in excess of 75%. Hydroforming plants made much of the toluene produced in the U.S.A. for the manufacture of T.N.T. during the 1939–1945 war.

(b) *Fluidized Bed Hydroforming*

As in fluidized cracking, a powdered catalyst containing 10% of molybdena and 90% of alumina is circulated between a reactor and a regenerator by the fluidized technique. Temperatures and pressures are similar to those with the fixed bed, but fluidization enables temperature to be controlled in the reactor to $\pm 2 \cdot 5°$F, preventing the excessive reforming, with production of gases, that takes place in fixed bed plants. Similarly, regeneration temperature is more closely controlled by use of cooling coils in the regeneration unit.

The overall result is better yields and higher octane numbers, e.g. from a Louisiana naphtha, a yield of 80% gasoline was obtained of octane number (unleaded).

5. *Platforming and Catforming*

Platinum is used in many processes involving reforming with hydrogen, since this catalyst requires little or no regeneration with feeds that have been pretreated to remove sulphur.

Platforming is the most important of these processes and uses a catalyst of platinic chloride on alumina. The catalyst is not regenerated *in situ*, but is replaced when operating temperatures cannot be increased further to maintain the octane number of the gasoline produced. 1 lb of catalyst is used per 200 barrels of feed. Several reactors are used, in series, at operating temperatures varying from 850°F (455°C) initially to 980°F (527°C) finally. Pressures of 500 to 700 lb/in^2 are used.

Reactor space velocities vary from 1·5 to 3 vol. feed/hr/vol. catalyst. Molar ratios of hydrogen : hydrocarbon vary from 4 to 8.

The recycle gas may be dehydrated and freed from hydrogen sulphide by scrubbing with mono and diethanolamines (Girbotol).

The two most important reactions are aromatization (endothermic), which takes place mainly in the first reactor, and hydrocracking (exothermic), which takes place in the later reactors; e.g.

$$n\text{-decane} + H_2 \rightarrow 3 \text{ methylpentane} + \text{butane}$$

Results vary with reforming severity, for example, using Venezuela naphtha as feed:

Low severity: Yield gasoline: 91·5%   O.N. unleaded: 85
High   ,,   ,,   ,,   85·2%   O.N.   ,,   95

Catforming is a similar process that permits the occasional regeneration of catalyst *in situ*. Intervals between regeneration vary from several months to 1 year.

SUPERFRACTIONATION

Whilst not a reforming process, superfractionation is a method for the separation of branched chain iso-paraffins from their isomers, the normal paraffins, which are poor in anti-knock properties; for example, *n*-hexane, B.P. 68°C (155°F), O.N. 26: neo-hexane, B.P. 49°C (120°F), O.N. 49: iso-hexane, B.P. 63°C (145°F), O.N. 94.

Separation is effected by:

(1) Increasing the number of plates in the fractionating column (up to 110) and taking out no side-streams.
(2) Increasing the reflux ratio up to 10 : 1.
(3) Reducing the number of components in the feed by pre-distillation.
(4) Introducing more precise feed flow and heat input control.

The separated branched chain paraffins are used for blending to produce high octane number gasolines.

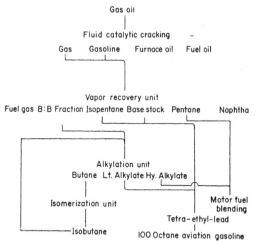

Fig. 55.1   Flow Sheet for Production of 100 Octane Aviation Gasoline.

REFERENCE

Modern Petroleum Technology, 3rd Edition, Institute of Petroleum, London, 1962.

ANTI-KNOCK RATING AND OCTANE NUMBERS

NATURE OF KNOCK IN SPARK IGNITION ENGINES

1. The efficiency of an engine operating on a constant volume cycle

   is given by $E = 1 - \left(\dfrac{1}{r}\right)^{\gamma - 1}$

   where r = the compression ratio and

   $$\gamma = \text{Ratio} \frac{\text{Sp. Ht. at constant } P.}{\text{Sp. Ht. at constant } V.} \simeq 1{\cdot}296$$

   for a weak petrol/air mixture.

   Consequently, the higher the compression ratio the greater the efficiency (see also Data Sheet No. 58).

2. With increase in pressure, the temperature developed before the spark rises, and, with high compression ratios, the temperature can reach the spontaneous ignition point of certain hydrocarbons.

3. Spontaneous ignition temperature is low with straight chain hydrocarbons and high with aromatics, e.g.

n-pentane, spontaneous ignition temp.		= 218°C
Diesel oil (paraffin type)	,, ,,	= 247°C
Toluene	,, ,,	= 550°C
Benzene	,, ,,	= 580°C

4. Spontaneous ignition before the spark passes causes sudden detonation, giving rise to knock. This is therefore more liable to occur with straight chain paraffins than with aromatics.

   Knock is the principal limiting factor to the development of power in a spark ignition engine. The phenomenon is apparent as a sharp metallic hammering from the engine cylinder. The effect is caused by detonation, producing a vibratory pressure wave that precedes the normal operating pressure development. The result is overheating and loss of power. The most important design factor is the compression ratio in the cylinder head. For any given fuel and engine there is an upper limit to the compression ratio that may be used without causing knock. Alternatively, the fuel that may be used in an engine with a given compression ratio is defined by its anti-knock rating.

5. *Ricardo*, in the early 20's, using a variable compression engine, found that toluene was a good fuel to use at high ratios and proposed a scale of knock ratings in which toluene was given a top rating of 100.

He also introduced the concept of "Highest useful compression ratio" (H.U.C.R.) for gasolines, to indicate the highest ratio that could safely be used, e.g.

Approx. Comp. of Gasoline			
Paraffins %	*Naphthenes* %	*Aromatics* %	*H.U.C.R.*
10	85	5	5·9
38	47	15	5·35
68	20	12	4·7

6. Edgar, in 1931, found that branched chain hydrocarbons, such as iso-octane, compare favourably with aromatics in anti-knock rating.

7. In 1931 a committee, called the "Co-operative Fuel Research Committee" was established to develop a suitable test engine for determining the knock rating of gasolines and a suitable scale of values. The result was a standard test engine—the C.F.R.—and an octane scale, in which iso-octane was taken as 100 and *n*-heptane as zero.

DEFINITION OF "OCTANE NUMBER"

1. The octane number of a fuel is the percentage by volume of iso-octane in an iso-octane/n-heptane mixture with the same knocking tendency as the fuel.

TEST METHODS

1. Four methods of test are available using the C.F.R. engine, called, repectively, the "Research", "Motor", "Aviation lean mixture" and "Aviation rich mixture" methods.

   The motor method is used for low octane number motor fuels, the research method is used for high octane number motor fuels, the aviation methods are used for high octane aviation fuels.

   Essential details of these methods are as follows:

Method	Research Method	Motor Method	Aviation Lean Mixture	Aviation Rich Mixture
C.R.C. number	F_1	F_2	F_3	F_4
Engine speed r.p.m.	600	900	1200	1800
Air intake temp. °C	Room	38	52	107
Mixture temp. °C	not controlled	149	104	—
Ignition advance	13°	variable	35°	45°
Coolant temp. °C	100	100	190	190
Indicator of detonation	Bouncing pin	Detonation meter	Thermal plug	Aural or Detonation meter

USE OF TETRA-ETHYL LEAD—"PERFORMANCE NUMBERS"

1. The addition of small quantities of T.E.L. to gasolines greatly increases their knock ratings, the maximum quantity used being about 6 cm^3 per gallon. Some gasolines respond better than others

and, with a properly prepared spirit, it is easily possible to increase the knock rating to a value in excess of iso-octane. Values above 100 O.N. are known as "Performance numbers" and the best aviation gasolines used today have P.N. of ca. 160. The standards used are mixtures of iso-octane and T.E.L., with the relationship between composition and performance number shown in Fig. 56.1. This method does not apply directly to motor engines, for

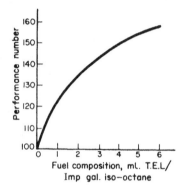

FIG. 56.1   Relationship between T.E.L. in Iso-octane and Performance Number.

which it is desirable that units above 100 O.N. should be approximately equal in value to those below 100 O.N. The A.S.T.M. and I.P. have agreed to the following relationship for octane numbers above 100:

$$O.N. = 100 + \frac{P.N. - 100}{3}$$

Fuels above 100 O.N. are tested in F_1 and F_2 engines, using iso-octane + T.E.L. as reference fuel.

T.E.L. is a solution of tetra-ethyl lead $(C_2H_5)_4Pb$, and ethylene dibromide in gasoline, plus an identifying dye.

2. *Lead Response*—Gasolines respond differently to the addition of T.E.L. The order of decreasing effect (called "Lead response") is paraffins → naphthenes → olefines → aromatics. Alcohols respond negatively, as do sulphur compounds and lubricating oils.

K

RELATIONSHIPS BETWEEN KNOCK RATING AND COMPOSITION

1. (a) Highest octane numbers are obtained with aromatics, e.g. benzene or toluene and iso-paraffins, highly branched, e.g. iso-octane.

   (b) With paraffins and olefines, octane numbers decrease with increasing chain length.

   (c) With isomeric olefines, O.N. increases as the double bond nears the centre of the molecule.

   (d) With aromatics, addition of side chains up to 3 carbon atoms length improves O.N. Afterwards, O.N. decreases in proportion to the length of the longest chain.

   (e) Naphthenes generally have lower O.N. than corresponding aromatics.

   (f) With naphthenes, the larger the size of the ring and the length of the side chains, the lower the O.N.

   (g) Olefines possess higher O.N. than corresponding N. paraffins.

BLENDING OCTANE NUMBERS

1. (a) Blends of two paraffins have O.N. directly proportional to the percentage of each.

   (b) With blends of aromatics and paraffins, O.N. of the blend is lower than expected from a linear relationship.

   (c) With blends of olefines and paraffins, O.N. of the blend is higher than expected.

REFERENCES

Modern Petroleum Technology, 3rd Edition, Institute of Petroleum, London, 1962.
SPIERS, H. M. *Technical Data on Fuels*, 5th Edition, London, 1952.

DIESEL FUELS—CETANE NUMBERS

COMPRESSION IGNITION (4-stroke cycle)

1. Air is compressed to between 440 and 670 lb/in^2: Temp. = 500 to 600°C.
2. For high speed diesels (2000 r.p.m.) fuel is injected near the top of the compression stroke, at 15° before top dead centre. The atomized fuel ignites spontaneously and pressure is increased by combustion to between 1000 and 1030 lb/in^2. Fuel injection ends at 5° after t.d.c. Combustion starts 8° before t.d.c.
3. Fuel used must be self igniting at least 30°C below the temperature of the compressed air.
4. Ignition takes place via droplets of oil in a high speed air stream. There is a delay period in which droplets are vaporized and heated to the spontaneous ignition temperature, this is followed by rapid combustion in the cylinder, with steady rise in pressure.
5. Most of the remaining injected oil burns steadily at the fuel jet.
6. Pressure begins to fall soon after the end of the injection period, e.g. at 10° after t.d.c.
7. After burning of oil (sprayed on to walls of cylinders and pistons) may then proceed.

CAUSE OF "DIESEL KNOCK"

1. In high speed diesels the period between start of ignition and first combustion (delay time) may be 0·6 msec and the injection period 1·7 msec.
2. With a good diesel fuel, the delay time is short.
3. With fuels of long delay times (high spontaneous ignition temperatures) much of the charge is injected into the cylinder before

ignition is initiated, causing violent combustion, sudden increase in pressure, and rough and bumpy running. This is called "Diesel knock".

SPONTANEOUS IGNITION TEMPERATURES OF OILS

	Typical Values
n-pentane (C_5H_{12})	218°C
Cetane ($C_{16}H_{34}$)	235°C
Toluene	550°C
Benzene	580°C

It is evident that straight paraffin hydrocarbons ignite more readily than aromatics and so are more suitable diesel fuels. In fact, all types of light fuel oils with low octane numbers are satisfactory high speed diesel fuels. High octane fuel oils are not satisfactory high speed diesel fuels. In other words, good spark ignition fuels make poor compression-ignition fuels, and vice versa.

CETANE NUMBERS

These are used to indicate the quality of a fuel oil for compression-ignition engines.

1. The straight chain hydrocarbon cetane $C_{16}H_{34}$ is perhaps the best high speed diesel fuel known, and is given a rating of 100.
2. Aromatic hydrocarbons are poor diesel fuels, and the aromatic hydrocarbon α-methyl-naphthalene is given a rating of O.
3. The *cetane number* of a diesel oil is the percentage by volume of cetane in a cetane/α-methyl naphthalene mixture that has the same performance in a standard compression ignition engine as that of the fuel.

Method of Determining the "Cetane Number" in Test Engine

1. Because of the high cost of pure cetane and α-methyl-naphthalene,

a number of standard reference fuel oils are available with a range of cetane numbers.
2. Two methods of test are specified, both of which may be carried out on any compression-ignition engine:

A. *Ignition Delay Test* (I.P. 41A)
The test is carried out at constant speed and load. The delay time is measured for the oil under test with an electronic delay meter and compared with standard reference fuels having delay periods shorter and longer than that of the sample fuel. The cetane number is obtained by interpolation.

B. *Throttling Test* (I.P. 41B)
The engine is run at the lowest load which gives steady conditions. A surge chamber and throttle device is attached to the engine intake port. This device reduces the surge chamber pressure and increases the delay period until a misfire occurs, which is indicated by a puff of white smoke. The air pressure at this point is related to the delay period and is a function of the cetane number. By bracketing the pressure for misfire on the sample fuel with reference fuels of higher and lower quality, the cetane value can be calculated.

Cetane Numbers of Suitable Diesel Fuels

High speed diesels not < 50
Medium ,, ,, ,, < 35
Slow speed diesels—not important but preferably > 15

DIESEL INDEX

An alternative method of expressing the quality of diesel oils is by use of the "Diesel Index", which does not necessitate the use of a test engine.

$$\text{Diesel Index} = \text{Aniline point in } °F \times \frac{\text{A.P.I. Gravity}}{100}.$$

This can only be used as a rough guide to cetane numbers and is not applicable to fuels containing additions for ignition quality improvement.

Aniline Point

This is the lowest temperature at which the oil is completely miscible with an equal volume of aniline. For a good quality diesel oil the aniline point is $> 70°F$.

$$A.P.I.\ Gravity = \frac{141 \cdot 5}{\text{sp. gr. at } 60°F} - 131 \cdot 5$$

This gives a higher result for paraffin oils than for aromatics, hence its use in the Diesel index formula.

REFERENCES

Modern Petroleum Technology, 3rd Edition, Institute of Petroleum, London, 1962.
SPIERS, H. M. *Technical Data on Fuels*, 5th Edition, London, 1952.

GASOLINES — PROPERTIES AND SPECIFICATIONS

A. AVIATION GASOLINES (Spark-Ignition Engines)

1. *Properties*

(a) *Maximum Power*

(i) This is achieved by increasing the compression ratio and the air/fuel flow through the engine by supercharging. The limiting permissible increase in the compression ratio is determined by the octane number of the fuel, with or without the addition of T.E.L.

Permissible increase in supercharge is determined by the air/fuel ratio.

The extra fuel in a rich mixture acts as an internal coolant, suppressing knock and enabling higher engine ratings to be obtained. Hence aviation gasoline specifications call for two knock ratings, known as the aviation lean mixture method (F_3) and the aviation rich mixture method (F_4) (cf. Data Sheet No. 56).

(ii) Mixture response. If air/fuel ratios are plotted against power output for a series of increments in supercharge, a position of incipient knock can be established on each curve. If such positions are connected by a further curve, known as the "Mixture response curve", the boundary between knock-free and knock conditions is established. Such a curve shows that much greater power can be obtained by boost (e.g. at take-off) with rich mixtures (air/fuel ratio ca. 11/1) than with lean mixtures (ca. 14/1 to 16/1).

(b) *Volatility and Boiling Range*

Volatility must be closely controlled since:

(i) The fuel must be burned in the engine in the vapour phase, but is supplied as liquid.

(ii) If the volatility is too low, difficulties are encountered in starting and in lubricating oil dilution.

(iii) Difficulties due to low volatility are accentuated by the use of ethylene dibromide in T.E.L.

(iv) If the volatility is too high, vapour occurs in tanks and pipe lines, causing pumping and metering difficulties and danger of explosion. A boiling range of 30°C to 150°C is satisfactory. Some gasolines require special starting fuels of high volatility, e.g. of boiling range 30°C to 75°C.

(c) *Vapour Pressure*

This is not measured accurately by the distillation range, particularly in relation to extremely volatile components, or to gaseous hydrocarbons and air dissolved in the fuel. With decreased atmospheric pressure at high altitudes, these gases or vapours come out of solution, causing vapour locks and faulty operation.

Boost pumps, fitted with deaerator cones, return vapour back to the tanks. The quantity of highly volatile constituents present is measured by the "Reid vapour pressure test" (cf. Data Sheet No. 62). Rvp specification limits are usually between 5·5 and 7·0 lb/in^2 at 100°F.

(d) *Calorific Value and Specific Gravity*

These items must be considered together to determine:

(i) Maximum power per unit of weight

(ii) Maximum power per unit of volume.

Hydrocarbons of low specific gravity (paraffins) possess the maximum thermal energy (calorific value) per gallon. Hydrocarbons of high specific gravity (aromatics) possess the maximum thermal energy per pound. However, the high calorific value of normal paraffins cannot be fully utilized because of their low anti-knock ratings. Aromatics produce more carbon deposits than paraffins. These considerations together favour the use of iso-paraffins for aviation gasolines.

The calorific value of gasolines is determined in the bomb calorimeter (Data Sheet No. 29). The "Aniline–gravity" product is sometimes specified as an alternative to calorific value. This is the product of the aniline-point, in °F, and specific gravity, in degrees API at 60°F. The product can be converted into net B.t.u./lb by the use of standard tables.

(e) *Freezing Point*

This should not exceed −60°C to avoid trouble due to crystal formation in feed lines and filters. Benzene is excluded on these grounds, but most other possible aviation gasoline components have freezing points below −60°C.

(f) *Flash Point and Inflammability Limits*

Flash point is not included in specifications for aviation gasolines, because the volatile components always provide sufficient vapour to form an inflammable mixture at ambient temperatures. Danger due to explosions of hydrocarbon vapours in air is determined by their inflammability limits (cf. Data Sheet No. 116). There is a close relationship between vapour pressure, atmospheric pressure, and concentration of vapour in air for any gasoline. These factors are expressed as "Explosivity bands", which define the altitude–temperature–inflammability limits for aviation fuels.

(g) *Water Solubility*

Aviation gasolines are substantially insoluble in water, but most specifications include a limit of 2 ml per 80 ml (determined by shaking with 20 ml of water and allowing to settle for 5 min). A more important requirement in this test is a clean interface between water and spirit. (Scum causes filter trouble.)

(h) *Storage Stability*

Storage stability for long periods is essential. Two effects of unstable fuels are unacceptable:

(i) Gum formation.
(ii) Loss of anti-knock properties due to precipitation of lead from T.E.L.

Gum may be "Existent" or "Potential". The latter is determined by an accelerated oxidation test.

Reformed gasolines containing T.E.L., necessitate the use of oxidation inhibitors to achieve given specification figures and to improve T.E.L. stability. These are usually complex phenols or amines, e.g. phenyl α or β-naphthylamine.

Zinc catalyses T.E.L. deterioration, so that galvanized drums may not be used for storage.

2. *Typical Specifications* (*abridged*)

	Grades	
	91/96	115/45
Application	For medium powered aircraft	For long range transports and high powered military aircraft
Colour	Blue	Purple
T.E.L. content ml/Imp. gal. max.	5·5	5·5
Knock rating, lean mixture min.		
by Motor method F_2	90 O.N.	—
by Aviation method F_3	91 O.N.	115 P.N.
by Aviation rich mixture F_4	96 O.N.	145 P.N.
Calorific value (net) B.t.u./lb min.	18,700	18,900
or Aniline gravity product min.	7500	9000
Distillation, fuel evaporated %		
at 75°C (167°F)	10 min. 40 max.	
,, 105°C (221°F)	50 min.	
,, 135°C (275°F)	90 min.	
Final boiling point	170°C (338°F) max.	
Sum of temps. of the 10 and 50% evaporated points	135°C (307°F) min.	
Freezing point	−60°C (−76°F) max.	
Gum: Existent mg/100 ml	3 max.	
Potential, 16 hr Residue mg/100 ml	6 max.	
Precipitate mg/100 ml	2 max.	

	Grades	
	91/96	115/45
*Sulphur, Total, % wt.	0·05	
*Corrosion, Copper Strip	Slight tarnish only	
Vapour Pressure (Rvp) lb/in² at 100°F	5·5 min. 7.0 max.	
Water reaction, vol. change ml	2 max.	

* See Data Sheet No. 62.

3. *Boost Fluids*

These are used to increase engine power at take-off. A 50/50 or 60/40 methanol (methyl alcohol)–water blend is found to be the most effective combined coolant and producer of knock-free power.

B. MOTOR GASOLINES

Properties

These compare with those required for aviation use as follows:

(a) *Maximum Power*

Considerations of performance and economy are more important in motors than the necessity for maximum power at take-off in aircraft.

(i) The Tizard and Pye formula for the efficiency of an ideal four-stroke Otto cycle engine, viz.

$$E = 1 - \left(\frac{1}{r}\right)^{\gamma - 1}$$

shows that efficiency increases with compression ratio. γ is 1·296 for weaker than theoretical air/fuel mixtures, and 1·2586 for theoretically correct mixtures. Values for indicated horsepower are lower than the values obtained by this formula.

Indicator tests on modern engines show efficiencies increasing from

35 to 45% by increasing the compression ratios from 7:1 to 11:1. Brake thermal efficiencies are usually 80% or less of indicated thermal efficiencies.

Recent tests by Cavis and Nelson[1] show that thermal efficiency and brake horsepower reach a maximum at 17:1 compression ratio.

(ii) *Air/Fuel ratios.* The theoretical air required for the combustion of a fuel may be calculated when the chemical composition or analysis is known.

1 lb of heptane, which may be taken as a typical hydrocarbon in motor gasoline, requires 15 lb of air for complete combustion.

The inflammability limits, on a weight basis, are 7 lb air (richest mixture) to 20 lb air (weakest mixture) per lb heptane.

Maximum power is obtained at an air/fuel ratio of 12·5:1.

Most economical mixture for normal cruising range is 17:1.

To obtain economical running with high performance at speed, main and compensating carburettor jets are used.

(iii) *Ignition timing.* Maximum power development depends upon compression ratio and ignition timing. This can only be developed, under non-knocking conditions, by firing before top dead centre, so that about half the pressure rise occurs before t.d.c.

(iv) *Octane number and compression ratio.* Octane number must be increased for increase in compression ratio to prevent knock. Design of engine affects this relationship. For the same engine, the octane number must be increased from ca. 80 to ca. 105 for an increase in compression ratio from 7:1 to 11:1.

(b) *Volatility and Boiling Range*

Volatility is determined by distillation range and by the Reid vapour pressure test. These affect the behaviour of the motor engine in much the same manner as the aircraft engine, except that such high altitudes are not encountered by motor engines. The temperature at which the first 10% distils is a measure of the ease of starting. The boiling range is from ca. 30°C to ca. 200°C.

(c) *Vapour Pressure*

The Reid vapour pressure of the components of motor gasoline varies from ca. 0.6 lb/in^2 at 100°F for octane to over 14.5 lb/in^2 for the more volatile components. The vapour pressure requirements should be adjusted to suit temperature and altitude to avoid vapour lock.

(d) *Calorific Value and Specific Gravity*

These affect the carburettor design and are not often specified. Benzole mixtures possess higher specific gravities than petroleum spirits, so are cheaper on a volume basis.

(e) *Freezing Point*

Benzene is a common component of motor gasolines particularly of "benzole mixtures" and alcohol–benzole–petrol blends. Benzene freezes at 5.5°C and *m*-xylene at -25°C. The remaining components of motor gasoline or benzole mixtures all freeze at temperatures below -50°C. The freezing point of motor gasoline is usually not specified, except, possibly, for use in arctic conditions.

(f) *Water Solubility*

Not specified.

(g) *Storage Stability*

Cracked gasolines containing olefines are liable to oxidation–peroxide–polymerization reactions, and require the addition of an oxidation inhibitor to prevent gum formation during storage.

Such inhibitors are complex amines or phenols and are used in amounts from 0.001% to 0.02% by weight (e.g. 2,4-dimethyl-6-tertiary-butyl phenol).

Metals, such as copper, accelerate gum formation.

Additives, called "Metal deactivators" are used to passify metals in contact with motor gasolines.

These also contain amino groups (e.g. *N,N*-disalicylidine-ethyl-ene-diamine).

Gum forming tests are usually included in motor gasoline specifications, as are the amount and nature of the additives.

Typical Motor Gasoline Specification

Octane number
  Motor (F_1) or
  Research (F_2)$_{min}$ 80   95

Distillation				
10% evaporation	min.	60°C (140°F)	max.	70°C (158°F)
50% ,,	,,	88°C (190°F)	,,	115°C (239°F)
90% ,,	,,	132°C (270°F)	,,	180°C (356°F)
Final boiling point			,,	205°C (401°F)

Reid vapour pressure lb/in^2
  at 100°F   12
Gum mg/100 ml   max.   6
Sulphur % by wt.   ,,   0·25
T.E.L. ml/100 Imp. gal   ,,   3·6   max.   5·5

Additives—Use of Phosphates

Sparking plugs deteriorate by the deposition of lead compounds from T.E.L. on the ceramic insulation. Tri-cresyl-phosphate and other phosphate additives to gasoline greatly reduce troubles of this character through the formation of lead phosphates, which are non-conducting at temperatures up to ca. 800°C. In addition, phosphates increase the "glow-point" of plug deposits and so reduce pre-ignition from this cause.

REFERENCES

1. CAVIS, D. F. and NELSON, E. E. *Trans. Auto Eng.* **67**, 112 (1959).
Modern Petroleum Technology, 3rd Edition, Institute of Petroleum, London, 1962.

KEROSINES — PROPERTIES AND SPECIFICATIONS

KEROSINES are distillation products of petroleum of boiling range 150 to 300°C (302 to 372°F). They fall between the gasoline and gas oil fractions. Fuel uses for kerosines fall into the four main groups:

1. Burning oils, for lighting and heating.
2. Power kerosines—tractor vaporizing oils.
3. Gas turbine fuels—aviation turbine kerosine (Jet engines).
4. Ram jet fuels.

1. BURNING OILS

The kerosine for this purpose is composed mainly of paraffin type hydrocarbons and should burn with a clear, white flame. It may be obtained by straight distillation of paraffin type crudes or by solvent extraction of distillates from mixed base crudes. Liquid SO_2 is the solvent most used for this purpose.

The Edeleanu Process

Using liquid SO_2, this process was developed to remove aromatics from Roumanian kerosines.

The oil is first carefully dried and then extracted by counter flow washing with liquid SO_2 in a packed tower. The extractor operates at 170 lb/in^2 at a temperature of $-30°C$. The liquid from the tower separates into an upper refined layer (the raffinate) and a lower layer of aromatics and SO_2, from which the SO_2 is recovered by evaporation. A final treatment with sulphuric acid and/or Fuller's earth is sometimes applied to the kerosine fraction.

The aromatics are blended with gasoline or power kerosine. To qualify as "heavy oils" for duty purposes in the U.K., the flash point (Abel) must not be less than 73°F; less than 50% must distil at 366°F (185°C) and less than 95% at 464°F (240°C).

Other important properties are volatility, freezing and pour points, viscosity, smoke point, char value and sulphur content.

Volatility

This affects ease of ignition and "smooth" vaporization during combustion.

Freezing and Pour Points

These indicate the temperatures at which handling difficulties can be expected in cold weather or in cold climates.

Since paraffins possess higher freezing points than naphthenes and aromatics, but are better lamp oils, careful blending is necessary with kerosines for use in arctic conditions.

Viscosity

Viscosity affects the amount of fuel that can be drawn through a wick to a flame by capillary attraction. The viscosity of kerosines for wick type burners should be < 2·5 centi-Stokes at the operating temperature.

Smoke Point

This is the height to which the flame may be turned before smoking commences, when the kerosine is burned in a standard lamp under closely controlled conditions.

Char Value

This is the amount of charred oil obtained from kerosine after burning in a standard wick and lamp at a standard rate for 24 hr. The weight of char is estimated from that present in the upper portion of the wick after washing with light petroleum spirit and drying at 100 to 110°C. Char value should be less than 30 mg per kg of kerosine.

Flash Point

This is the temperature to which an oil must be heated in a specified instrument for sufficient vapour to be given off to form an inflammable mixture with air under the prescribed conditions. Further details of these tests are given, with other standard tests for oils, in Data Sheet No. 62.

Typical Specification for Burning Kerosines

Specific Gravity at 60°F	0·778 to 0·790
Distillation:	
I.B.P.	150°C (302°F) to 175°C (347°F)
% at 170°C (338°F)	1 to 10
% at 200°C (392°F)	30 to 55
% at 240°C (464°F)	80 to 95
F.B.P.	250°C (482°F) to 280°C (536°F)
Flash point °F	110 to 120
Freezing point °C	−42 to −47
Pour point °F	−55 to −60
Kinematic viscosity at 70°F c.S.	1·85 to 1·87
Gross C.V. B.t.u./lb	19,950 to 20,000
Net C.V. B.t.u./lb	18,750 to 19,000
Sulphur % by wt.	0·02 to 0·06
Smoke point, min.	40 to 33
Char value, mg/kg	2 to 10
Residue on evaporation mg/100 ml	1
Hydrocarbon analysis:	
Paraffins % vol.	60 to 58
Naphthenes % vol.	36 to 33
Aromatics % vol.	4 to 9

2. POWER KEROSINES—TRACTOR VAPORIZING OILS (T.V.O.)

These are low volatility oils, of high flash point (ca. 90°F) with a minimum distillate of 40% at 200°C (392°F) and designed as nondutiable fuels for tractors. Final boiling point is ca. 275°C (527°F). Knock rating is poor, usually 50 to 60 octane number by the F_2 test. Naphthenic stocks are preferred to improve O.N., or blends with aromatics from the SO_2 treatment of burning oils.

T.V.O. should be free from gum and gum-forming components. Otherwise little refining is practised. The engine cycle is similar to that of the 4-stroke motor engine. A cold start on gasoline is necessary because of the low volatility of the fuel. A heat exchanger (vaporizer) is also fitted between carburettor and inlet manifold to vaporize the fuel when hot. The engine efficiency is low, so that the modern trend is to replace T.V.O. tractor engines by Diesels.

3. GAS TURBINE FUELS—AVIATION TURBINE KEROSINE

The open cycle gas turbine consists of an air compressor and a turbine wheel mounted on a common shaft. Air is the working fluid. Its temperature and pressure are increased in the compressor and fuel is injected, ignited, and burned in the hot compressed air.

The air/fuel ratio is limited, and sufficient cold, secondary, air is admitted to ensure that the temperature of the products of combustion will not harm the turbine blading, i.e. ca. $< 1670°F$ (910°C).

The gas turbine can burn a range of fuels, from gasoline to heavy residual fuel oils, but the design of the combustion unit must be modified to suit various grades of fuel. For aviation use other factors, such as altitude, volatility of fuel and safety, must be considered.

On these counts, kerosines, or near related oils, are most suitable for aviation turbines and only these will be considered here.

Prime requirements of aviation turbine kerosines are:

(a) Good atomization over a wide range of fuel flow—mainly dependent upon volatility and composition. Paraffins and iso-paraffins are most suitable. They are stable and clean burning; of high calorific value per unit of weight and are relatively inert to aircraft and engine constructional materials.

Aromatics are good solvents for plastics and cause smoke and carbon deposits. They are usually restricted to a maximum of 25%.

Olefines are unsuitable because of high chemical activity and gum forming tendencies.

Sulphur content is restricted to a maximum of 0·4% because of corrosion possibilities. Mercaptans are specifically restricted because of odour and solvent activity.

Good atomization is obtained in some cases by preheating the fuel before passing into the primary combustion zone.

(b) Only fuels of low freezing point may be used, e.g. kerosines of F.P. < 40°F (− 40°C) or related fuels with improved volatility (Reid vapour pressure ca. 2 to 3 lb).

(c) Distilled fuels only are permissible to prevent the formation of ash deposits.

(d) Variations in specific gravity are restricted to permit satisfactory metering and fuel supply control.

(e) Viscosity is restricted to reduce feed line pressure losses and to ensure that injection nozzles operate at design levels. Viscosity also affects pump life, and kerosines are the most satisfactory fuels to use on this account.

(f) Volatility — Kerosines have low volatility and boiling range (150 to 250°C). These are controlled in specifications by flash point and distillation values.

Wide cut fuels have high volatility and wide boiling range (50 to 250°C), which are specified by distillation values and Reid vapour pressure.

High initial volatility (high Rvp) is helpful for starting but increases vapour loss from tank vents and may cause vapour locks in pipe lines.

Danger of explosion is related to inflammability limits. Though kerosines can form explosive mixtures on the ground at tropical temperatures, wide cut fuels are much more dangerous in temperate and cold climates.

(g) Heat content—weight and volume basis. Operators prefer a fuel with high calorific value on a volume basis, to fuel with high

C.V. on a weight basis. This means a kerosine of high specific gravity, preferably based on Venezuelan crude (156,000 B.t.u./gal: cf. 148,900 B.t.u./gal for Middle East product).

Typical (Abridged) Specification for Aviation Kerosine

Specific gravity at 60°F	0·775 to 0·845
Calorific value, B.t.u./lb	18,300 to 18,400, min.
Aromatics, vol. %	20 to 25, max.
Olefines, vol. %	5 max.
Smoke point, min.	18 to 20
Existent gum, mg/100 ml	7 max.
Potential gum, mg/100 ml	14 max.
Sulphur, total % wt.	0·4 max.
Mercaptan sulphur, % wt.	0·003 max.
Freezing point °C, °F	−40 max.
Viscosity c.S.	16·5 at −30°F max.
*Corrosion, copper strip	1, 2 hr. at 212°F max.
Flash point °F	110 to 150 min.
Distillation:	
10% min. evap. at	400°F (205°C)
Final B.P.	550°F (288°C)

* cf. Data Sheet No. 62.

4. RAM JET FUELS

In ram jet units, compression of air for combustion is effected by ram pressure caused by forward motion at high speeds.

Kerosines are suitable fuels because of low vapour pressure at high altitudes and high thermal capacity per unit volume.

Ram jet fuel requirements are:

(1) Thermal stability—better than that of any existing turbo-jet fuel.
(2) Low vapour pressure.
(3) High thermal capacity on a volume basis.
(4) Excellent combustion quality at low air pressures and high air velocities—this requires a fuel of high hydrogen content.

(5) High specific heat. This is required to improve fuel cooling capacity and to reduce heat exchange areas. The range now varies from 0·47 to 0·50 B.t.u./lb°F at 60°F.

(6) Handling—must be capable of pumping under all flight conditions and stable during storage.

Typical (Abridged) Specification

Gravity, °A.P.I.	32·5 to 45
Specific gravity at 60°F	0·788 to 0·863
Aromatics, vol. %	5 max.
Olefines, vol. %	1 max.
Smoke point	20 to 35 max.
Existing gum, mg/100 ml	3 to 7 max.
Potential gum, mg/100 ml	6 to 14 max.
Sulphur, total % wt.	0·007 max.
Mercaptan sulphur, % wt.	0·005 max.
Freezing point	−40°F max.
Viscosity, c.S.	60 at −30°F max.
Flash point	110°F min.
Distillation:	
10% evap. at	338 to 480°F
Final B.P.	518 to 600°F max.

REFERENCE

Modern Petroleum Technology, 3rd Edition, Institute of Petroleum, London, 1962.

DIESEL FUELS—GAS OILS—
SPECIFICATIONS

GAS oils are petroleum distillates boiling within the range 400 to 700°F (204 to 370°C). They may be divided into the following classes, based upon their applications:

1. Diesel oils.
2. Gas oils, proper, for use,
    (a) in carburetted water gas and oil-gas plants (cf. Data Sheet Nos. 108 and 110),
    (b) in small furnaces, including domestic and office heating,
    (c) as a solvent in stripping benzole and other vapours from permanent gases.

DIESEL OILS

The characteristics of compression-ignition engines and the relationships between chemical type and engine performance have been discussed in Data Sheet No. 57. The remaining physical and chemical characteristics of diesel fuels are discussed here:

(a) *Boiling Range*

This exceeds that of the gas oils proper. High speed diesels may use oils with initial boiling point as low as 140°C (284°F), which may be properly termed heavy kerosines, while modern slow speed marine diesels operate on heavy residual fuel oils. The latter require preheating before use to reduce viscosity to an acceptable level. For high speed diesels, the 50% distillation point should not exceed 300°C (570°F).

(b) *Specific Gravity*

Since automotive fuels are sold on a volume basis, an increase in specific gravity increases the amount of heat purchased per gallon. The extent to which this increase in specific gravity is permissible depends upon the cetane number of the fuel, since an increase in specific gravity also means a decrease in paraffin content.

(c) *Viscosity*

This determines the flow of fluid through the fuel injector mechanism. An increase in viscosity reduces the leakage past the fuel pump plunger, increasing the maximum power obtainable from a given engine. In one example, a change of oil from a specific gravity of 0·812 to a specific gravity of 0·851 resulted in an increased calorific value of 3·75%. The corresponding increase in viscosity was from 1·8 to 4·96 at 100°F. The measured increase in maximum power from the engine was 9·8%.

(d) *Carbon Residue Values, Sulphur, and Ash*

(Cf. Data Sheet No. 62.) Carbon residues may be considered in conjunction with sulphur content and, in the case of marine engines using residual fuel oils, ash content.

High carbon residues, sulphur, and ash, are together responsible for fouling engine parts and excessive wear, particularly in the case of slow speed diesels.

High speed diesel oils contain lower proportions of sulphur and (virtually) no ash.

Adverse effects due to sulphur can be reduced by the use of heavy duty lubricating oils.

In all cases, if the cetane number of the fuel is too low to give smooth running, engine fouling increases.

GAS OILS

Direct fuel applications include domestic, office, and small industrial furnaces. Indirect applications include the manufacture of carburetted water gas, and other gases made from oil by reaction with steam in the presence of catalysts or refractories.

The specification requirements for these applications are less exacting as regards chemical type than is the case with diesel oils.

For domestic and small scale industrial heating the main requirements are:

1. Viscosity at 60°F < 100 Redwood seconds, to enable the oil to be atomized without preheat.
2. Low sulphur, preferably < 0·5%, to reduce corrosion and atmospheric pollution from acid gases.

For use in gas manufacture, the principal requirement is low sulphur and low specific gravity, indicating a paraffinic type oil. The lighter grades of gas oil produce higher yields of gas and lower yields of tar and carbon than the heavier grades.

Specification for all these oils are generally similar, but those for domestic, industrial and marine fuels do not normally include cetane numbers or diesel indices.

1. *High Speed Diesel Fuels and Domestic Oils*
(based on B.S. 2869: 1957).

	Diesel	*Domestic*
Viscosity at 100°F, c.S.	1·6 to 7·5	7·5 max.
Cetane number, min.	45	—
Carbon residue, Conradson, % wt	0·1 max.	0·2 max.
Distillation, recovery at 357°C %	90 min.	—
Flash point, closed, °F	130 min.	130 min.
Water, % vol.	0·1 max.	0·25 max.
Sediment, % wt.	0·01 max.	0·25 max.
Ash, % wt.	0·01 max.	0·01 max.
Sulphur, % wt.	1·3 max.	2·0 max.

2. *Industrial and Gas Making*

Specific gravity at 60°F	0·835 to 0·935
Viscosity, at 122°F, c.S.	36 max.
at 100°F, R. sec	32 to 220

Flash point, closed, °F	150 min.
Carbon residue, Conradson, % wt.	0·2 to 1·5 max.
Pour test, °F	20 to 35 max.
Water, % vol.	0·05 to 0·5 max.
Sediment, % wt.	0·01 to 0·1 max.
Ash, % wt.	0·01 max.
Atomizing temperature	ambient to 160°F
Calorific value, gross, B.t.u./lb	18,000 to 19,600

3. *Marine Engine Fuels*

	Range
Specific gravity at 60°F	0·935 to 0·950
Viscosity, at 122°F, c.S.	36 to 690 max.
at 100°F, R. sec	250 to 3500 max.
Flash point, closed, °F	150 min.
Pour test, °F	35 to 70 max.
Water, % vol.	0·5 to 1·5 max.
Sediment, % wt.	0·15 to 0·25 max.
Calorific value, gross, B.t.u./lb	18,800 to 19,300

REFERENCES

Modern Petroleum Technology, 3rd Edition, Institute of Petroleum, London, 1962.
British Standard Specification No. 2869, 1957, *Oil Fuels*.

FUEL OILS—PROPERTIES AND SPECIFICATIONS

A. SOURCES

Fuel oils based on petroleum comprise a number of products obtained by the processes of distillation and reforming described in previous data sheets. They may be straight-run products obtained by atmospheric and vacuum distillation, or blends of these with residual oil fractions obtained by reforming processes.

Viscosity is the main factor determining the atomization equipment used for the combustion of these oils. Low viscosity is an inherent property of light weight fractions, e.g. kerosines and gas oils. The high viscosity of residual oils may be reduced by blending with less viscous products, or by the process of "Visbreaking".

Visbreaking is a mild thermal cracking process designed for the purpose of reducing the viscosity of heavy residual oils. This data sheet will be confined to a discussion of the heavier, more viscous, fuel oils.

B. PROPERTIES IN RELATION TO USE

Important physical and chemical properties of fuel oils are:

1. Viscosity and viscosity-temperature relationships. These determine the flow of the oil to the burner and the type of atomizer (cf. Fig. 61.1).
2. Pour point. This determines the temperature at which the oil storage tanks are maintained to ensure flow into the feed lines.
3. Sludge and sediment formation. These determine the possible life of the oil during storage. Unsatisfactory blending, or the presence

of unstable, oxidizable, components of an oil cause the separation in time of sludge, emulsions, and sediments, that cause clogging of filters or nozzles and corrode storage tanks and pipe lines. Cracked oils are particularly bad in this respect. Oxidation and corrosion inhibitors are sometimes added to reduce these troubles, but improved catalytic refining processes are more effective.

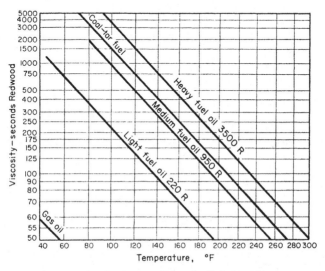

FIG. 61.1   Temperature/Viscosity Relationships.

4. Carbon–hydrogen ratio of oil. High carbon, low hydrogen, oils burn with a more luminous flame than low carbon, high hydrogen oils. The result is to increase the transfer of heat by radiation, because of the high emissivity factor of such flames (cf. Data Sheets Nos. 64 and 116).

The calorific value decreases and the specific gravity increases with increasing carbon: hydrogen ratio. The calorific values of the heaviest residual oils, specific gravity > 0.970 and C:H ratio ca. 8:1, are little over 18,000 B.t.u./lb (gross). For light, paraffinic type distillates, corresponding values are:

Sp. gr. 0·777; C:H ratio 6:1; C.V. 19,800 B.t.u./lb.

In general, also, the higher the C:H ratio, the greater the reduction in viscosity with increase in temperature.

5. Sulphur. The sulphur content of residual oils varies from ca. 0·2 to 4%. High sulphur in a fuel,
   (a) raises the dew-point of the flue gases
   (b) increases the formation of sulphate deposits in boiler passes, economizers, and air heaters
   (c) increases back-end corrosion
   (d) reduces efficiency of combustion by limiting the permissible temperature reduction of the flue gases
   (e) contaminates products in direct contact with the furnace gases, such as glass or steel
   (f) accelerates the formation of gum and sediment during storage.

6. Ash. The maximum amount present is usually < 0·2%. Its composition is important, since certain constituents, such as sodium vanadium and sulphur, have the following effects on boiler and furnace operation:
   (a) Attack the surface of hot refractories, causing erosion, corrosion, and spalling.
   (b) Reduce availability and output by the build-up of deposits on boiler tubes, economizers and air heaters.
   (c) Cause severe corrosion of superheater tubes by deposition of low melting deposits of sodium vanadates, m.p. 600 to 900°C.
   (d) Contaminate products in course of manufacture by contact with furnace gases, e.g. glass and ceramics.

7. Uniformity. Uniform quality, to an agreed specification, is essential for satisfactory operation. This can only be achieved by adequate quality control at the refinery.

C. SUMMARIZED PROPERTIES OF RESIDUAL OILS

Physical and chemical properties of typical residual fuel oils are summarized in Tables 61.1 and 61.2.

TABLE 61.1

PHYSICAL PROPERTIES OF TYPICAL RESIDUAL FUEL OILS

| Country of Origin | Specific Gravity at 60°F | Closed Flash (Pensky-Marten) °F | Viscosity at | | | | Pour point, A.S.T.M. °F | Sulphur % | Gross Calorific Value B.t.u./lb |
			60°F Redwood No. 1 sec	100°F Redwood No. 1 sec	120°F Saybolt Furol sec				
S. America:									
Venezuela	0·976	235	—	5700	290	35	2·0–2·5	18,500
Curaçao	0·965	250	—	5700	290	25	1·9–2·0	18,650
Mexico	0·968	230	—	2900	150	15	3·3–3·5	18,600
Roumania	0·950	200	—	1300	71	55	0·3–0·4	18,800
Trinidad	0·985	210	—	1050	60	10–20	1·0–1·2	18,400
Russia:									
Baku	0·910	230	120	300	—	15	0·1–0·2	19,200
Grozny	0·909	160	730	172	—	35	0·1–0·2	19,250

TABLE 61.2

ANALYSES OF FUEL OILS FROM PETROLEUM

	Carbon	Hydrogen	Sulphur	Calorific Value B.t.u. per lb	Specific Gravity at 60°F	Flash Point °F	Visc. at 100°F Redwood No. 1	Type
Mexican	83·52	11·68	3·27	18,750	0·95	above 150	1500	Asphalt base
Texas	86·3	12·22	1·33	19,200	0·928	160	176	Naphthene base
Persian	86·0	12·3	1·7	19,200	0·897	above 150	88	Mixed base
Borneo	86·74	10·67	0·03	18,830	0·962	225	42	Asphalt base

D. SPECIFICATIONS FOR FUEL OILS

Fuel oils are often specified, loosely, as light, medium and heavy, with maximum viscosities, 200 Redwood No. 1 sec, 950 sec and 3500 sec, at 100°F, respectively.

Standard specifications included in B.S. 2869, Classes E, F and G, refer to the above three grades.

Trade specifications for these three grades are summarized in Table 61.3.

TABLE 61.3

Oil Item	B.P. Britoleum	Shell Heavy Fuel Oil	Shell Heavy Fuel Oil, B.
Sp. gr. at 60°F	0·935	0·95	0·97
Flash point, closed, °F, min.	150	150	150
Viscosity, Red. No. 1 sec. at 100°F max.	220	950	3500
Pour test °F max.	35	70	70
C.V. gross, B.t.u./lb	18,800	18,600	18,300
Water, % vol. max.	0·5	1·0	1·0
Sediment, % wt. max.	0·1	0·2	0·25
Storage temp. °F min.	45	65	75
Atomizing temp. °F	140 to 160	180 to 220	220 to 260

REFERENCES

Modern Petroleum Technology, 3rd Edition, Institute of Petroleum, London, 1962.
British Standard Specification No. 2869, 1957, *Oil Fuels*.

TEST METHODS FOR PETROLEUM PRODUCTS

1. SPECIFIC GRAVITY

This is the ratio of the density of a substance to that of water at the same temperature. The temperature usually specified is 60°F (15°C).

Specific Gravity Bottle

The most accurate method of determining the specific gravity of an oil is to weigh a known volume in a specific-gravity bottle at 60°F. If it is not convenient to carry out the determination at 60°F a correction may be applied by measuring the specific gravity at some convenient temperature near 60°F and adding or subtracting 0·00034 per °F above or below 60°F. A convenient specific-gravity bottle for doing this, with ground-in thermometer for measuring temperature, is illustrated in Fig. 62.1.

FIG. 62.1   Specific-gravity Bottle.

Hydrometer

The most rapid method is by means of a set of hydrometers. A hydrometer is placed in the oil sample at 60°F and allowed to come to rest. The specific gravity is shown on the scale at the point co-incident with the surface of the oil.

A.P.I. Gravity

In the U.S., specific gravity of oil is often expressed as degrees A.P.I. (American Petroleum Institute).

$$\text{A.P.I. gravity} = \frac{141 \cdot 5}{\text{Sp. gr. at } 60°F} - 131 \cdot 5$$

The specific gravity is an indication of the type of hydrocarbon present, being highest for aromatics and lowest for paraffins. The A.P.I. gravity reverses this relationship.

2. VISCOSITY

(a) *Redwood Viscometer*

The Redwood viscometer, illustrated in Fig. 62.2 consists essentially of a standard cylindrical oil cup containing a standard agate orifice at the lower end, into which fits a spherical valve. The oil cup is surrounded by an oil-jacket containing a heater and stirring device. The oil in the outer bath is heated 2 or 3° above or below the required temperature of the determination, dependent upon the relative temperatures of the oil and the surrounding atmosphere. The oil sample, free from solid matter, is heated approximately to the desired temperature and poured into the oil cup up to a standard level. When equilibrium has been reached, i.e. when the oil in the inner cup remains steady at the desired temperature, the oil level is adjusted, the valve is opened and the time in seconds is taken for 50 ml to run out. This time interval is recorded as the viscosity in Redwood

L

Seconds at the specified temperature. The temperature must remain steady during the determination, within $\pm 0.5°$ F for temperatures below 150°F and within $\pm 2°$F for temperatures above 150°F.

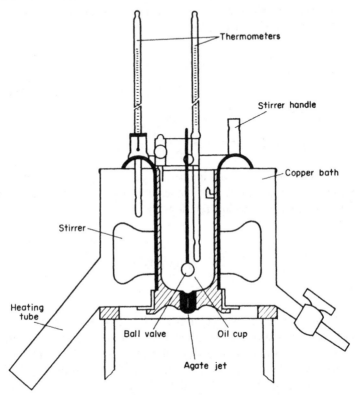

FIG. 62.2 Detail of Redwood No. 1 Viscometer.

(b) *U-tube Viscometer*

Principle of Method

U-tube glass viscometers allow an accurately reproducible volume of liquid to pass through a capillary at a constant temperature by the application of an accurately reproducible force. The time taken for a liquid to flow is proportional to the ratio of the dynamic viscosity to the density of the fluid, hence to its kinematic viscosity. The constant of proportionality for the instrument is obtained by carrying out a determination in the viscometer with a fluid of known viscosity.

The kinematic viscosity of a fluid of viscosity greater than 10 centi-Stokes is given by the expression

$$v = Ct$$

where C is the viscometer constant, and
    t is the time of flow in seconds.

When the fluid has a viscosity of 10 centi-Stokes, or less, a second coefficient is used to correct for changes in kinetic energy at the exit to the capillary. The expression then becomes

$$v = Ct - \frac{B}{t}$$

where B is the coefficient of kinetic energy, which may be determined experimentally, or eliminated by choosing long flow times.

The viscometer constant is determined by use of standard solutions of known kinematic viscosity, e.g. 40 % sucrose: $v = 4 \cdot 39$ cS at 25°C.

Determination

A filtered sample of the oil under test is introduced into the viscometer by suction or by pipetting into the wide tube (HG in Fig. 62.3) so that air bubbles are absent and the level of oil stands a few millimetres above the level. The viscometer is then placed in a thermostat, maintained at the required temperature, and adjusted so that it is exactly vertical. After a time, varying from 20 min for temperatures near the normal to 30 min at 100°C, the oil is blown or sucked into the tube A to a point 1 cm above the etched level B. The oil is then allowed to flow freely back down the capillary, taking the time of fall from the mark B to the mark C by means of an accurate stopwatch reading to 1/5 sec. The experiment is repeated until duplicate tests are repeatable within 0·2 %.

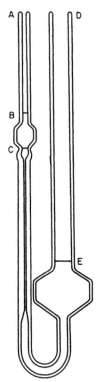

FIG. 62.3   U-tube Viscometer.

(c) *Viscosity Index*

The viscosity index is a number that expresses the temperature–viscosity relationship of an oil. Oils containing a high proportion of paraffins have relatively high viscosity indices (maximum value 100). Naphthenes have low V.I. (minimum 0).

The viscosity index of an oil is determined by measuring its viscosity at two temperatures and comparing the results with those for a standard oil of V.I. = 100 and for a standard oil of V.I. = 0.

$$\text{Viscosity Index} = \frac{L - U}{L - H} \times 100$$

where U = Saybolt viscosity of sample at 100°F
$\quad L$ = Saybolt viscosity at 100°F of a standard oil (V.I. = 0)
$\quad\quad$ with the same viscosity at 210°F as the sample
$\quad H$ = Saybolt viscosity at 100°F of a standard oil (V.I. = 100)
$\quad\quad$ with the same viscosity at 210°F as the sample.

In practice L and H are obtained from tables, after the viscosity of the sample at 100°F has been determined.

The Saybolt viscometer is used in the U.S. in place of the Redwood instruments. Results are expressed as "Saybolt Seconds Universal", at any given temperature.

3. FLASH POINT

The flash point is the temperature to which the oil must be heated, in a standard instrument, to give an inflammable mixture with air under the prescribed conditions. The Pensky–Marten apparatus is the British standard instrument for flash points above 120°F and the Abel apparatus is used for more volatile oils, with flash points below 120°F.

(a) Pensky–Marten Closed Cup Test

The apparatus, illustrated in Fig. 62.4, consists of a brass cup, mounted in an air bath and heated by a gas flame. A propeller-type stirrer, operated by a flexible drive, extends from the centre of the cover into the cup. The cover has four openings: one for a thermometer, and the others fitted with sliding shutters for the introduction of a pilot flame and for ventilation. The temperature of the oil in the cup is raised at 9 to 11°F/min. The stirrer is rotated at ca. 60 r.p.m. When the temperature has risen to ca. 30°F from the anticipated flash point, the pilot flame is dipped into the oil vapour for 2 sec every 2°F rise in temperature up to 220°F. Above 220°F, the flame is introduced every 5°F rise in temperature. The flash point is the temperature at which a distinct flash is observed when the pilot flame meets the vapour in the cup.

Open flash point. This may be determined after the closed flash point by removing the cover and continuing the heating until a distinct flash occurs across the open cup.

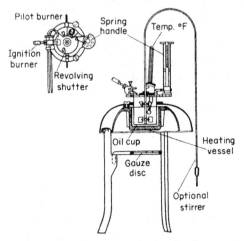

FIG. 62.4　Pensky–Marten's Flash-point Apparatus.

(b) *Abel Closed Cup Test*

The Abel apparatus consists of a brass cup sealed in a small water bath which is immersed in a second water bath. The cover of the brass cup is fitted in a manner similar to that in the Pensky–Marten apparatus. For oils with flash point $< 90°F$, the outer bath is filled with water at $130°F$ and is not heated further. The oil under test is then placed inside the cup. When the temperature reaches $66°F$, the pilot flame is introduced every $1°F$ until a flash is obtained. For oils with flash points $> 90°F$, $< 120°F$, the inner water bath is filled with cold water to a depth of $1\frac{1}{2}$ in. The outer bath is filled with cold water and heated at a rate of $2°F/min$. The flash point is obtained as before.

4. CALORIFIC VALUE

The same apparatus and procedure are used as for coal (see Data Sheet No. 29).

5. REID VAPOUR PRESSURE

This is a measure of the vapour pressure of an oil at 100°F, expressed in pounds pressure or as millimetres of mercury.

The apparatus consists of a metal cylinder, or "bomb", fitted with an accurate dial pressure gauge, or a mercury manometer. The bomb consists of two parts: an upper expansion chamber and a lower liquid chamber. The oil is cooled and poured into the lower chamber until full. The temperature of the air in the upper chamber is taken and the two chambers are connected together in a gas-tight manner. The bomb is immersed upright in a water bath at 100°F and shaken repeatedly until a constant pressure reading is obtained. This is corrected, from tables, for initial air temperature and pressure.

6. CLOUD AND POUR POINTS

The cloud point is the temperature at which a haze or cloud first appears in a sample of oil when cooled in a prescribed manner. The pour point is 5°F above the temperature at which the oil ceases to flow under the prescribed conditions. The oil is contained in a glass test tube fitted with a thermometer and immersed in one of three baths containing coolants, as shown in Fig. 62.5.

(a) *Cloud Point*

The oil sample is dehydrated and filtered at a temperature > 25°C above the anticipated cloud point. It is then placed in a test tube and cooled progressively in coolants held at 30 to 35°F; 0 to −5°F and −30 to −25°F, respectively. The sample is inspected for cloudiness at temperature intervals of 2°F.

(b) *Pour Point*

The sample is first heated to 115°F and cooled in air to 90°F before the tube is immersed in the same series of coolants. It is inspected at temperature intervals of 5°F by withdrawal and holding

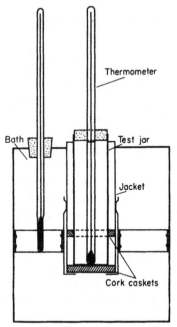

Fig. 62.5 Cloud and Pour-point Apparatus.

horizontal for 5 sec, until no flow is observed during this time interval.

7. ANILINE POINT AND DIESEL INDEX

(a) *Aniline Point*

This is an approximate measure of the aromatic content of a mixture of hydrocarbons. It is defined as the lowest temperature at which an oil is completely miscible with an equal volume of aniline.

Since aromatics dissolve aniline (itself an aromatic substance) more readily than paraffins or iso-paraffins, the lower the aniline point the higher the proportion of aromatics in the oil. Since, also, the higher the aromatic content of an oil, the lower the cetane number (cf. Data Sheet No. 57) the aniline number can be used to indicate the probable behaviour of an oil in a diesel engine.

(b) *Diesel Index*

This is an expression developed to correlate aniline point and A.P.I. gravity (cf. Item 1, above) with cetane number.

$$\text{Diesel Index} = \frac{GA}{100}$$

where G is the A.P.I. gravity of an oil,
      A is the aniline point of the oil.

Method of Test

5 ml each of a carefully dried sample of oil and aniline are placed in a test tube fitted with a thermometer and stirrer and enclosed in a larger tube to act as an air jacket. If, on stirring, the oil and aniline are completely miscible, the apparatus is cooled until the mixture is opaque. The temperature is then raised at 1°C/min until the thermometer bulb is just visible. The temperature is then recorded as the aniline point.

If, at atmospheric temperature, the oil and aniline are not completely miscible, the temperature is raised until this occurs. The mixture is then cooled at 1°C/min until the thermometer bulb is just obscured, when the temperature is recorded as the aniline point.

8. GUM IN MOTOR FUEL

(a) *Existent Gum*

50 ml of sample are evaporated in a glass dish of specified size on a steam bath for 1 hr, or until evaporation is complete, while heated air from a small jet impinges on the surface. The dish is transferred to a drying oven for 1 hr, and weighed after cooling. The weight in mg/100 ml is reported as "Existent gum".

(b) *Gum Stability*

This is an approximate measure of the tendency to form gum during storage.

50 ml of the gasoline are placed in a glass dish inside a stainless steel bomb, which is filled with oxygen at 100 lb/in². The bomb assembly is placed in a boiling water bath and connected to a sensitive pressure/time recorder. The time interval in minutes between placing the bomb in the water bath and recording a drop of 2 lb/in² from the maximum pressure, is recorded as the induction period (oxygen stability).

9. SULPHUR

(a) *Total*

By combustion in a bomb calorimeter. This is best carried out in the bomb calorimeter in conjunction with the determination of calorific value (cf. Item 4, above). The contents of the bomb are washed with distilled water into a beaker with distilled water. Hydrochloric acid is added and the solution raised to boiling point. Barium chloride is added drop by drop to the boiling solution to precipitate the sulphuric acid as granular barium sulphate. After cooling, and standing for 24 hr, the precipitate is filtered off on an ashless paper, washed, ignited and weighed as barium sulphate.

$$\% \text{ wt. of sulphur} = \frac{\text{Wt. of barium sulphate} \times 13 \cdot 73}{\text{Wt. of oil sample}} .$$

(b) *Corrosion Sulphur—by copper strip test.*

A piece of mechanically cleaned pure sheet copper, 3 in. × ½ in. is placed in a test tube with 40 ml of the sample, so that the copper is completely immersed. The tube is closed with a vented cork and heated in a boiling water bath for 3 hr. The copper strip is then compared visually with a new strip of copper for signs of tarnish.

The results are recorded as:

No change ⎫
Slight discoloration ⎬ result negative
Brown shade ⎭
Steel grey

Black, not scaled $\left.\right\}$ result positive, corrosive sulphur present.
Black, scaled

10. WATER AND SEDIMENT

(a) *Water*

This is best determined by the Dean and Stark method. The apparatus consists of a round-bottom flask of capacity 50 ml connected to a Liebig condenser by a receiving tube of capacity 25 ml, graduated in 0·1 ml (Fig. 62.6). 100 ml of oil are placed in the flask

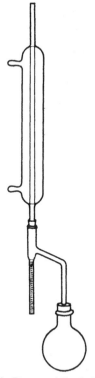

FIG. 62.6 Dean and Stark Apparatus.

with 25 ml of dry toluene. The flask is heated gently until the 25 ml of toluene have distilled into the graduated tube. The water, distilled with the toluene, separates to the bottom of the tube. Its volume is recorded as ml, or the weight as mg or percent.

(b) *Sediment*

This is best carried out by solvent extraction in the apparatus shown as Fig. 62.7. Inside a 1-litre Erlenmeyer flask is suspended a

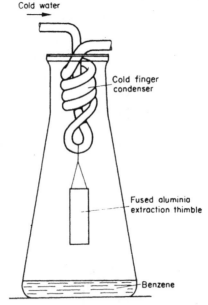

Cold water

Cold finger condenser

Fused aluminia extraction thimble

Benzene

Fig. 62.7   Determination of Sediment by Extraction.

cold finger condenser, which drops into a porous alumina thimble of dimensions $2\frac{3}{4}$ in. × 1 in. The thimble is cleaned with benzene and dried before the test and 10 g of oil sample are introduced. Approximately 100 ml of benzene are placed in the flask, which is heated until the condensed benzene vapour, dripping from the cold finger through the thimble, has extracted all the oil. The thimble is then dried, re-weighed, and the increase in weight recorded as percent, or as mg sediment/100 ml oil.

11. ASH CONTENT

This is the percentage by weight of inorganic residue obtained by the combustion of an oil in a porcelain, silica, or platinum dish. The temperature of combustion is not specified, but the final temperature reached is preferably 800°C.

20 g of oil are placed in a clean, dry, weighed silica dish. This is placed inside a cold electric muffle furnace. The temperature is raised slowly until the oil burns when a flame is applied to the surface. When combustion is complete, the temperature of the muffle is raised to 800°C and kept at this temperature for a further hour. The crucible and ash are then cooled, re-weighed and the weight of ash obtained by difference.

12. CARBON RESIDUE

(a) *Conradson Carbon*

This is the more usual test for measuring the "carbon" obtained by destructive distillation. The apparatus used is shown in Fig. 62.8 and consists of a large porcelain crucible, placed inside two iron crucibles and heated by a Meker gas burner until all oil vapours are driven off. A known weight of oil (e.g. 10 g) is placed inside the porcelain crucible and the apparatus assembled and heated at such a rate that the vapours start to burn in about 10 min. The flame is then adjusted so that they burn at the top of the chimney for a further 21 to 23 min. The crucibles are then heated to a cherry red heat for a further 7 to 8 min, giving a total time of 30 ±2 min. After cooling, the porcelain crucible is re-weighed and the result recorded as % wt., Conradson carbon.

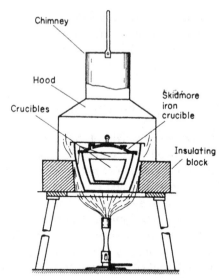

FIG. 62.8   Conradson Carbon Residue Apparatus.

(b) *Ramsbottom Carbon Residue Test*

In this test a known weight of oil (proportional to the anticipated weight of residue) is heated in a hemi-spherical glass bulb of standard dimensions by a bath of molten solder at 550°C for 20 min. The residual carbon is weighed and recorded as % wt., "Ramsbottom coke".

13. DISTILLATION

Distillation of oil is carried out in a standard round bottom distillation flask of 250 ml capacity attached to a water cooled condenser. The thermometer bulb is placed at the opening to the side arm of the flask.

100 ml of oil are placed in the flask and heated by a small gas flame so as to produce 10 ml of distillate every 4 or 5 min. The temperature of initial distillation is recorded; the temperature at which each further 10 ml distils and the final boiling point are also recorded.

REFERENCE

Test Methods for Petroleum Products, Institute of Petroleum, London.

OIL PRODUCTS DERIVED FROM COAL — MOTOR BENZOLE

MOTOR benzole is a mixture of the three lower aromatic hydrocarbons, benzene, toluene and xylene in the approximate proportions 75, 15 and 10%, respectively. Small proportions of other hydrocarbons and impurities may be present, usually less than 10%.

Crude benzole is recovered from coke-oven gas and from other coal gases produced at high temperatures, by scrubbing the gas with gas oil, or creosote oil, or by absorption on active carbon, after tar vapours, water and ammonia have been removed (see Data Sheet No. 105). A small percentage of benzole is also present in coal tar, from which it may be recovered by distillation.

Crude benzole may contain as impurities sulphur compounds (e.g. carbon disulphide and thiophene), phenols, pyridine, indene, coumarone, naphthalene, and traces of scrubbing oil.

REFINING MOTOR BENZOLE

The usual refining process to produce motor benzole contains the following steps:

1. A wash with dilute caustic soda to remove phenols.
2. A wash with 40% sulphuric acid to remove pyridine.
3. Fractional distillation to remove (a) carbon disulphide and low boiling hydrocarbons in the first runnings and (b) naphthalene and traces of wash oil as end runnings. The motor benzole fraction boils between ca. 70 and 170°C.
4. A wash with 2% of concentrated sulphuric acid to remove gum forming constituents (indene and coumarone) and thiophene.

5. A final wash with dilute soda.
6. A second distillation.
7. Addition of 0·001 to 0·02% of an oxidation inhibitor.

Sometimes the hydrocarbons benzene, toluene, and xylene are recovered separately, but not for use as motor fuel.

PROPERTIES AND USES AS MOTOR FUEL

The freezing point of pure benzene is 5·5°C and its boiling point 80°C. Its carbon/hydrogen ratio is extremely high, e.g. 12:1, so that it is difficult to burn without the production of carbon. These three properties make benzene an unsatisfactory motor fuel when used alone, but its high knock rating (O.N. > 100) and, particularly, its high blending octane number (90 to 98) make it particularly suitable for blending with gasolines of relatively low octane number. Toluene and xylene possess much lower freezing points and even better knock ratings (P.N. > 100 to 145).

Motor benzole is therefore usually sold as a blend with gasoline— "Benzole mixture"— in proportions between 5% and 30%.

It is also sometimes used in ternary blends with gasoline and alcohol, or with tetralin and alcohol. (See Data Sheets Nos. 65 and 67.)

PHYSICAL PROPERTIES OF PURE AROMATIC HYDROCARBONS

	Benzene	Toluene	Xylene	
			Ortho	Meta
Formula	C_6H_6	C_7H_8	C_8H_{10}	
m.p. °C	5·5	−95·1	−25·2	−53·5
b.p. °C	80·4	111	142	139
Sp. gr. at 60°F	0·884	0·872	0·884	0·869
Blending octane number				
Motor method	90·5	107	102·5	124
Research method	98·5	123	120	145

SPECIFICATION FOR MOTOR BENZOLE

Specific gravity at 60°F	0·870 to 0·886
Distillation range	≮ 60% at 100°C
	≮ 95% at 155°C
Crystallization point	< 5°C
Sulphur	< 0·4%
Calorific value, gross, B.t.u./lb	18,050
net, B.t.u./lb	17,280
Limits of inflammability, % lower	2·65
upper	6·50

The net calorific value of motor benzole is ca. 8% lower than that of gasoline of average composition (18,750 B.t.u./lb), but its density is 19% higher. Consequently, when bought by gallon (the usual method of sale), gasoline is 11% dearer than motor benzole on a thermal value basis.

OIL PRODUCTS DERIVED FROM COAL — COAL TAR FUELS

A. DESCRIPTION

Coal tar fuels are liquid fuels obtained by blending coal tar distillation products. They comprise a series of products numbered C.T.F. 50 to C.T.F. 400.

The numbers designate the temperature in °F at which the viscosity of each fuel is 100 Redwood seconds. At this viscosity they can be atomized efficiently in conventional oil-fuel atomizers.

C.T.F. 50 and 100 consist of creosote oil. C.T.F. 200 to 400 contain varying and increasing proportions of anthracene oil and pitch.

B. DISTILLATION OF COAL TAR

Coal tar is now usually distilled in some form of tube still, which is attached to a distillation column, a fractionating column, and a series of condensers and heat exchangers on similar lines to a single stage distillation unit for petroleum oil (cf. Data Sheet No. 53).

Steam is used in the mid-sections of the distillation column to assist the vaporization of the heavy oils.

The plants commonly used are the Wilton or Foster–Wheeler in Great Britain, the Koppers in the U.S.A. and the G.f.T. in Germany. The latter includes a vacuum stage.

C. YIELDS, TEMPERATURES AND TYPE OF PRODUCTS

These depend upon the source of the tar and the nature of the products required.

With tar from high temperature carbonization processes (without steaming) naphthalene and anthracene are important distillates and are normally recovered separately. In tar from lower temperature carbonization, or where steaming is practised as in continuous vertical retorts (cf. Data Sheet No. 24), low proportions of these substances make separate recovery not worthwhile.

Typical cuts are as follows:

Fraction	Temperature Range	Typical Yields (Coke oven practice)
Carbolic oil	170 to 200°C (340 to 390°F)	3 to 4%
Naphthalene oil	200 to 230°C (390 to 445°F)	5 to 7%
Creosote oil	230 to 300°C (445 to 570°F)	15 to 24%
Anthracene oil	300 to 360°C (570 to 680°F)	14 to 17%
Medium pitch	Residue	60 to 70%

D. VARIATION IN TAR TYPE WITH CARBONIZATION PROCESS

The table shows the increase in specific gravity, free carbon, naphthalene and pitch, and the decreasing yield of phenolics obtained with increasing severity of carbonizing conditions.

Yields of tar are in the reverse order, being approximately 50% of Gray–King assay yields (cf. Data Sheet No. 28) for higher temperature carbonization and up to 80% of assay yields for low temperature carbonization.

Properties of Tar

Carbonization Process	C.V. B.t.u./lb	Sp. gr.	"Free Carbon" %	Phenols %	Naphthalene %	Light Oil < 200°C %	Middle Oil 200°–270°C %	Heavy Oil 270°–360°C %	Pitch %
Low temp.	16,800	1·05	trace	20	trace	8	30	24	38
Continuous vertical	16,600	1·10	4	9	1	6	23	19	52
Intermittent vertical	16,500	1·15	3	5	1·5	5	18	17	60
Coke ovens narrow	15,800	1·20	15	4	5	4	8	18	70

The term "Free carbon" refers to complex polynuclear hydrocarbons that are insoluble in benzene.

E. VARIATION IN ULTIMATE ANALYSIS OF TAR WITH CARBONIZATION PROCESS

The above changes in tar with carbonizing severity are also reflected in ultimate analyses of tars produced from the same coal, e.g.

Ultimate Analysis of Tar	Source of Tar		
	Horizontal Retort	Vertical Retort	Low Temperature
Carbon %	85·9	85·7	83·5
Hydrogen %	6·3	6·3	8·5
Sulphur %	1·2	1·6	0·8
Oxygen plus nitrogen %	6·6	6·4	7·2

F. SPECIFICATIONS FOR COAL TAR FLUIDS

Property	C.T.F. 100	C.T.F. 200	C.T.F. 300	C.T.F. 400
Viscosity, Redwood seconds				
at 100°F, max.	100	1500		
at 200°F, max.		100		
at 300°F, max.			100	
at 400°F, max.				100
Water, % vol. max.	1·0	1·0	0·5	0·5
Toluene insol. % wt. max.	0·5	15·0	26·0	30·0
Ash, % wt. max.	0·05	0·25	0·3	0·75
Gross C.V. B.t.u./lb min.	16,500	16,500	16,000	16,000
Sulphur, % wt. max.	1·0	1·0	1·0	1·0
Flash point, closed, min. °F	150	150		
*Ring and ball softening point, °C			36	73 to 80

* Refers only to pitch.

G. COMBUSTION CHARACTERISTICS OF COAL TAR FUELS

1. As with benzene, all C.T.F. are lower in calorific value on a weight basis, and higher on a volume basis, than corresponding petroleum fuel oils.

2. Also, the C : H ratio of C.T.F. average ca. 14 : 1, compared with petroleum fuel oils which average 6 : 1.

3. In consequence, C.T.F. burn with a smoky, or luminous flame, which has a high emissivity factor. As shown in Data Sheet No. 165, transmission of heat by radiation from a flame is proportional to (a) the 4th power of the difference of absolute temperature between the flame and the substance heated, (b) directly as the radiating area, and (c) directly as the emissivity factor.

   i.e. $M = CAE\,(T_1{}^4 - T_2{}^4)$

   C is the Stefan–Boltzmann constant, with the value
   $17\cdot23 \times 10^{-10}$
   E is the emissivity factor.

   The emissivity factor range is from about 0·1 to 0·9 and is related to luminosity. For highly luminous flames the value approaches 0·9.

   Since flames from aromatic hydrocarbons are more luminous than those from paraffin hydrocarbons the emissivity factor for coal tar fuels is some 25 % higher than for residual fuel oils. It is therefore possible to use 10 to 12 % less coal tar fuel than petroleum fuel oil for steel billet heating, though its calorific value is 10 to 12 % lower on a weight basis.

4. The sulphur content of coal tar fuels is generally much lower than for corresponding petroleum fuel oils—usually < 0·5 % as compared with up to 4·0 %. This also is important in metallurgical practice, since sulphur absorption destroys the surface structure of metals.

5. The lighter C.T.F. can be atomized in much the same way as corresponding petroleum fuel oils. The heavier grades of C.T.F. are more difficult to atomize.

   Steam atomization is suitable (see Data Sheet No. 69). Preheated compressed air, or mixtures of preheated air and steam are most effective, giving short, luminous flames.

6. Specific heat of C.T.F. varies from 0·3 to 0·4.

REFERENCE

Coal Tar Fuels, Association of Tar Distillers, 1944.

LIQUID FUELS DERIVED FROM COAL — HYDROGENATION PRODUCTS

A. NATURE OF THE PROCESS

Coal can be converted into oils by reaction with hydrogen under pressure in the presence of catalysts, with yields up to 75% by weight of the coal processed. This process is known as hydrogenation.

Although the yields are high, on the basis of coal processed, power and fuel requirements are also very high, so that the net yield on the total coal used is about 20%.

In addition, capital and maintenance charges are high, so that the process is not attractive commercially when natural petroleum oil is available cheaply.

Creosote oil and tars can be more easily hydrogenated, at lower costs, so these processes are more attractive when raw material costs are sufficiently low.

B. HISTORICAL

An experimental intermittent process was developed by Bergius in Germany in 1924 and a smaller scale duplicate was installed at the Fuel Research Station, Greenwich, in 1926.

The commercial hydrogenation of lignite and lignite tar by a continuous process commenced in Germany in 1930 and the application of a similar process to bituminous coals by I.C.I. at Billingham followed soon after.

The plant was modified in 1939 to hydrogenate creosote oil.

During the early stages of the 1939–1945 war Germany produced some $3\frac{1}{2} \times 10^6$ ton of fuel oil (including $2\frac{1}{4} \times 10^6$ ton of petrol) by hydrogenation processes.

Bergius Process

In the Bergius process a mixture of 20 parts of coal, 8 parts of tar and 1 part of catalyst ("Luxmasse"—chiefly iron oxide) was hydrogenated at 450 to 480°C at 200 atm pressure for several hours. Hydrogen consumption was 1 cwt. of hydrogen per ton of bituminous coal. The yield of liquid products was 10 cwt. of oils, of which 2 cwt. boiled below 200°C.

C. TWO-STAGE COMMERCIAL PROCESS

1. *Liquid Phase*

Coal, ground to a paste with heavy oil from the process and ca. 0·1% of tin chloride as catalyst, is pumped with hydrogen at 250 atm pressure, via a preheater, to the base of the reactor at 400 to 480°C. The exit reaction products and excess hydrogen are cooled, reduced to atmospheric pressure, and are separated into oil and gas in a fractionating column.

The reaction time is about 2 hr.

The reaction is exothermic and cooling of the reactor is obtained by the introduction of cold hydrogen.

Gross yield of oil   ≃ 170 gal/ton coal processed
Yield of oil b.p. < 170°C ≃ 40 gal/ton coal processed
Hydrogen used   ≃ 30,000 ft^3/ton coal processed
                          = 160 lb/ton coal (7%).

The products from the liquid phase hydrogenation are separated into 3 fractions, (a) motor spirit, b.p. < 170°C; (b) middle oil, b.p. 170 to 230°C; (c) heavy oil, b.p. > 230°C.

Sludge, containing coal ash, unconverted fusain, and catalyst, is distilled to yield heavy oil and coke residue. The heavy oil is returned to the process as paste. The middle oil is subjected to vapour phase hydrogenation in the second stage of the process.

2. Vapour Phase

The middle oil and hydrogen are preheated under pressure and passed as vapours through a reactor containing pellets of a catalyst consisting of molybdenum and/or tungsten sulphide. Pressure is ca. 200 atm and temperature 460 to 500°C.

The products are cooled and fractionated. The unconverted middle oils are recycled. Gaseous hydrocarbons are processed to form hydrogen, for use in the process, with recycled hydrogen.

Yield of motor spirit, b.p. < 170°C ≈ 170 gal/ton coal processed
Hydrogen consumption   ≈ 18,000 ft³/ton coal
                                          processed.

D. PROPERTIES OF MOTOR SPIRIT PRODUCED

The properties depend mainly upon the nature of the catalysts and the temperature and pressure of the operations, particularly the vapour phase process.

(a) *Low temperature* (ca. 400°C)—high yield of naphthenic product —good response to T.E.L. Sp. gr. 0·836. Suitable for diesel engines.

(b) *Intermediate temperature* (ca. 460°C)—medium yield of product, capable of isomerization to improved octane gasoline. Good response to T.E.L.

(c) *High temperature* (ca. 500°C)—smaller yield of product of aromatic nature. Octane number fairly high without further treatment.

E. HYDROGENATION OF CREOSOTE AND LIGHT TARS

These are more readily hydrogenated than coal either by single stage or two-stage processes. There is no problem of pasting or disposal of ash/inerts.

With creosote, a two-stage process is preferred, using a dispersed tungsten sulphide catalyst in the first stage and an iron oxide catalyst in the vapour phase.

The amount of hydrogen used in the vapour phase is limited and ammonia is removed from the feed to prevent over-hydrogenation and to increase catalyst life.

Typical results (according to Gordon[1]) are:

	1st stage	2nd stage
Tons feed/m³ cat/hr	1·2	1·0
Hydrogen m³/ton feed	2800	1700
Cooling gas m³/ton feed	1900	850
Temperature °C	385	370
Motor spirit yield, % wt.	—	75
Hydrocarbon gas yield, % wt.	1·5	27·5
Hydrogen consumed, % wt.	5·1	3·5
Octane number, motor	—	77

F. TETRALIN—TETRAHYDRONAPHTHALENE, $C_{10}H_{12}$

1. *Description*

Tetralin is readily produced by the hydrogenation of naphthalene under conditions similar to those used for creosote. It is an excellent Diesel fuel. Tetralin cannot be used alone as a motor fuel because of its high boiling point (206°C) and low vapour pressure at normal temperatures (0·5 mm Hg). It is used as a ternary blend with motor benzole and alcohol. Maximum proportion of tetralin is 25%.

2. *Physical Properties*

Specific gravity at 60°F	0·975
Boiling point	206°C
Freezing point	−35°C
Flash point	175°F
Mean specific heat	0·464
Latent heat of evaporation, B.t.u./lb	145
Calorific value, gross B.t.u./lb	18,250
Calorific value, net B.t.u./lb	17,400

3. *Motor Fuel Blend*

The principal motor fuel blend has been "Reichkraftstoff", in Germany, of the following composition:

Motor benzole	50%
Tetralin	25%
Industrial alcohol	25%

REFERENCE

1. GORDON, K. *J. Inst. Fuel*, **20**, 42, 1947.

DATA SHEET No. 66

LIQUID FUELS DERIVED FROM COAL—SYNTHESIS—THE FISCHER–TROPSCH PROCESS

A. NATURE OF PROCESS

This is a catalytic process for the synthesis of hydrocarbons from water gas, enriched with hydrogen to a ratio of $H_2 : CO = 2 : 1$. Water gas is made by passing steam over red hot coke in an intermittent process (cf. Data Sheet No. 107).

The Fischer–Tropsch process was developed on a large commercial scale in Germany before the 1939–1945 war and, with the hydrogenation of lignite and lignite tars, was able to supply much of Germany's gasoline requirements during that war.

Since the war, new catalysts and operation under pressure have improved the economics of the process, which is now also used in South Africa, where cheap coal is available.

B. DEVELOPMENTS IN GERMANY

1. The original process developed by Fischer and Tropsch in 1925, operated at atmospheric pressure and 200°C. The catalyst consisted of nickel and cobalt oxides.
2. The reaction gas must be nearly sulphur free (< 0.1 g S per 100 ft^3) to ensure reasonable catalyst life.
3. The reaction produces straight chain paraffin hydrocarbons by the reaction:

$$nCO + (2_{n+1})H_2 \rightarrow C_nH_{2n+2} + nH_2O$$

4. The reaction is strongly exothermic (ca. 7000 B.t.u./lb of product) and the reactor is cooled by the circulation of cooling water in pipes placed within the reaction bed.

5. The oils formed range from paraffin type hydrocarbon gases (C_3 and C_4) to solid paraffin waxes (C_{35} and higher). The octane number of the oils is low, ca. 52, and the cetane number high, ca. 105. They are therefore more suitable for diesel engines than for motor engines. The products may be cracked catalytically (see Data Sheets Nos. 54 and 55) to give high yields of gasoline of octane number 68, with a good response to T.E.L.

6. Post-war operation at 15 atm pressure and 240°C, in the presence of iron catalysts, has improved throughput ($\times 15$), decreased costs, and increased total yield.

7. Typical Results:

Product	Yield % wt	
	Atmospheric pressure	15 atm pressure
Methane	18	14
C_3–C_4 gases	11	6
Motor spirit < 200°C	43	33
Light oil < 300°C	20	26
Paraffin wax	8	21
g product/m³ synthesis gas	120	135

C. POST-WAR DEVELOPMENTS IN THE U.S.A.

The iron based catalyst, in the form of finely graded pellets, was maintained as a fluidized bed by the reaction gases. Operating conditions were 320°C and 27 atm pressure. A large commercial plant was built at Brownsville, Texas, but design production was not achieved and the process is not now operating commercially.

REFERENCES

BRAME, J. S. S. and KING, J. G. *Fuel—Solid, Liquid and Gaseous*, London, 1956.
SCHROEDER, W. C. and FIELDNER, A. C. *Synthetic Liquid Fuels*, 4th World Power Conference, Section CZ, Paper No. 1, London, 1950.

OTHER OIL FUELS—SHALE OILS—ALCOHOLS

A. SHALE OILS

1. Occurrence

Oil shales, containing between 5 and 30% of oil, exist in many parts of the world, notably in Scotland, Tasmania, New South Wales, U.S.S.R. and U.S.A. Estimated oil reserves from this source are $22,000 \times 10^6$ ton, i.e. twice the known world reserves of petroleum oil.

2. Utilization

Commercial operation has so far been mainly confined to Scotland and Tasmania, but the U.S.A. deposits at Rifle, Colorado, have been mined and exploited on a large experimental scale (production up to 1350 metric tons shale/day, or 300 barrels crude oil/day).

(a) *Scottish Shale Industry*

(i) Started by James Young on Torbanite in 1851 at Bathgate.

(ii) When Torbanite was worked out, distillation of oil shale commenced; in 1861.

(iii) Modern production is in Westwood continuous vertical retorts. Use of steam (40% by wt. of shale) gives maximum yield of oil and ammonia. Residual shale is used for sand/lime brickmaking, after burning out residual carbon with air, plus steam.

(iv) Retorts are 34 ft high, and taper from 33 in. at top to 56 in. at bottom. Capacity 10 ton/day. Temperature in flues; 480°C at top, 700°C at base. Upper 15 ft of retorts are made of cast iron to facilitate heat transfer.

M

(v) Gas is burned in flues to provide heat, after the recovery of oil vapours and ammonia.

(vi) Crude oil yield (including motor spirit) is about 28 gal/ton. The oil is similar to paraffinic type petroleum oil. Present production is ca. 100,000 ton/annum.

(vii) The oil is distilled in pipe stills and fractionated into crude gasoline, wax-free oil, and wax-bearing oil. The wax is recovered by cooling and pressing at 20°F.

(viii) The wax-free oils are refined by alkali and acid washing, followed by distillation to diesel oil and heavy oil fractions. The heavy oil is pressure cracked to gasoline (O.N. 58, Sp. gr. 0·723); Diesel oil (cetane number 53, Sp. gr. 0·843) and pitch.

(ix) Typical yields/ton shale are:

Gasoline, gal	3
Diesel oil, gal	11
Wax, lb	13
Pitch or coke, lb	5
Ammonium sulphate, lb	30

(b) *Experimental Production—Rifle, Colorado*

(i) Gross oil yield of crude oil is 27·5 gal (Imp.) per ton (metric).

(ii) Refining is by conventional cracking and fractionation.

(iii) Improved yields of light spirit can be obtained by pressure cracking to a coke residue, with hydrogenation of the distillate. Recovery of the hydrogenated product is 75 to 85 % of the crude oil, consisting of 40 % gasoline and 60 % oil.

B. TAR SANDS

1. *Occurrence*

These consist of heavy petroleum oils, or bitumen, impregnating sand or clay near the surface of the earth. Vast quantities exist, notably at Athabasca in North Alberta, and in Iran.

Total world quantity of tar sands is equivalent to ca. $50,000 \times 10^6$

tons of oil, but commercial exploitation has not yet been achieved.

The oil is of asphaltic type (Sp. gr. 1·002 to 1·003; sulphur 4 to 5%, and calorific value, ca. 18,000 B.t.u./lb).

2. *Experimental Production*

The most promising method is to mill with 10% by weight of hot water at 185°F, followed by flooding with a larger volume of hot water and settling. An oil foam floats to the surface, from which it is skimmed.

The foam consists of oil 65% (80% of the estimated yield); mineral matter 5%, and water 30%. Oil yield is ca. 13 lb/ft³ of sand. Straight distillation of the crude oil yields 15% kerosine and 85% fuel oil.

C. ALCOHOLS

Alcohols of importance as motor fuels are methyl alcohol (methanol), CH_3OH; and ethyl alcohol (ethanol), C_2H_5OH. They are used alone, in special engines, or as blends with gasoline, or with gasoline and motor benzole.

1. *Manufacture*

(a) *Methyl Alcohol*

Formerly obtained as a by-product of the carbonization of wood in metal retorts (cf. Data Sheet No. 2), methyl alcohol is now mainly obtained by synthesis on lines generally similar to the Fischer–Tropsch process (cf. Data Sheet No. 66) by the reaction:

$$2H_2 + CO \rightarrow CH_3OH$$

The process is carried out at 400°C and 200 lb/in² in the presence of ZnO/Cr_2O_3 catalyst.

The product is a mixture of 75% methanol and 25% of higher alcohols, which are separated by fractional distillation.

(b) *Ethyl Alcohol*

This is manufactured by the fermentation of sugars, followed by fractional distillation of the product. Its use as a fuel is not wide-spread because its value as a chemical is greater, whilst tax considerations make its use in pure form difficult in most countries.

2. *Properties of Alcohols*

(a) *Physical*

	Sp. gr. at 15°C	B.P. °C	Sp. ht.	C.V. B.t.u./lb	Latent heat B.t.u./lb	Octane number
Methyl alcohol	0·796	64·7	0·57	9600	487	90
Ethyl alcohol	0·794	77·8	0·53	12800	370	95

(b) *Behaviour as Motor Fuel*

  (i) Alcohols differ from gasoline (and benzene) in their higher latent heat (cf. 140 B.t.u./lb for gasoline), lower calorific value, and complete miscibility with water.

 (ii) Because of the high latent heat, a cooler fuel/air stream is drawn into the cylinder, giving a denser charge and a greater power output.

(iii) Because of the low calorific value, the high power output is only achieved by a higher fuel consumption than with gasolines.

(iv) The cooling effect of the high latent heat of alcohols is responsible for their excellent anti-knock properties when used alone or as blends.

 (v) The inflammability limits for alcohols are higher than for gasoline or benzene, so that easier starting is obtained, in spite of the higher latent heat. (Inflammability limits for ethyl alcohol are: lower, 4·0%; upper, 13·7%.)

(vi) Alcohol blends are more liable to vapour lock than straight gasolines.

(vii) The addition of alcohols to gasolines up to 20% improves the fuel: addition of benzole to these mixtures reduces the tendency to separate in the presence of water.

(viii) Alcohols are excellent solvents for gums formed in engines from petroleum spirits and they do not form gums or carbon during combustion. An alcohol blend of motor spirit is therefore cleaner running than gasoline, or a gasoline/benzole mixture.

(ix) Common ternary blends of gasoline, alcohol and benzole are:

	Gasoline %	Benzole %	Alcohol %
Great Britain	70	15	15
Germany	45	10	45
Argentine	50	—	50

REFERENCES

BRAME, J. S. S. and KING, J. G. *Fuel—Solid, Liquid and Gaseous*, London, 1956.
SCHROEDER, W. C. and FIELDNER, A. C. *Synthetic Liquid Fuels*, Proc. 4th World Power Conference, Sec. CZ, Paper No. 1., London, 1950.

THE COMBUSTION OF FUEL OILS — KEROSINE

KEROSINE is perhaps the most versatile, economical, and convenient form of oil fuel for use in small scale isolated applications as an illuminant and as a heating agent.

Three main types of lamps are available,

1. Yellow flame wick lamp.
2. Wick fed mantle lamp.
3. Pressure fed mantle lamp.

In the yellow flame burner, the vapour produced at the wick surface is not completely burned there, and incandescent carbon particles, burning above the wick, radiate light.

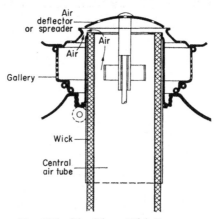

FIG. 68.1   Blue Flame Wick Burner.

The use of a mantle greatly increases the illuminating power of the wick lamp. In blue flame lamps, a circular wick is used; air is introduced at both sides of the wick, and an air deflector or spreader, on which the mantle rests, is placed immediately above the wick (see Fig. 68.1). The efficiency of this lamp is nearly as high as that of the coal gas mantle lamp.

The efficiency of the pressure burner (also used for heating, q.v.) is appreciably higher.

The relative efficiencies of these lamps, expressed as mean candle power per watt, and with the wire filament electric lamp for comparison, are given below:

Source of Illumination	*Mean candle power per watt*
Kerosine burner, yellow flame, wick fed	0·02 to 0·04
Kerosine burner, wick fed, with mantle	0·083
Gas burner, with mantle	0·095 to 0·159
Kerosine burner, pressure fed, with mantle	0·165
Metal filament electric lamp, 100 watt	0·8 to 1·44

KEROSINE IN SMALL HEATING APPLIANCES

The above lamps are efficient flueless burners, and all the heat in the fuel is available for heating. In other words, the efficiency for heating is 100%. With kerosine at 25d. per gallon and calorific value 150×10^3 B.t.u./gal the cost per useful therm is 16·5d., which compares favourably with any other form of space heating. (The cost per useful therm is the cost of heat available for heating, i.e. the cost per therm ÷ efficiency.)

The thermal output of flueless kerosine burners is limited to about 10,000 B.t.u./hr.

1. *Yellow and Blue Flame Burner*—as described above.

2. *Pressure Vaporizing Burner* (Fig. 68.2)

This consists of a reservoir, of sturdy construction, in which the pressure over the kerosine can be raised by a small hand pump. To light the burner, the head is preheated by burning methylated spirits in the trough until the kerosine vaporizes.

The vaporized kerosine mixes with most of the air required for combustion in the burner head. This mixture issues through perforations in the burner cap, where it burns with a blue flame. Some

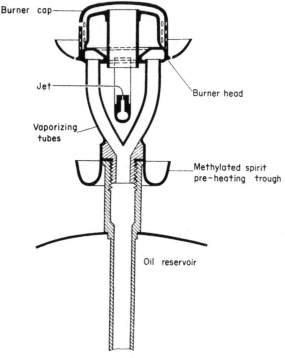

FIG. 68.2 Pressure Burner.

of the heat generated is conducted down the vaporizing tubes, ensuring adequate vaporization prior to combustion.

KEROSINE IN LARGE HEATING APPLIANCES

Large heating appliances use a variety of burners, including "Pot" and "Pressure jet" (cf. Data Sheet No. 69). All such appliances can be fitted with thermostatic controls to obtain efficient, economic, operation.

Space heaters may be of the radiation or convector type, or a combination of both. Only the most common type of burner is described here.

Pot Burner (Fig. 68.3)

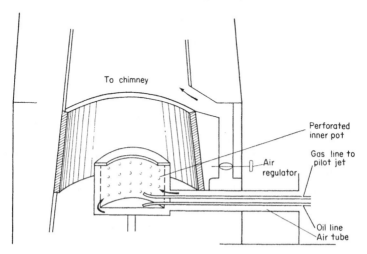

To chimney

Perforated
inner pot

Gas line to
pilot jet

Air
regulator

Oil line
Air tube

FIG. 68.3   Pot Type Burner.

This requires a flue, with an air regulator to obtain efficient control of combustion.

Kerosine is fed by gravity into the bottom of a pot by pipe, or by drip feed. The oil vapour is ignited either by a pilot gas flame, or electrically, and burns in air drawn through perforations in the walls of the pot. The blue flame normally burns a few inches above the rim of the pot.

Maximum output of such burners is ca. 30,000 B.t.u./hr.

THE COMBUSTION OF FUEL OILS — FURNACE OIL BURNERS

FUEL oils burn readily only in vaporized or gaseous state. The pot type vaporizing burner (Data Sheet No. 68) can be used for the lighter fractions of gas oils, but combustion appliances using heavier fuel oils require special atomizing equipment for efficient combustion.

Fuel oil atomizers operate on two principles.

A. Atomization by mechanical means, e.g. pressure jet and rotary cup atomizers.

B. Atomization by means of an atomizing fluid, e.g. air at low, medium or high pressures, or steam.

Oil fuel burners will be discussed under the above two main headings.

A. ATOMIZATION BY MECHANICAL MEANS

1. *Pressure jet burner*

This is the oldest type of mechanical atomizer and is still commonly used for large land and marine boilers.

(a) The fuel is preheated to a temperature at which the viscosity is < 100 Redwood seconds, and is forced at a pressure between 50 and 1000 lb/in^2 through tangential slots in the burner head into a turbulence or swirl chamber and thence through the burner tip into the furnace (Fig. 69.1).

(b) The atomized film issues as a hollow cone, with angular velocity 150 ft/sec at 150 lb/in^2 oil pressure.

(c) Output is controlled by viscosity and pressure.

(i) Viscosity is a function of temperature.

    (ii) Output and velocity vary as square root of the oil pressure. Fineness of spray varies inversely as the square root of the pressure. Maximum operating pressure is ca. 1000 lb/in².

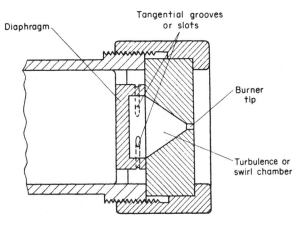

Fig. 69.1   Pressure Jet Burner Tip.

    (iii) Oil capacities for a simple pressure jet burner operating at 150 lb/hr vary from about 100 lb/hr for a 2-hole orifice plate to about 1000 lb/hr for a 6-hole orifice plate.

(d) Ratio of rated output to minimum operable output (called "Turn-down" ratio) is low with simple pressure jet burners (e.g. 2:1). Modified pressure jet burners give turn-down ratios of < 15:1.

These burners include the following types:

    (i) *Spill-back burners*—A portion of the oil from the swirl chamber is bled back to the oil feed in controlled amounts.

    (ii) *Variable entry grooves*—The effective swirl groove area is varied by use of a sliding piston.

    (iii) *Duplex or triplex burners*—The burner has two or three sets of swirl grooves, the supply of oil to each being independently controlled.

The maximum capacity of these modified pressure jet burners is higher than for the simple type. Burners are available to burn up to 2 ton oil/hr.

(e) Small fluctuations in load are controlled by varying the oil pressure; large variations, by shutting down or starting burners in a multiple burner system.

(f) Advantages over fluid atomization types:
   (i) Simplicity of operation and control.
   (ii) Low cost—because no atomization fluid required.
   (iii) No provision of separate fan or compressor for primary air.

(g) Disadvantages are:
   (i) Higher temperature and pressure of oil is required.
   (ii) Lack of flexibility in operation.

2. *Rotary Cup Burner*

A comparatively new burner, suitable for use with small installations and capable of using a variety of oil feeds without major modification.

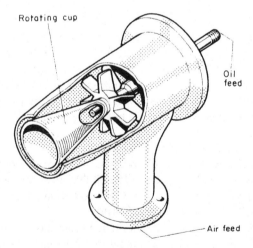

FIG. 69.2   Rotary Cup Burner.

(a) Oil is fed into the narrow end of a tapering cup, rotating about a horizontal axis at > 3500 r.p.m. (Fig. 69.2). A film of oil travels down the cup and is ejected at the wide end by centrifugal force as a fine mist. A high velocity air stream, supplied by a fan on the rotating cup and/or a separate compressor, surrounds the emerging oil film and moulds this into a cone.

(b) Advantages over simple pressure jet:
  (i) Turn-down ratio up to 5:1.
  (ii) Can handle efficiently oils at viscosities 50 to 350 R. sec.
  (iii) Is more economical in preheat.

(c) Major disadvantage: More liable to fouling by carbon from the radiant heat of the furnace.

B. ATOMIZATION BY FLUIDS
(Blast-type or twin-fluid burners)

Atomization is produced by the shearing effect of a high velocity stream of air or steam on oil flowing through an orifice at low pressure.

For the vast majority of applications, air is the atomizing fluid (at low, medium or high pressures).

For high viscosity coal-tar fuels and residual fuel oils, steam is the preferred fluid, because it supplies both heat and pressure.

The main advantage of atomization by fluids over mechanical atomization is the more complete control of output (turn-down ratio 10:1) and shape of flame. The main disadvantage is the cost of supplying the fluid under pressure.

A typical arrangement of a wide-range steam atomized burner is shown in Fig. 69.3.

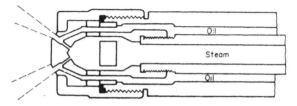

FIG. 69.3 Wide-range Steam Atomizer (Babcock and Wilcox).

The velocity of air or steam issuing from the nozzle varies from ca. 500 to 600 ft/sec.

1. *Low Pressure Air*

(a) 0·5 to 1·5 lb/in² pressure—primary air > 20% of the total requirement, and supplied through the burner, may be preheated to a maximum of 500°F (260°C). The remainder is supplied by furnace draught.

(b) If all air is supplied through the burner, the size of the air passage at the burner nose determines the maximum oil consumption. Range of outputs can be obtained by varying burner nose size. For reduced oil outputs the air pressure is varied proportionally (volume $\alpha \sqrt{P}$).

(c) With 20% of air supplied through the burner, turn-down ratio is 5:1.

(d) This type of burner is perhaps the most efficient, reliable, flexible, and economical of all oil burners.

2. *Medium Pressure Air*

(a) 2 to 15 lb/in² pressure. Up to 10% of theoretical air is supplied through the burner—remainder is supplied by furnace draught.

(b) Large range of output is obtained by maintaining air for atomization constant and varying supply of secondary air passing over the burner nose.

(c) Bulk of air supplied can be preheated to give high thermal efficiency.

(d) Suitable for small boilers where adequate draught permits good control of secondary air. Not very suitable for metallurgical furnaces.

3. *High Pressure Air*

Pressure > 15 lb/in²: supplied by compressor. < 5% of air is used for atomization; remainder is supplied as secondary air by furnace draught. Increased cost of compressing air is only justified when high preheat of secondary air is required.

4. *Steam Atomization*

Steam serves as a convenient fluid, already under pressure, and as a source of heat to reduce the viscosity of heavy oil fuels. The steam used should be supplied dry, and the amount kept under careful control. Normal consumption in boilers is ca. 3% of boiler output. With wear of atomizers this quantity can rise unduly. Except in the open-hearth steel melting furnace, steam atomization is rarely used in metallurgical practice because its use reduces flame temperature. Steam atomization is much used for ships' boilers.

C. COMBUSTION CHARACTERISTICS OF FUEL OILS

1. Combustion takes place initially in the vapour phase, so that evaporation or atomization must be sufficient to initiate combustion.
2. After ignition, heat is supplied by the flame and by surrounding heated surfaces. With heavy residual oils and coal tar products, a large oil film area is necessary to maintain combustion.
3. Distillation takes place at the surface of droplets of oil, leaving carbon particles which burn with a luminous flame. The more aromatic the fuel, i.e. the greater the carbon/hydrogen ratio, the more luminous the flame and the higher the emissivity factor.

	Type of Oil	*Emissivity Factor*
Typical values are:	Gas oil	0·5 to 0·7
	Fuel oil	0·6 to 0·8
	Creosote oil	0·8 to 0·9
	Soft pitch	0·9

4. Most fuel oils require about 14 lb of air per lb of oil for complete combustion. Optimum efficiency is obtained when using a small proportion of excess air. With oil fuels this proportion can be as low as 10%.
5. The shape and size of flame affect efficiency. They depend upon the design of the burner, the amount of air supplied, and its mode of distribution.
   (a) Correct flame pattern is normally short. Impingement on walls

or tubes causes carbon formation. Too short a flame suggests excessive air. Optimum conditions are obtained with a slight smoke haze at the stack, indicating about 10% excess air.

(b) The amount of primary air is determined by burner design. The amount of secondary air is controlled by adjustable vanes, which also direct the flow of air.

A high degree of swirl surrounding the flame reduces flame length. In some cases, particularly with steam atomization or rotary cup burners, the secondary air is arranged to swirl in the opposite direction to that of the flame.

(c) The flame cone can be adjusted to an included angle from ca. 60 to 120°, depending upon the angle of the nozzle and the viscosity of the oil.

6. With 10 to 20% of excess air, preheated to 200°C, the flame temperature obtained from fuel oils is 1600 to 1700°C. With an emissivity factor of 0·5, this flame would radiate energy at a rate of 100,000 to 150,000 B.t.u./ft^3 of combustion volume.

7. Theoretical evaporation by residual oil fuel of 18,700 B.t.u./lb is 19·3 lb water per lb oil. This compares with 12·4 lb water per lb of coal of calorific value 12,000 B.t.u./lb.

8. Although free from most of the troubles due to impurities in coal, residual oil fuels contain high proportions of sulphur and small proportions of ash, both of a corrosive nature.

(a) High sulphur leads to high dewpoint in the exit gases (up to 160°C). Corrosion is at a maximum some 30°C below the acid dewpoint.

(b) Sodium and vanadium in the ash form low melting, corrosive, deposits on the hot pressure parts of boilers, particularly on superheater tubes. Attempts to neutralize these troubles by the addition of ammonia or metal oxides to the flue gases are only partially successful (cf. Data Sheet No. 162).

REFERENCES

B.S. 2869, 1957, *Oil Fuels*, British Standards Institution.

Modern Petroleum Technology, 3rd Edition, Institute of Petroleum, London, 1962.

THE COMBUSTION OF FURNACE OILS — ANCILLARY EQUIPMENT

INDUSTRIAL fuel oil systems comprise the following items:
1. Storage tank or tanks, with pipe connection to (2).
2. Pumping, filtering, and heating equipment.
3. Pipe lines to burners; usually by the "Ring-main" system when using multiple burners.

When heavy fuel oils are burned, provision must be made for heating the stored oil and the oil lines, with efficient lagging to prevent waste of heat. The following details relate to such equipment, as used in a heavy oil system. Light oils require little heat, or none if the viscosity is < 100 Redwood seconds at 60°F.

A. STORAGE TANKS—USUALLY MADE OF WELDED STEEL

Requirements—see Fig. 70.1.

(a) Well lagged to preserve heat—an unlagged, sheltered, tank loses ca. 1·0 B.t.u./ft^2 surface/°F difference in temperature between the oil and the atmosphere. A tank lagged with 2 in. of 85% magnesia loses ca. 0·3 B.t.u./ft^2/°F.

(b) Protected from the weather—this is best done by surrounding by a brick/concrete building, with manholes from the roof for easy access.

(c) Equipped with filling, sludging and level indicators—sludging connections should be at the lowest level, to enable water and sludge to be drawn off. In the case of coal tar fuels, specific gravity > 1·0, water separates out at the top of the fuel. Tanks normally used for petroleum oils should not be used for coal-tar fuels and vice versa. Nor should these fuels be mixed.

(d) Equipped with vent pipe to remove inflammable vapours.

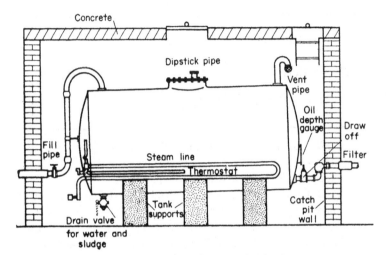

FIG. 70.1   Fuel Oil Storage Tank.

(e) Equipped with heating coils to reduce viscosity to < 1000 R. sec
for ease of flow. These are normally steam coils, but one tank
should be fitted with an electric immersion heater to enable a
cold start to be made.

Specific heat of fuel oil $\simeq 0.35$

Heat from steam coils $\simeq 20$ B.t.u./hr/ft^2 heating surface/°F
difference between steam and oil temperatures.

For lagged tanks, 7 ft^2 steam pipe surface suffices per 10,000 gal
oil $\equiv 7.5$ kW.

Heating should be controlled by thermostat.

(f) Fitted with draw-off connections near the base of the tank, but
above the sludge cock and on the opposite side of the tank.

(g) Minimum storage temperatures for petroleum fuel oils are:
light, 45°F; medium, 80°F; heavy, 100°F.

B. PUMPS

Positive displacement pumps are most suitable (ram type) capable
of handling oils of viscosity 30 to 3500 R. secs. Each pump is fitted
with a totally enclosed relief valve across delivery and suction.

When steam is available, this should be used for power, with an electrical pump as standby. If no steam is available, electric pumps are used.

C. OIL FILTERS

These are placed before and after the pumps, in duplicate, fitted with by-passes to facilitate cleaning.

Self-cleaning or duplex filters may be used. Corrosion resisting metal gauze is the most frequent filling.

For single stage filtration—120 mesh/linear inch.

For two stage filtration   —coarse—20 mesh/linear inch.

                                          —fine—120 mesh/linear inch.

Pitch of holes $\backsimeq$ 1·6 times diameter.

D. PIPE LINES AND VALVES

Pipe lines are mild steel. Valves are of "Full-way" type, with cast iron bodies and steel fittings. Suction lines are twice the diameter of pressure lines, and are fitted with steam tracer lines, or are wrapped with electrically heated cable, to ensure easy flow to pumps.

Average heat loss from oil in unlagged line $\backsimeq$ 1·75 B.t.u./ft^2/°F between oil and atmosphere

Average heat loss from oil in lagged line $\backsimeq$ 0·45 B.t.u./ft^2/°F.

E. OIL HEATERS AND RING-MAIN SYSTEM

Oil heaters are placed between pumps and burners in a ring-main system.

Capacity should be sufficient to heat the maximum quantity of oil flowing through the ring-main through a temperature rise of 150°F. Quantity of oil in ring main > 25% above maximum capacity of all burners in the system. A typical layout of a ring-main oil firing system for heavy oils is shown in Fig. 70.2.

Atomizing temperatures are:

Light fuel oil	150°F
Medium fuel oil	200°F
Heavy fuel oil	250°F
Coal tar fuel 200	200°F

F. PRESSURE RELIEF VALVES, AIR VENTS AND SAFETY DEVICES

Pressure relief valves and air vents are fitted as shown in Fig. 70.2.

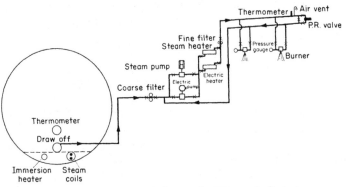

FIG. 70.2 Diagrammatic Layout for Ring-main System.

Safety devices are fitted to all burners to ensure that oil vapour is not fed to furnaces without igniting. The usual type is a flamestat, which operates on the principle of a thermostat, shutting down the oil firing equipment should a flame failure occur whilst the pump is running, or should the oil fail to ignite on starting up.

G. AUTOMATIC CONTROL

1. For small installations, three controls are used:
   (a) Thermostat to control temperature. This is connected to the oil feed to vary amount with load.

(b) Flamestat to shut down furnace in case of oil flame failure.

(c) Relay system for controlling the pump output, with lamp to indicate a fault and with a re-setting switch.

2. For large steam installations, the fuel/air ratio is controlled as follows:

(a) Pressure of steam in the boiler can be used to control the delivery pressure of fuel to the burners, when using the simple pressure jet, or to control the return pressure with the spill burner.

(b) The air is controlled by running fans at constant speed and reducing the quantity of air delivered by the automatic operation of dampers.

(c) The viscosity of the oil at the burners can be measured continuously and the variations used to control the admission of steam to the heaters.

(d) Provision is made for starting up automatically, and immediately, a spare oil pump in the event of failure of the main operating pump.

3. With rotary cup burners, a graduated and automatic oil feed rate is used to control fuel consumption.

4. With air atomization, two systems of control are used.

(a) *High–low Flame*

The oil to the burner is supplied through two valves. One is open continuously to give a low flame. The other is opened intermittently by the automatic control device to give a high flame. The motor which operates the second valve also actuates a butterfly valve in the air supply line to give the correct fuel/oil ratio.

(b) *Air/Vacuum Regulation*

The vacuum created at the burner jet is proportional to the velocity of the air flowing past the jet through the nose of the burner. Oil is maintained at a constant level in the jet by a float-operated valve. The vacuum at the jet draws the oil into the air stream. The automatic operation of the air control, in response to temperature fluctuations, maintains the correct fuel feed and fuel/air ratio.

REFERENCE

The Efficient Use of Fuel, H.M.S.O., London, 1958.

COMBUSTION OF FUEL OILS—APPLICATIONS

INDUSTRIAL applications of fuel oils (including coal tar fuels) may be considered conveniently under four main headings:

    A. Steam raising
    B. Industrial—general
    C. Industrial—metallurgical
    D. Gas making—This application will be dealt with in Section C, Vol. II.

A. STEAM RAISING

1. By far the most important burner used in large installations is the pressure-jet burner.
2. By far the most important oil used in large installations is residual fuel oil.
3. The maximum size of burner is limited by practical considerations, viz. difficulty in obtaining fine atomization with large sizes and correct length of flame in relation to combustion space. Consequently increase in output per boiler is best obtained by increase in number of burners rather than by increase in size above about 1 ton/hr. The flame from a burner handling 1 ton/hr is ca. 30% shorter than one handling 2 ton/hr.
4. Preheated air for operating the burners is supplied through a common windbox at a pressure up to 10 in. W.G., issuing at a velocity of ca. 300 ft/sec. The initial velocity of the oil is ca. 400 ft/sec. These factors reduce flame size and give direction to the flame.

5. Multiple burners are arranged to provide the maximum flame path within the combustion space, as with pulverized fuel (cf. Data Sheet No. 17).

   Common arrangements are:

   (a) In banks on the front wall, firing horizontally.

   (b) On the side walls, firing horizontally in opposite directions.

   (c) At the corners, firing crosswise and horizontally.

   (d) At the front of the roof of the combustion space, firing downwards.

6. Because of the low turn-down ratio of pressure jet burners, which is limited by windbox pressure, air-blast burners may be used for low loads. Otherwise air pressure must be reduced with decrease in load.

7. For smaller boilers, using high viscosity coal tar fuel or residual fuel oils, a hybrid burner combining steam and pressure jet atomization is effective.

8. For smaller boilers, the rotary cup burner, using low viscosity fuel oil, or gas oil, is effective and simple in operation.

B. INDUSTRIAL — GENERAL

1. Bakery ovens heated by side flues require a long lazy flame, obtained by low pressure air burners with controlled admission of secondary air. When side and top flues are used, the whole of the air for combustion passes through the burners and recirculation of combustion gases ensures uniform heating. Low viscosity oil is preferred.

2. Grain driers.

   Conveyor type. No overheating is permissible and the quantity of water evaporated is large. The burner is operated in a separate chamber and the products of combustion are diluted to 300°F. Low viscosity distillate oil is required and low pressure air burners.

   Pneumatic type. Time of drying is much reduced. Temperature of drying gases ca. 900°F. Medium pressure air burner is preferred, with low viscosity oil. This provides low sensitivity to chilling, with minimum production of soot, which would contaminate the product.

3. Regenerative glass melting—low ash, low sulphur oil fuel is required to prevent contamination of glass. Coal tar fuels may damage refractories due to deposition of carbon. Medium or high pressure air burners are used; 2 per tank of 22 ton capacity. Each burner is used alternately for half-hour periods, with reversals through the regenerators to give preheated secondary air at ca. 1000°C. 5% air is used in the burners for atomization. Output, ca. 11 ton glass melted per 24 hr.

C. INDUSTRIAL—METALLURGICAL

1. *General*

Where combustion gases come into contact with the product, air control is important to prevent scale formation and sulphur in oil must be low.

In many applications, medium air pressure burners are used, with 5% of air for atomization. Secondary air is heated by recuperation and is supplied at slight pressure.

2. *Crucible Furnaces*

Low pressure air burner is used, inserted tangentially to give a rotary motion round the crucible. This increases heat transfer rate. Atmosphere is not important. Recovery of heat is not possible. Thermal efficiency, 12 to 15%.

3. *Annealing and Heat Treatment Furnaces*

Atmosphere and temperature are both important. Medium pressure air burners are used with atomizing air at 3 lb/in². Secondary air is supplied at up to 4 in. W.G. pressure. Oil pressure is between 3 and 7 lb/in². Oil and air pressures are automatically controlled to give correct temperature and atmosphere. Oil consumption, 6 to 9 gal/ton. Thermal efficiency, 28 to 31 %.

4. *Bar Furnace for Sheet Mill*

Temperature of bars is 850°C. Preheated secondary air at 300°C is obtained by recuperation. Medium pressure air or steam jet burners are used. Oil consumption, 8 to 10 gal/ton. Thermal efficiency, 25 to 28 %.

5. *Open Hearth Furnace*

High pressure air–steam jet hybrid burner is used (0·5 steam/lb oil), with coal tar fuel to obtain maximum radiation efficiency. Long narrow angle flame is directed on to product. Excess air is 10 to 15 %. Fuel consumption, 20 gal/ton. Thermal efficiency, 18 %.

6. *Rotary Iron Melting Furnace* (*malleable cast iron*)

Requires close control of atmosphere. This is obtained by metering both air and oil. Medium pressure burner is used. Secondary air is preheated by recuperator to 500°C. Temperature of melt, 1550°C. Total air used is 15 % less than theoretical requirements. Oil consumption, 30 gal/ton. Efficiency, 19 %.

REFERENCE

RODDAN, M. *Fuel Oil in Furnaces*, Joint Conf. Inst. Pet. and Inst. Fuel, 'Modern Application of Liquid Fuels', Birmingham, 1948.

COMBUSTION DATA ON OIL FUELS

A. COMBUSTION CALCULATIONS — FUEL OILS

Calculations of theoretical and actual air requirements, dry and wet flue gases, and carbon dioxide in flue gases are carried out as described in Data Sheet No. 15. Typical results for a medium grade petroleum fuel oil and for a coal tar fuel are listed below:

Ultimate Analysis	Petroleum Fuel Oil	Coal Tar Fuel 200
Carbon %	86·2	90·0
Hydrogen %	12·0	6·0
Oxygen %	0·4	3·6
Sulphur %	1·4	0·4
Calorific value B.t.u./lb		
Gross	19,000	16,400
Net	17,870	15·820
Theoretical air lb/lb	14·0 = 182·5 ft³/lb	12·4 lb = 162 ft³/lb
Flue gases at N.T.P. wet	193 ft³/lb	168 ft³/lb
Flue gases at N.T.P. dry	170 ft³/lb	157 ft³/lb
CO₂ in dry flue gases %	15·9	18·2

B. HEAT LOSSES DUE TO HYDROGEN IN FUEL

1. Gross and Net Calorific Values

Because of the high percentages of hydrogen in petroleum oil fuels, the differences between gross and net calorific values are much greater than for coals, or for coal tar fuels. Typical differences are:

> 1130 B.t.u./lb for petroleum oils
> 580   ,,   ,,   ,, coal tar fuels
> 500   ,,   ,,   ,, bituminous coals.

2. *Wet Flue Gas Losses*

These vary with the exit gas temperature. Heat losses due to hydrogen in a typical petroleum fuel oil for different flue gas temperatures are shown in Fig. 72.1.

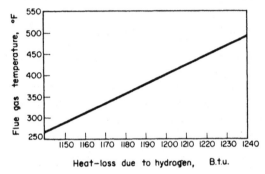

FIG. 72.1   Heat Losses due to Hydrogen.

3. *Dry Flue Gas Losses*

The dry flue gas losses at different exit gas temperatures and percentages of excess air are shown in Fig. 72.2, as percentages of the gross C.V., for a typical petroleum type fuel oil of composition given above. The percentages of carbon dioxide in the dry flue gases are also given for each percentage of excess air.

C. ADVANTAGES OF FUEL OILS OVER COAL

1. Oil can be stored more compactly than coal. On a weight/ calorific value basis oils contain 50% more heat than coals. On an area-coverage basis, because of limitations on height for coal, oil can be stored nearly five times as compactly.
2. Oil can be handled more readily than coal. Pumps, pipes, and controls, are easier and cheaper than the cumbersome equipment required for coal.

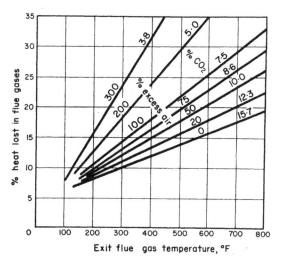

FIG. 72.2   Dry Flue Gas Losses.

3. The higher calorific value of oil fuels enables much greater furnace outputs to be obtained from a given weight.

4. The combustion of oil fuel is more easily regulated, and variation in the patterns of heating can be obtained by the use of burners designed to give a flame of a particular shape, or by the use of multiple burners, strategically placed.

5. Oil burners can be regulated, or designed, to burn efficiently over a wide range of heat output. Sudden fluctuations in heat demand are more readily met with oil than with coal.

6. There is no need to maintain banked boilers or furnaces with oil firing, as with coal, because starting up is easy and rapid.

7. Oils can be burned at higher combustion rates than coal, except in pulverized form. By using a smaller excess of air, higher flame temperatures are obtained and by the use of aromatic type oils the luminous flames have a greater emissivity factor, leading to greater transfer of heat by radiation. These effects enable greater thermal outputs to be obtained per unit of heat in the fuel.

8. Deliveries of oil are more uniform in composition than coal deliveries. There is no dust nuisance during unloading and loading, as with coal.

9. Oils contain extremely small proportions of ash. There is no heat wasted in ashes, or clinker nuisance. Troubles due to "bird-nesting" in boilers are non-existent with oils.

10. Coal is liable to spontaneous combustion and deterioration during storage. Oil is not subject to these troubles.

11. Low-viscosity distillates (e.g. gas oils and kerosines) contain much less sulphur than coals and are therefore extremely suitable for central heating and domestic applications.

D. ADVANTAGES OF COAL OVER OILS

1. No special provision need be made for storage, in the way of tanks, heaters, lagging, or pipe lines. Any hard flat surface will suffice.

2. Because of the lower hydrogen content, a greater proportion of the gross calorific value of coal can be utilized than is the case with oils.

3. The sulphur content of coals is, on the average, less than half the average for heavy residual fuel oils. Consequently, there is less pollution of the atmosphere due to sulphur oxides emission and less corrosion of "back-end" equipment, such as air heaters.

4. Coal ash is substantially free from vanadium compounds, which are present in oil and which form corrosive deposits on hot pressure parts of boilers.

5. Coal may be converted on site to the convenient pulverized form, which has many of the advantages of oil fuels, listed above.

6. Coal is an indigenous fuel in Great Britain and therefore should be cheaper than imported oil fuels.

Made in the USA
Las Vegas, NV
13 March 2022